Progress Chart

This chart lists the topics in the book. Once you have
completed each page, stick a star in the correct box below.

Page	Topic	Star	Page	Topic	Star	Page	Topic	Star
2	Numbers	★	15	Adding	☆	28	Telling time	☆
3	Place value	☆	16	Subtracting	☆	29	Tables and graphs	☆
4	Multiplying by 10	☆	17	Subtracting	☆	30	Necessary information	☆
5	Ordering	★	18	Choosing the operation	☆	31	Number pairs	☆
6	Rounding	★	19	Multiplying	☆	32	2 times table	☆
7	Polygons	★	20	Multiplying	☆	33	Multiplying by 2	☆
8	Identifying patterns	☆	21	Dividing	☆	34	Dividing by 2	☆
9	Odds and evens	☆	22	Dividing	☆	35	Using the 2 times table	☆
10	Addition fact families	☆	23	Choosing the operation	☆	36	Using the 2 times table	☆
11	Fractions	☆	24	Word problems	☆	37	Using the 2 times table	☆
12	Fractions	☆	25	Word problems	☆	38	5 times table	☆
13	Ordering decimals	☆	26	Problems with measures	☆	39	Multiplying by 5	☆
14	Adding	☆	27	Telling time	☆	40	Dividing by 5	☆

0 zero　1 one　2 two　3 three　4 four　5 five　6 six　7 seven　8 eight　9 nine　10 ten

Extra Practice Section

When you have completed the progress chart
in this book, fill in the certificate on page 202.

Ages 8-9

Grade 3

Math Workbook

Math Made Easy

Expanded Canadian Edition

Author Sean McArdle
Canadian math consultant Marilyn Wilson

Numbers

Write the number in words.

567   Five hundred sixty-seven

Write the number in standard form.

Four hundred eighty-six.   486

Write each number in words.

85   eighty - five ✓

26   twenty - six ✓

43   Fourty - three ✓

38   thirty - eight ✓

Write the numbers in standard form.

Forty-seven.   47   Fifty-eight.   58

Seventy-three.   73   Three hundred eighty-two.   382

Sixty-one.   61   Seven hundred twenty-four.   724

Write each number in words.

207   two hundred and seven

46   fourty - six ✓

58   fiffty - eight ✓

39   thirty - nine

Write the numbers in standard form.

Three hundred twenty-one.   321   Two hundred seven.   207

Eighty-two.   82

Place value

645 is the same as:
6 hundreds, 4 tens, 5 ones
or
645 is the same as 600 + 40 + 5

Write the correct number in the space.

945 = 900 + 40 + 5   312 = ___ + 10 + 2

749 = 700 + ___ + 9   263 = 200 + ___ + 3

294 = ___ + 90 + 4   742 = ___ + 40 + 2

176 = ___ + 70 + 6   375 = ___ + 70 +5

264 = ___ + 60 + 4   286 = ___ + 80 + 6

Write the number that is the same as:

Two hundred eighty-four

One hundred sixty-nine

Eight hundred seventy-two

Two hundred sixty-six

Four hundred twenty-seven

Nine hundred forty-three

Two hundred ten

One hundred three

Three hundred eleven

Three hundred thirty-eight

Look at these numbers: 8 3 0 7

Arrange these digits to make the largest number you can.

Arrange these digits to make the smallest number you can.

Multiplying by 10

Multiply each number by 10.

7 70   12 120   3 30   13 130

Multiply each of these numbers by 10.

6 60   14 140   12 120   17 170   20 200
9 90   15 150   13 130   2 20   23 230
1 10   19 190   24 240   28 280   22 220
5 50   3 30   26 260   11 110   25 250

Multiply each of these numbers by 10.

20 200   17 170   12 120   14 140   6 60
23 230   2 20   13 130   15 150   9 40
22 220   28 280   24 240   19 190   1 10
25 250   11 110   26 260   3 30   5 50

Multiply each of these numbers by 10.

56 560   48 480   67 670   39 390   82 820
69 690   32 32   74 74   57 570   43 430
95 950   63 630   55 550   77 770   40 400

Multiply each of these numbers by 10.

38 380   67 670   48 480   56 560   74 740
32 320   69 690   82 820   63 630   95 950
43 430   57 570   99 990   40 400   77 770

4

Ordering

Write these numbers in order, from smallest to largest.

675	830	390	617
390	617	675	830

Write these numbers in order, from smallest to largest.

574	683	847	563	563	574	683	847
473	670	371	421	371	421	473	670
389	726	995	843	389	726	843	995
562	264	923	674	264	562	674	923
853	567	684	557	557	567	684	853
241	785	538	647	241	538	647	785

Write these numbers in order, from smallest to largest.

705	390	903	704	390	704	705	903
67	809	330	35	35	67	330	809
207	380	105	127	105	127	207	380
45	28	36	106	28	36	45	106
104	140	410	800	104	140	410	800

Write these numbers in order, from smallest to largest.

780	365	968	89	89	365	780	898
890	78	678	999	78	678	890	999
950	230	845	102	102	230	845	950
804	800	840	980	804	840	800	980
679	375	753	573	375	573	679	753

Rounding

What is 132 rounded to the nearest ten?

```
100   110   120   130   140   150   160   170   180
|...|...|...|...|...|...|...|...|...|...|...|...|...|...|...|...|
                      ↑
```

132 rounded to the nearest 10 is 130 .

Round each number to the nearest ten.

247 250   306 340   493 _____   733 _____

834 _____   651 _____   379 _____   215 _____

Round each number to the nearest ten.

```
120   130   140   150   160   170   180   190   200
|...|...|...|...|...|...|...|...|...|...|...|...|...|...|...|...|      ✓160
                          ↑
```

```
320   330   340   350   360   370   380   390   400
|...|...|...|...|...|...|...|...|...|...|...|...|...|...|...|...|      350
              ↑
```

```
220   230   240   250   260   270   280   290   300
|...|...|...|...|...|...|...|...|...|...|...|...|...|...|...|...|      270
                        ↑
```

```
480   490   500   510   520   530   540   550   560
|...|...|...|...|...|...|...|...|...|...|...|...|...|...|...|...|      550
                                      ↑
```

```
700   710   720   730   740   750   760   770   780
|...|...|...|...|...|...|...|...|...|...|...|...|...|...|...|...|      ✓720
          ↑
```

```
60    70    80    90    100   110   120   130   140
|...|...|...|...|...|...|...|...|...|...|...|...|...|...|...|...|      ✓110
                        ↑
```

```
450   460   470   480   490   500   510   520   530
|...|...|...|...|...|...|...|...|...|...|...|...|...|...|...|...|      ✓500
                      ↑
```

```
170   180   190   200   210   220   230   240   250
|...|...|...|...|...|...|...|...|...|...|...|...|...|...|...|...|      ✓250
                                        ↑
```

```
640   650   660   670   680   690   700   710   720
|...|...|...|...|...|...|...|...|...|...|...|...|...|...|...|...|      700
                              ↑
```

```
500   510   520   530   540   550   560   570   580
|...|...|...|...|...|...|...|...|...|...|...|...|...|...|...|...|      530
              ↑
```

Polygons

Match the polygon with a solid figure.

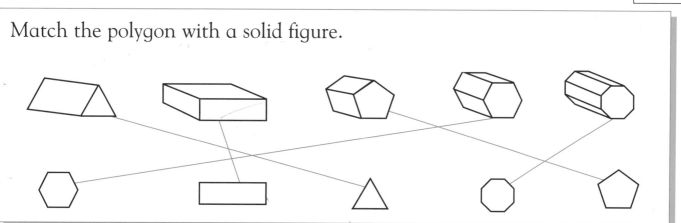

Circle the octagon.

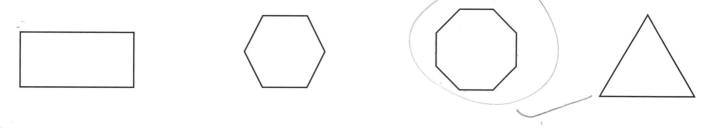

Circle the rectangle.

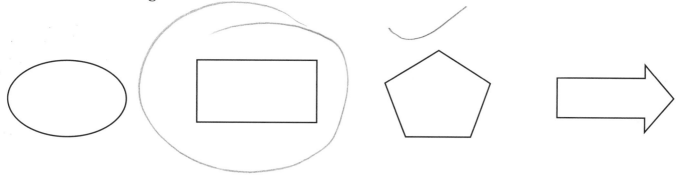

Match the polygon to the solid object in which it appears.

hexagon   octagon   rectangle   pentagon   triangle

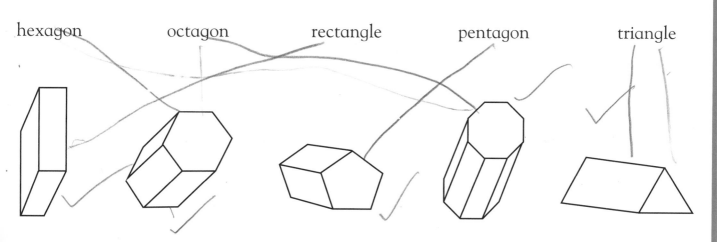

Continue each pattern.

0	6	12	18	24	30
0	7	14	21	28	35
60	52	44	36	28	20

Continue each pattern.

3	9	15	21				
2	9	16	23				
1	9	17	25				
7	15	23	31				
7	13	19	25				
7	12	17	22				

Continue each pattern.

71	65	59	53				
90	82	74	66				
56	49	42	35				
72	66	60	54				
96	88	80	72				
48	42	36	30				

Continue each pattern.

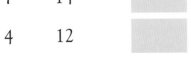

36	43						85
61	55					25	19
0	7	14					49
7	14						56
4	12			36			

Odds and evens

Multiply the odd number by the odd number. $7 \times 5 = \boxed{35}$

Multiply the even number by the even number. $6 \times 8 = \boxed{48}$

Multiply the odd number by the odd number.

$5 \times 7 = \boxed{35}$ $3 \times 9 = \boxed{27}$ $1 \times 5 = \boxed{5}$ $3 \times 5 = \boxed{15}$

$7 \times 3 = \boxed{21}$ $3 \times 7 = \boxed{}$ $7 \times 1 = \boxed{7}$ $7 \times 7 = \boxed{}$

$3 \times 3 = \boxed{9}$ $3 \times 1 = \boxed{3}$ $5 \times 9 = \boxed{45}$ $1 \times 1 = \boxed{1}$

$5 \times 3 = \boxed{15}$ $9 \times 3 = \boxed{27}$ $5 \times 5 = \boxed{25}$ $7 \times 5 = \boxed{35}$

What do you notice about the numbers in your answer boxes?

_____

Multiply the even number by the even number.

$2 \times 8 = \boxed{}$ $6 \times 4 = \boxed{}$ $6 \times 10 = \boxed{}$ $2 \times 6 = \boxed{}$

$4 \times 4 = \boxed{}$ $8 \times 2 = \boxed{}$ $6 \times 8 = \boxed{}$ $6 \times 6 = \boxed{}$

$4 \times 6 = \boxed{}$ $10 \times 4 = \boxed{}$ $4 \times 8 = \boxed{}$ $2 \times 4 = \boxed{}$

$2 \times 2 = \boxed{}$ $8 \times 6 = \boxed{}$ $6 \times 2 = \boxed{}$ $10 \times 10 = \boxed{}$

What do you notice about the numbers in your answer boxes?

_____

Multiply the odd number by the even number.

$3 \times 6 = \boxed{}$ $10 \times 5 = \boxed{}$ $7 \times 4 = \boxed{}$ $2 \times 9 = \boxed{}$

$4 \times 7 = \boxed{}$ $3 \times 10 = \boxed{}$ $4 \times 9 = \boxed{}$ $10 \times 7 = \boxed{}$

$5 \times 8 = \boxed{}$ $6 \times 9 = \boxed{}$ $8 \times 5 = \boxed{}$ $6 \times 7 = \boxed{}$

$9 \times 6 = \boxed{}$ $6 \times 3 = \boxed{}$ $9 \times 4 = \boxed{}$ $10 \times 3 = \boxed{}$

What do you notice about the numbers in your answer boxes?

_____

Addition fact families

Circle the number sentence that is in the same fact family.

| 12 − 5 = 7
5 + 7 = 12 | 12 − 4 = 8 | (7 + 5 = 12) | 12 + 12 = 24 |
| 10 − 8 = 2
8 + 2 = 10 | 8 − 6 = 2 | (2 + 8 = 10) | 8 − 2 = 6 |

Circle the number sentence that is in the same fact family.

7 + 8 = 15 8 + 7 = 15	7 + 5 = 12	15 − 8 = 7	8 − 7 = 1
17 − 6 = 11 11 + 6 = 17	17 − 11 = 6	17 + 6 = 23	5 + 6 = 11
14 − 5 = 9 14 − 9 = 5	9 − 3 = 6	14 + 9 = 23	5 + 9 = 14
9 + 7 = 16 7 + 9 = 16	16 − 9 = 7	16 + 7 = 23	9 − 7 = 2
19 − 9 = 10 19 − 10 = 9	9 + 3 = 12	9 + 10 = 19	18 − 8 = 10
4 + 7 = 11 11 − 4 = 7	11 + 4 = 15	7 + 4 = 11	7 + 7 = 14

Write the fact family for each group of numbers.

5, 6, 11	6, 10, 4	5, 13, 8

Fractions

Write the fraction for the part that is shaded.

How many shaded circles? 3

How many circles? 8

So, the fraction of circles shaded = $\frac{3}{8}$ $\frac{\text{numerator}}{\text{denominator}}$

Circle the fraction that shows the part that is shaded.

$\frac{2}{5}$ $\frac{2}{3}$ $\frac{3}{5}$

$\frac{3}{4}$ $\frac{4}{7}$ $\frac{3}{7}$

Write the fraction for the part that is shaded.

$\frac{3}{4}$

$\frac{5}{8}$

$\frac{1}{3}$

$\frac{4}{9}$

$\frac{5}{8}$

$\frac{4}{8}$

$\frac{5}{7}$

$\frac{2}{6}$

$\frac{5}{12}$

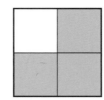 # Fractions

Colour $\frac{3}{4}$ of each shape.

Colour $\frac{2}{3}$ of each shape.

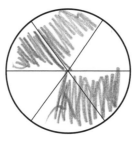
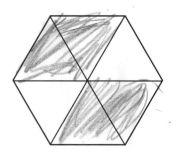

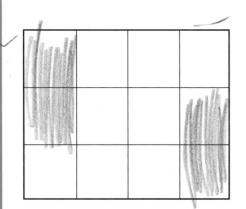
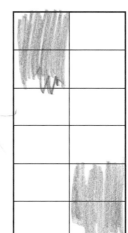
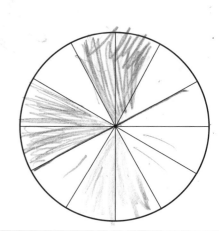

Colour $\frac{3}{4}$ of each shape.

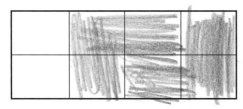
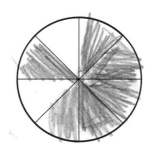
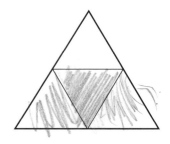

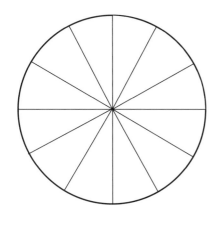
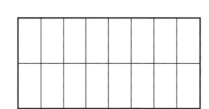
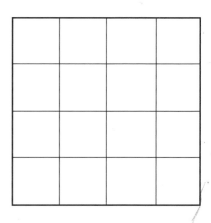

Ordering

Write these numbers in order, from smallest to largest.

606   303   707   505   90 | 90 | 303 | 505 | 606 | 707 |

Write these numbers in order, from smallest to largest.

320	230	421	124	35	35	124	230	320	421
160	762	85	146	641	85				
76	189	99	340	430					
460	64	237	173	426					
701	189	89	382	328					

Write these numbers in order, from smallest to largest.

99	119	201	911	319					
746	47	647	747	74					
673	701	77	637	360					
700	160	155	70	17					
89	390	93	244	98					

Write these numbers in order, from smallest to largest.

692	291	270	39	401					
125	81	18	89	99					
75	750	260	140	350					
280	340	460	180	230					
530	480	290	190	350					

Adding

Write the answer between the lines.

```
  34        28        75
+ 42      + 11      + 14
  76        39        89
```

Write the answer between the lines.

```
  24        36        45        61
+ 14      + 23      + 13      + 17
____      ____      ____      ____


  63        71        48        53
+ 14      + 16      + 10      + 16
____      ____      ____      ____


  60        46        54        83
+ 36      + 21      + 33      +  6
____      ____      ____      ____


  28        53        74        38
+ 31      + 36      + 25      + 21
____      ____      ____      ____


  57        65        79        47
+ 22      + 14      + 10      + 12
____        79      ____        59


  35        46        57        68
+ 13      + 22      + 31      + 40
____        68        88      ____


  44        53        26        62
+ 25      + 34      + 33      + 17
____      ____      ____      ____


  50        47        66        45
+ 37      + 11      + 22      + 32
____      ____      ____      ____
```

Adding

Write the answer between the lines.

```
  15          25          55
+ 20        + 40        +  5
  35          65          60
```

Write the answer between the lines.

```
  50          70          90          20
+ 25        + 15        +  5        + 45
  75          85          95          65

  65          25          35          85
+ 30        + 40        + 50        + 10
                          85          93

  30          60          55          75
+ 25        + 35        + 30        + 20
                          85          95

  25          45          65          15
+ 15        +  5        + 25        + 15
              50          90          30

  75          15          35          45
+ 10        + 25        + 25        + 15
                                      60

  65          45           5          55
+ 35        + 25        + 65        + 35
                                      90

  35          45          15          75
+ 45        + 35        + 30        +  5
                                      80

   5          50          45          80
+ 95        + 35        + 45        + 15
                                      95
```

Subtracting

Write the answer between the lines.

36	25	57
− 14	− 13	− 26
22	12	31

Write the answer between the lines.

27	35	47	63
− 14	− 12	− 32	− 20
13	23	15	

54	38	47	56
− 23	− 16	− 12	− 21
31	82	35	

44	57	65	78
− 32	− 24	− 32	− 35
12	33		

66	75	84	93
− 26	− 35	− 64	− 33
40	40 50		

87	76	67	49
− 34	− 45	− 33	− 28
53	31		

56	73	47	54
− 35	− 40	− 25	− 32
21	33		

79	45	76	75
− 38	− 21	− 43	− 12
41	27		

43	55	67	53
− 30	− 12	− 33	− 12
13			

Subtracting

Write the answer between the lines.

1 13	2 14	3 13
2̶3̶	3̶4̶	4̶3̶
− 16	− 17	− 18
7	17	25

Write the answer between the lines.

36	41	53	65
− 28	− 35	− 46	− 47

44	35	62	73
− 27	− 18	− 24	− 44

56	37	43	68
− 46	− 18	− 26	− 49

34	45	63	37
− 12	− 18	− 46	− 15

60	47	63	86
− 43	− 24	− 40	− 29
			57

73	56	48	80
− 34	− 47	− 36	− 45
			35

54	70	37	53
− 38	− 45	− 18	− 26
	25	19	

34	71	25	83
− 18	− 44	− 17	− 29
16			

17

Choosing the operation

Write either + or − in the box to make each problem correct.

15 + 25 = 40   30 − 8 = 22   50 − 25 = 25

Write either + or − in the box to make each problem correct.

45 − 12 = 33   48 + 14 = 34   31 + 15 = 46

17 + 13 = 30   60 − 35 = 25   70 + 35 = 35

27 − 15 = 12   26 + 18 = 44   50 + 12 = 62

65 − 25 = 40   80 − 35 = 45   63 + 23 = 40

Write either + or − in the box to make each problem correct.

12 m + 5 m = 17 m   34 cm − 18 cm = 16 cm

29 cm − 17 cm = 12 cm   42 cm + 20 cm = 62 cm

28 cm + 28 cm = 56 cm   60 cm − 15 cm = 45 cm

40 cm − 8 cm = 32 cm   90 cm − 35 cm = 55 cm

28 cm + 15 cm = 43 cm   70 m − 29 m = 41 m

90 cm − 12 cm = 78 cm   28 m + 21 m = 49 m

Write the answer in the box.

I start with 12 apples and end up with 18 apples. How many have I added or subtracted?

A number is added to 14 and the result is 20. What number has been added?

I start with 14 pens. I finish up with 9 pens. How many pens have I lost or gained?

I take a number away from 30 and have 12 left. What number did I take away?

MIMZY The last
The last MIMZY

Multiplying

Solve the problems.

2	1	5	5
x 2	x 3	x 4	x 2
4	3	20	10

Solve the problems.

1	3	4	2
x 4	x 3	x 2	x 4
4	9	8	8

5	4	4	3
x 4	x 3	x 4	x 2
20	12	16	6

5	7	2	6
x 3	x 2	x 3	x 2
15	24	6	18

Solve the problems.

8	8	6	9
x 2	x 3	x 3	x 2
24			

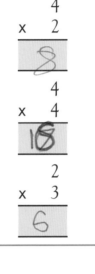

The last MIMZY is my favourite movie. In other words Silas favourite movie the last MIMZY

3	5	10	10
x 4	x 7	x 2	x 7
12			

5	3	2	4
x 5	x 5	x 5	x 5

1	7	9	8
x 5	x 5	x 5	x 5

10	10	10	20
x 5	x 6	x 3	x 2

Multiplying

Solve each problem.

16 x **4** = (10 x 4) + (6 x 4)

   = 40 + 24

   = 64

10	6
x 4	x 4
40	24

40 + 24 = 64

Solve each problem.

8 x 4	5 x 6

7 x 5	4 x 7

9 x 3	6 x 6

13 x 4	16 x 5

14 x 6	12 x 4

12 x 7	14 x 4

Dividing

Write the answer to each division problem.

$27 \div 3 =$ 9 $40 \div 10 =$ 4

$$\begin{array}{r} 7 \\ 5\overline{)35} \\ -35 \\ \hline 0 \end{array}$$

Write the answer to each division problem.

$30 \div 10 = $ 3	$28 \div 4 = $ 7	$18 \div 2 = $	$40 \div 5 =$
$20 \div 10 = $ 2	$40 \div 4 = $	$20 \div 2 = $	$35 \div 5 =$
$60 \div 10 = $ 6	$24 \div 4 = $	$16 \div 2 = $	$45 \div 5 =$
$90 \div 10 = $ 9	$32 \div 4 = $	$14 \div 2 = $	$30 \div 5 =$

Write the answer in the box.

$5\overline{)25}$ $3\overline{)15}$ $4\overline{)24}$ $2\overline{)12}$ $3\overline{)21}$

$2\overline{)8}$ $10\overline{)70}$ $5\overline{)20}$ $3\overline{)30}$ $2\overline{)10}$

Write the answer in the box.

What is the remainder when 15 is divided by 2?

How many groups of 5 are there in 45?

How many groups of 3 are there in 21 and what is the remainder?

What is the remainder when 63 is divided by 10?

Divide 27 by 3.

How many groups of 4 are there in 26?

Dividing

Write the answer to each division problem.

$14 \div 3 =$ 4 r 2 $18 \div 5 =$ 3 r 3 $2 \overline{)9}$ 4 r 1
$\phantom{2\overline{)}}\underline{-8}$
$\phantom{2\overline{)}9}1$

Write the answer in the box.

$15 \div 3 =$ ⬜ $25 \div 5 =$ ⬜ $10 \div 10 =$ ⬜ $24 \div 4 =$ ⬜

$12 \div 3 =$ ⬜ $20 \div 5 =$ ⬜ $60 \div 10 =$ ⬜ $36 \div 4 =$ ⬜

$24 \div 3 =$ ⬜ $35 \div 5 =$ ⬜ $40 \div 10 =$ ⬜ $16 \div 4 =$ ⬜

$30 \div 3 =$ ⬜ $30 \div 5 =$ ⬜ $80 \div 10 =$ ⬜ $24 \div 4 =$ ⬜

Write the answer in the box.

$3 \overline{)15}$ $5 \overline{)15}$ $10 \overline{)40}$ $4 \overline{)12}$ $3 \overline{)25}$

$3 \overline{)9}$ $5 \overline{)14}$ $10 \overline{)41}$ $4 \overline{)20}$ $10 \overline{)69}$

Write the answer in the box.

What is the remainder when 36 is divided by 10? ⬜

How many whole sets of 3 are there in 16? ⬜

How many sets of 4 are there in 30 and what is the remainder? ⬜

What is the remainder when 44 is divided by 40? ⬜

Divide 26 by 3. ⬜

Divide 40 by 6. ⬜

Choosing the operation

Write either x or ÷ in the box to make the product correct.

12 ÷ 2 = 6   12 × 2 = 24   10 ÷ 2 = 5

Write either x or ÷ in the box to make the product correct.

18 ☐ 3 = 6   20 ☐ 10 = 2   6 ☐ 3 = 18

2 ☐ 9 = 18   20 ☐ 2 = 10   12 ☐ 4 = 3

7 ☐ 10 = 70   24 ☐ 3 = 8   30 ☐ 10 = 3

27 ☐ 3 = 9   18 ☐ 3 = 6   14 ☐ 2 = 28

16 ☐ 4 = 4   24 ☐ 4 = 6   30 ☐ 3 = 10

3 ☐ 8 = 24   5 ☐ 10 = 50   6 ☐ 2 = 3

Write either x or ÷ in the box to make the product correct.

27 cm ☐ 3 = 9 cm   40 cm ☐ 10 = 4 cm   15 cm ☐ 3 = 5 cm

18 cm ☐ 2 = 9 cm   4 m ☐ 5 = 20 m   10 cm ☐ 4 = 40 cm

30 cm ☐ 10 = 3 cm   50 cm ☐ 5 = 10 cm   60 cm ☐ 2 = 30 cm

5 m ☐ 8 = 40 m   4 cm ☐ 2 = 2 cm   4 m ☐ 2 = 8 m

20 cm ☐ 5 = 4 cm   20 cm ☐ 4 = 5 cm   20 cm ☐ 2 = 40 cm

12 m ☐ 2 = 6 m   1 cm ☐ 10 = 10 cm   4 m ☐ 3 = 12 m

Write the answer in the box.

Which number multiplied by 3 equals 24? ☐

Which number divided by 10 equals 7? ☐

Which number divided by 8 equals 5? ☐

Which number multiplied by 6 equals 6? ☐

Which number multiplied by 9 equals 36? ☐

Which number multiplied by 5 equals 30? ☐

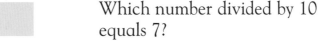

Word problems

Write the answer in the box.

I multiply a number by 6 and the answer is 24.

What number did I begin with? 4

Write the answer in the box.

A number multiplied by 7 equals 35. What is the number?

I divide a number by 10 and the answer is 3. What number did I divide?

I multiply a number by 4 and the answer is 20. What is the number I multiplied?

After dividing a piece of wood into four equal sections, each section is
4 cm long. How long was the piece of wood I started with?

A number multiplied by 6 gives the answer 24. What is the number?

Some money is divided into five equal amounts. Each amount is 10 cents.
How much money was there before it was divided?

I multiply a number by 4 and the result is 24. What number was multiplied?

A number divided by 6 is 3. What number was divided?

Three children share 18 peanuts equally among themselves.
How many peanuts does each child receive?

A number divided by 4 is 4. What is the number?

I multiply a number by 6 and the answer is 30. What is the number?

Four sets of a number equal 16. What is the number?

A number divided by 5 is 5. What is the number?

A child divides a number by 4 and gets 2. What number was divided?

Three groups of a number equal 9. What is the number?

I multiply a number by 10 and the result is 100. What is the number?

Word problems

Write the answer in the box.

A child is given four dimes. How much money does she have altogether? 40¢

Write the answer in the box.

A box contains 6 eggs. How many boxes would I need to buy to have 18 eggs?

A boy is given three bags of candy. There are 4 pieces in each bag. How many pieces of candy does the boy have in total? 12

Four lifeboats carry a total of 20 people. How many people are in each boat?

A shepherd had 100 sheep but 70 were lost in a snowstorm. How many sheep does the shepherd have left?

Three women win the lottery and share $90 equally among themselves. How much does each woman receive?

A truck contains 50 barrels of oil. It delivers 27 barrels to one garage. How many barrels are left on the truck?

Andrej has a collection of 150 baseball cards. He sells 30 of them to a friend. How many cards does he have left?

When Peter multiplies his apartment number by 3, the result is 21. What is his apartment number?

One photograph costs 70¢. How much will two photographs cost?

A dog buries 20 bones on Monday, 30 bones on Tuesday, and 40 bones on Wednesday. How many bones has the dog buried altogether?

A car trip is supposed to be 18 kilometres long but the car breaks down half-way. How far has the car gone when it breaks down?

A teacher has 32 children in her class. 13 children are out with the flu. How many children are left in class?

Problems with measures

Which would be the best unit to use
for the length of a worm?

centimetre

Choose the most appropriate unit for the measurements below.

metre litre kilometre millilitre gram kilogram centimetre

Write the best unit for each of the following.

The length of a garden path.   M

The mass of a brick.   cm

The mass of a thimble.   cm

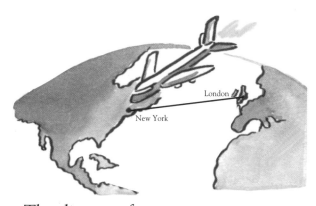

The distance from
London to New York.   Km

The length of a tortoise.   cm

The capacity of a bucket.   cm

Telling time

What time is shown by these clocks?

   28 minutes to 7

   14 minutes past 3

What time is shown by these clocks?

7: 45

4: ~~XX~~ 10

5:52

6: 25

10: 50

10:54

10: 54

2: 35

12: 08

27

Telling time

Draw the time on each clock face.

Twenty-six minutes past four.

Draw the time on each clock face.

Twelve minutes to eight

Twenty to nine

Seventeen minutes past four

Eleven minutes to six

Twenty-seven minutes
past twelve

Tables and graphs

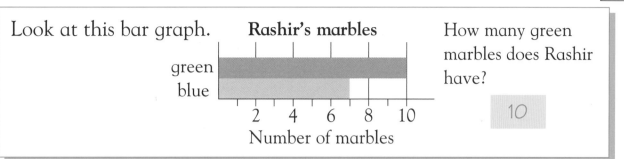

Look at this bar graph.

Rashir's marbles

green
blue

2   4   6   8   10
Number of marbles

How many green marbles does Rashir have?

10

Look at this bar graph.

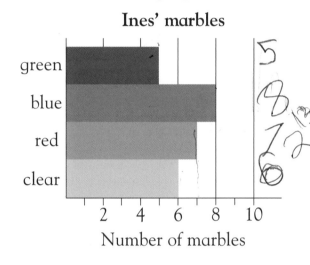

Ines' marbles

green
blue
red
clear

2   4   6   8   10
Number of marbles

How many green marbles does Ines have?

5

Ines has 7 marbles of which colour?

blue   red

How many clear marbles does Ines have?

6

Of which colour does Ines have the most marbles?

blue

How many marbles does Ines have altogether?

26

Complete the table.

Favourite pets

	tally marks	total
hamsters	++++ | |	
mice		4
gerbils	| | |	
rats		5

Pets

Number of children

How many more children have hamsters than have rats? 2

Which animal is owned by 4 children? Mice

Necessary information

Write the missing information you need to have to answer the question.

Tim wants to buy juice for his friends. Each box of juice costs 79¢. How much will it cost in all?

You need to know   *the number of friends for whom Tim is buying juice.*

Write the missing information you need to have to answer the question.

On Saturday, 367 people saw the first of five movies playing at the local theatre. How many people went to the movies on Saturday?

You need to know

Patsy has $5.25. She wants to buy a pop for $1.00. She also wants a sandwich. Does she have enough money?

You need to know

Seashells cost 35¢, 50¢, or 75¢ depending upon their size. Sara bought four shells that had the same price. How much money did she spend?

You need to know

Martina divided her class into 5 teams of students. How many students were on each team?

You need to know

Katya made sandwiches for her mother, her father, her three brothers and her sisters. She also made herself a sandwich. How many sandwiches did she make?

You need to know

Carl bought two paperback books for $6.99 each. He spent 35¢ on a pen and $1.75 on a notepad. How much money did he have left?

You need to know

Number pairs

Write the number pairs of the letter A.

A = (2,1)

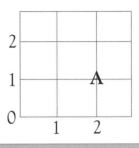

Look at this grid and write the number pairs of each letter.

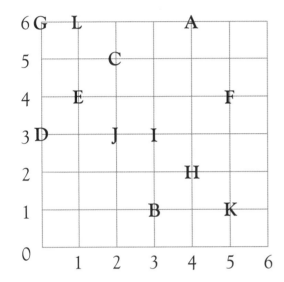

A =   G =

B =   H =

C =   I =

D =   J =

E =   K =

F =   L =

Use the grid to write the number pairs.

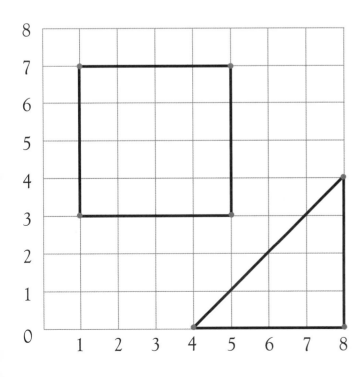

Write the number pairs of each corner of the square.

Write the number pairs of each corner of the triangle.

31

2 times table

Count in 2s, colour, and find a pattern.

1	2	3	4	5
6	7	8	9	10
11	12	13	14	15
16	17	18	19	20
21	22	23	24	25

Write the answers.

1 x 2 = 2   2 x 2 = ☐   3 x 2 = ☐   4 x 2 = ☐

5 x 2 = ☐   6 x 2 = ☐   7 x 2 = ☐   8 x 2 = ☐

9 x 2 = ☐   10 x 2 = ☐

How many ears?

 5 sets of 2   5 x 2 = 10 ears

 ☐ sets of 2   ☐ x ☐ = ☐ ears

 ☐ sets of 2   ☐ x ☐ = ☐ ears

 ☐ sets of 2   ☐ x ☐ = ☐ ears

Multiplying by 2

Write the problems.

How many pairs of feet?

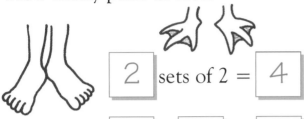

2 sets of 2 = 4

2 x 2 = 4

How many pairs of feet?

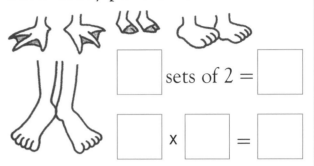

☐ sets of 2 = ☐

☐ x ☐ = ☐

How many pairs of feet?

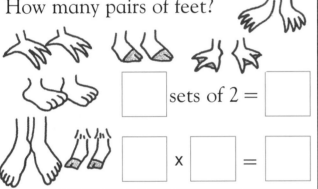

☐ sets of 2 = ☐

☐ x ☐ = ☐

How many pairs of feet?

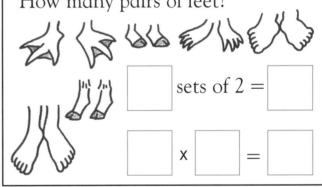

☐ sets of 2 = ☐

☐ x ☐ = ☐

How many pairs of feet?

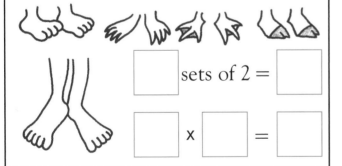

☐ sets of 2 = ☐

☐ x ☐ = ☐

How many pairs of feet?

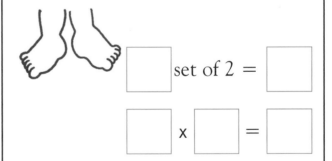

☐ set of 2 = ☐

☐ x ☐ = ☐

Draw different pictures to go with these problems.

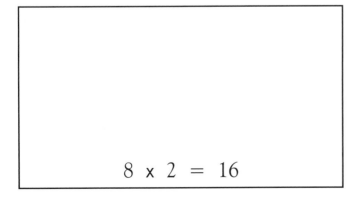

8 x 2 = 16

10 x 2 = 20

Dividing by 2

Share the eggs equally between the nests.

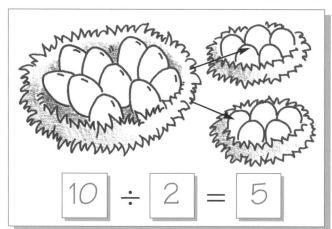

$$10 \div 2 = 5$$

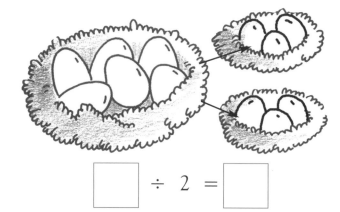

$$\boxed{} \div 2 = \boxed{}$$

$$\boxed{} \div 2 = \boxed{}$$

$$\boxed{} \div 2 = \boxed{}$$

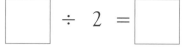

$$\boxed{} \div 2 = \boxed{}$$

$$\boxed{} \div 2 = \boxed{}$$

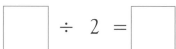

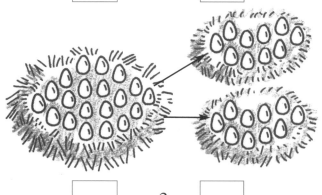

$$\boxed{} \div 2 = \boxed{}$$

$$\boxed{} \div 2 = \boxed{}$$

Using the 2 times table

Write the problems to match the stamps.

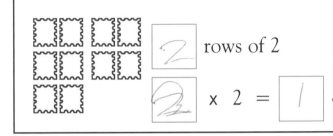

6 rows of 2

6 x 2 = 12

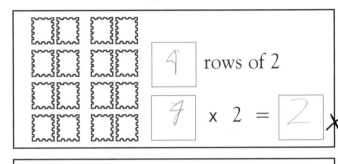

4 rows of 2

4 x 2 = 2 ✗

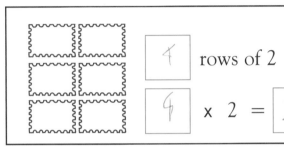

4 rows of 2

4 x 2 = 2 ✗

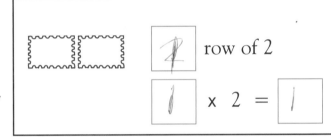

2 rows of 2

2 x 2 = 1 ✗

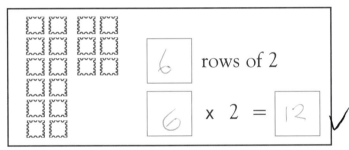

6 rows of 2

6 x 2 = 12 ✓

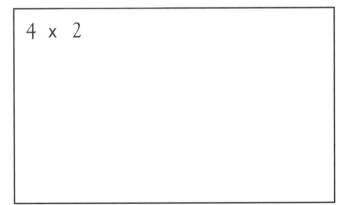

1 row of 2

1 x 2 = 1   2

Draw the stamps to match these problems.

3 x 2	4 x 2

2 x 2	7 x 2

Using the 2 times table

Each face stands for 2. Join each set of faces to the correct number.

2

6

8

10

12

14

16

20

Using the 2 times table

How many eyes?

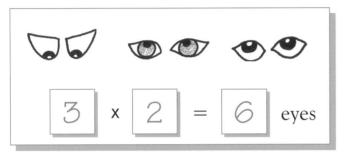

$3 \times 2 = 6$ eyes

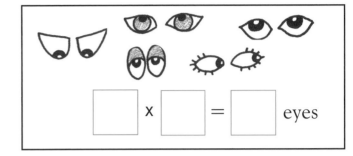

$\boxed{} \times \boxed{} = \boxed{}$ eyes

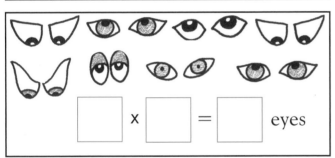

$\boxed{} \times \boxed{} = \boxed{}$ eyes

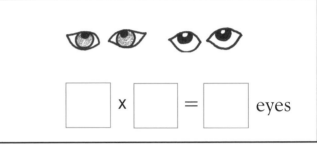

$\boxed{} \times \boxed{} = \boxed{}$ eyes

$\boxed{} \times \boxed{} = \boxed{}$ eyes

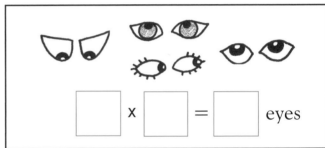

$\boxed{} \times \boxed{} = \boxed{}$ eyes

Draw your own pictures to match these number sentences.

$2 \times 2 = 4$

$10 \times 2 = 20$

$3 \times 2 = 6$

$7 \times 2 = 14$

37

5 times table

Count in 5s, colour, and find a pattern.

1	2	3	4	5	6	7	8	9	10
11	12	13	14	15	16	17	18	19	20
21	22	23	24	25	26	27	28	29	30
31	32	33	34	35	36	37	38	39	40
41	42	43	44	45	46	47	48	49	50
51	52	53	54	55	56	57	58	59	60
61	62	63	64	65	66	67	68	69	70
71	72	73	74	75	76	77	78	79	80
81	82	83	84	85	86	87	88	89	90
91	92	93	94	95	96	97	98	99	100

Write the answers.

$1 \times 5 = \boxed{5}$ $2 \times 5 = \boxed{10}$ $3 \times 5 = \boxed{15}$ $4 \times 5 = \boxed{20}$

$5 \times 5 = \boxed{25}$ $6 \times 5 = \boxed{30}$ $7 \times 5 = \boxed{30}$ 35 $8 \times 5 = \boxed{40}$

$10 \times 5 = \boxed{50}$ * $9 \times 5 = \boxed{45}$ *

How many candies?

 $\boxed{4}$ sets of 5 $\boxed{4} \times \boxed{5} = \boxed{20}$ candies

 $\boxed{3}$ sets of 5 $\boxed{3} \times \boxed{5} = \boxed{15}$ candies

 $\boxed{8}$ sets of 5 $\boxed{8} \times \boxed{5} = \boxed{40}$ candies

 $\boxed{7}$ sets of 5 $\boxed{7} \times \boxed{5} = \boxed{30}$ candies

Multiplying by 5

Draw a ring around rows of 5. Complete the problem.

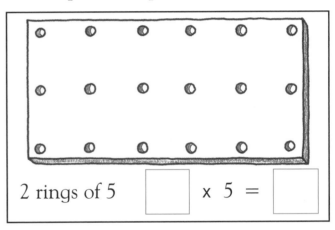

3 x 5 = 15

Draw a ring around rows of 5. Complete the problem.

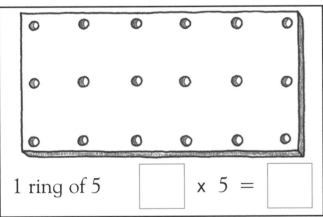

5 rings of 5   ☐   x 5 = ☐

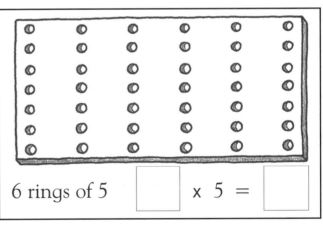

2 rings of 5   ☐   x 5 = ☐

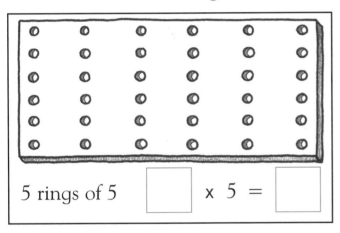

1 ring of 5   ☐   x 5 = ☐

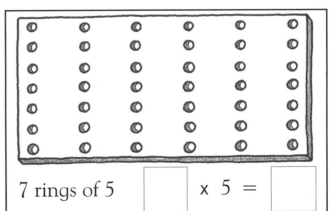

6 rings of 5   ☐   x 5 = ☐

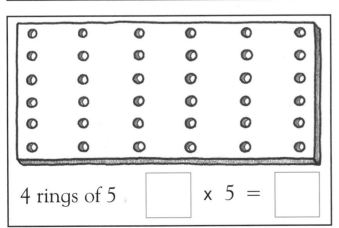

4 rings of 5   ☐   x 5 = ☐

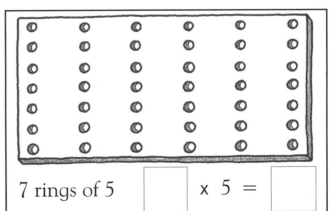

7 rings of 5   ☐   x 5 = ☐

Dividing by 5

Write a number sentence to show how many cubes are in each stack.

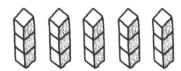

15 cubes altogether

5 stacks

15 ÷ 5 = 3

Write a number sentence to show how many cubes are in each stack.

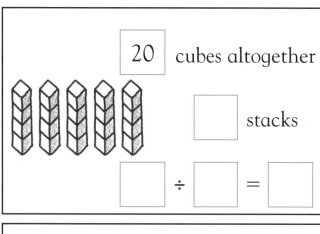

20 cubes altogether

☐ stacks

☐ ÷ ☐ = ☐

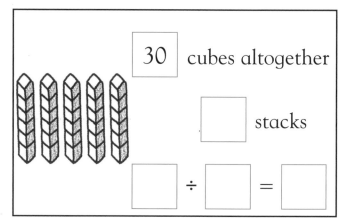

30 cubes altogether

☐ stacks

☐ ÷ ☐ = ☐

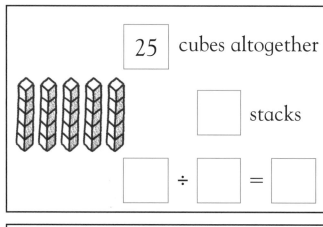

25 cubes altogether

☐ stacks

☐ ÷ ☐ = ☐

10 cubes altogether

☐ stacks

☐ ÷ ☐ = ☐

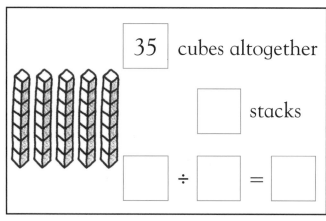

35 cubes altogether

☐ stacks

☐ ÷ ☐ = ☐

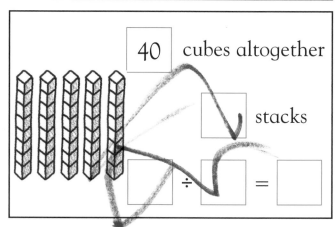

40 cubes altogether

☐ stacks

☐ ÷ ☐ = ☐

Using the 5 times table

Write the number that is hiding under the star.

 x 5 = 20

Write the number that is hiding under the star.

 x 5 = 10   3 x 5 =

 x 5 = 25   1 x 5 =

 x 5 = 50   8 x 5 =

x 5 = 45   0 x 5 =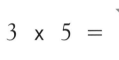

 x 5 = 35   6 x 5 =

Using the 5 times table

Each frog stands for 5. Join each set of frogs to the correct number.

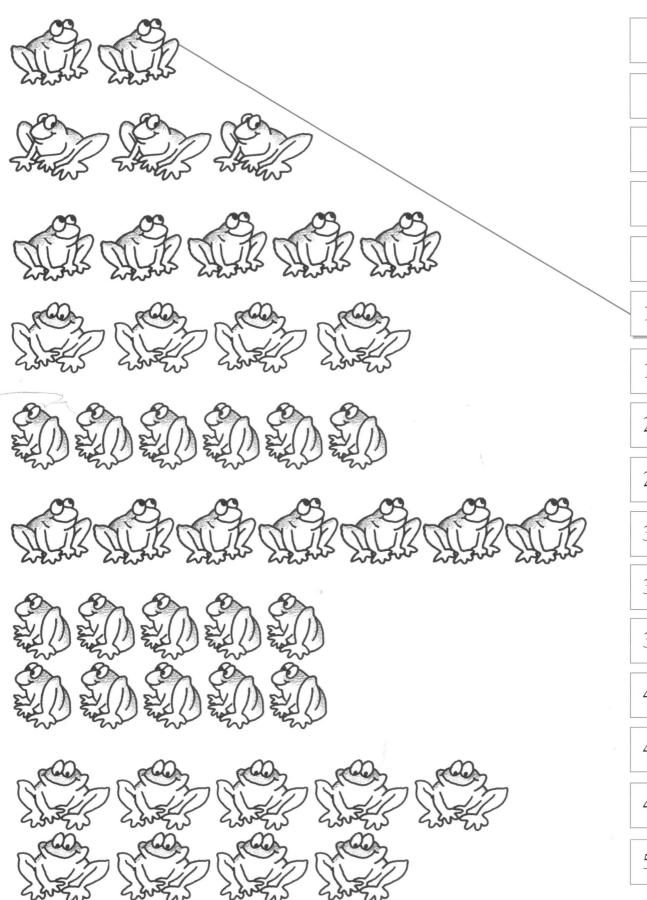

1

2

4

5

8

10

15

20

25

30

35

36

40

45

48

50

Using the 5 times table

How many altogether?

Georgia had 7 cats. Each cat had 5 kittens.
How many kittens were there altogether?

$\boxed{7} \times \boxed{5} = \boxed{35}$ kittens

How many altogether?

Charlie had 6 boxes. He had 5 trains in each box. How many trains did he have altogether?

$\boxed{} \times \boxed{} = \boxed{}$ trains

Zoe had 3 jackets. Each jacket had 5 buttons. How many buttons were there altogether?

$\boxed{} \times \boxed{} = \boxed{}$ buttons

Yan had 8 fish tanks. Each tank had 5 fish in it. How many fish were there altogether?

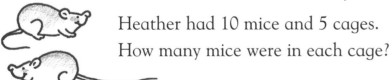

$\boxed{} \times \boxed{} = \boxed{}$ fish

How many in each?

Joe had 45 pencils and 5 pencil cases.
How many pencils were in each case?

$\boxed{45} \div \boxed{5} = \boxed{9}$ pencils

How many in each?

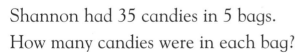

Heather had 10 mice and 5 cages.
How many mice were in each cage?

$\boxed{} \div \boxed{} = \boxed{}$ mice

Shannon had 35 candies in 5 bags.
How many candies were in each bag?

$\boxed{} \div \boxed{} = \boxed{}$ candies

Mark put 25 seeds into 5 pots.
How many seeds were in each pot?

$\boxed{} \div \boxed{} = \boxed{}$ seeds

10 times table

Count in 10s, colour, and find a pattern.

1	2	3	4	5	6	7	8	9	10
11	12	13	14	15	16	17	18	19	20
21	22	23	24	25	26	27	28	29	30
31	32	33	34	35	36	37	38	39	40
41	42	43	44	45	46	47	48	49	50
51	52	53	54	55	56	57	58	59	60
61	62	63	64	65	66	67	68	69	70
71	72	73	74	75	76	77	78	79	80
81	82	83	84	85	86	87	88	89	90
91	92	93	94	95	96	97	98	99	100

Write the answers.

1 x 10 = 10   2 x 10 =   3 x 10 =   4 x 10 =

5 x 10 =   6 x 10 =   7 x 10 =   8 x 10 =

10 x 10 =   9 x 10 =

Each box contains 10 crayons. How many crayons are there altogether?

 2 sets of 10   2 x 10 = 20 crayons

 _ sets of 10   _ x _ = _ crayons

 _ sets of 10   _ x _ = _ crayons

 _ sets of 10   _ x _ = _ crayons

Multiplying and dividing

Each pod contains 10 peas. How many peas are there altogether?

How many pods? 2

2 x 10 = 20 peas

Write how many peas.

 How many pods? ☐

☐ x 10 = ☐ peas

 How many pods? ☐

☐ x ☐ = ☐ peas

 How many pods? ☐

☐ x ☐ = ☐ peas

How many pods? ☐

☐ x ☐ = ☐ peas

How many pods did the peas come from?

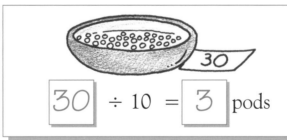

30 ÷ 10 = 3 pods

Write how many pods.

☐ ÷ 10 = ☐ pod

☐ ÷ 10 = ☐ pods

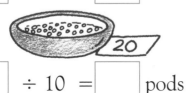

☐ ÷ 10 = ☐ pods

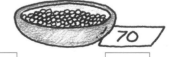

☐ ÷ 10 = ☐ pods

Dividing by 10

One dollar is worth the same as ten dimes.

How many dollars are there?

30 dimes

$30 \div 10 = \$ \ 3$

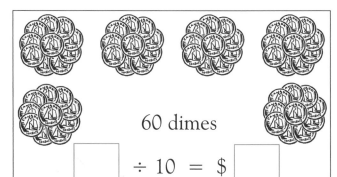

60 dimes

$\div 10 = \$$

40 dimes

$\div 10 = \$$

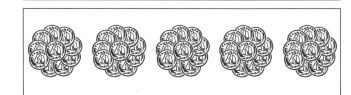

50 dimes

$\div 10 = \$$

90 dimes

$\div 10 = \$$

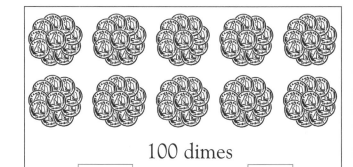

100 dimes

$\div 10 = \$$

10 dimes

$\div 10 = \$$

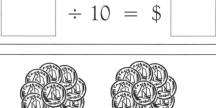

20 dimes

$\div 10 = \$$

Using the 10 times table

How many altogether?

The squirrels had 4 food dens. Each den had 10 acorns. How many acorns were there altogether?

$\boxed{4}$ x $\boxed{10}$ = $\boxed{40}$ acorns

How many altogether?

The monkeys had 6 trees. There were 10 bananas in each tree. How many bananas did they have altogether?

$\boxed{}$ x $\boxed{}$ = $\boxed{}$ bananas

The frogs had 2 ponds. Each pond had 10 lily pads. How many lily pads were there altogether?

$\boxed{}$ x $\boxed{}$ = $\boxed{}$ lily pads

The snakes had 5 nests. Each nest had 10 eggs in it. How many eggs were there altogether?

$\boxed{}$ x $\boxed{}$ = $\boxed{}$ eggs

The lions had 7 cubs. Each cub already had 10 teeth. How many teeth did the cubs have altogether?

$\boxed{}$ x $\boxed{}$ = $\boxed{}$ teeth

How many in each?

The crows had 40 eggs and 10 nests. How many eggs were in each nest?

$\boxed{40}$ ÷ $\boxed{10}$ = $\boxed{4}$ eggs

How many in each?

There were 90 mice living in 10 nests. How many mice were in each nest?

$\boxed{}$ ÷ $\boxed{}$ = $\boxed{}$ mice

There were 60 foxes hiding in 10 dens. How many foxes were in each den?

$\boxed{}$ ÷ $\boxed{}$ = $\boxed{}$ foxes

Using the 10 times table

Match each dog to the right bone.

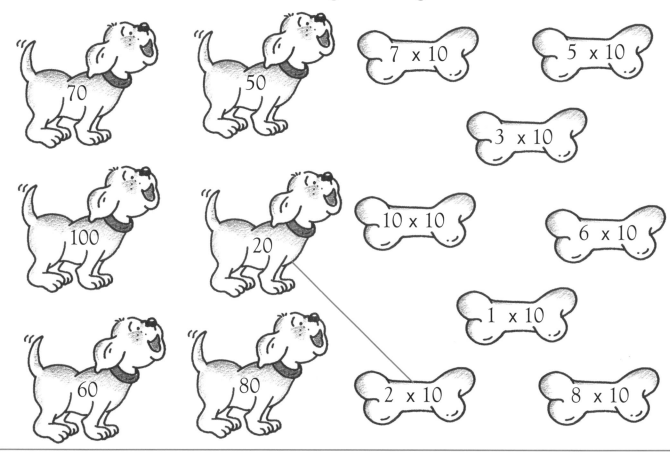

Match each mouse to the right cheese.

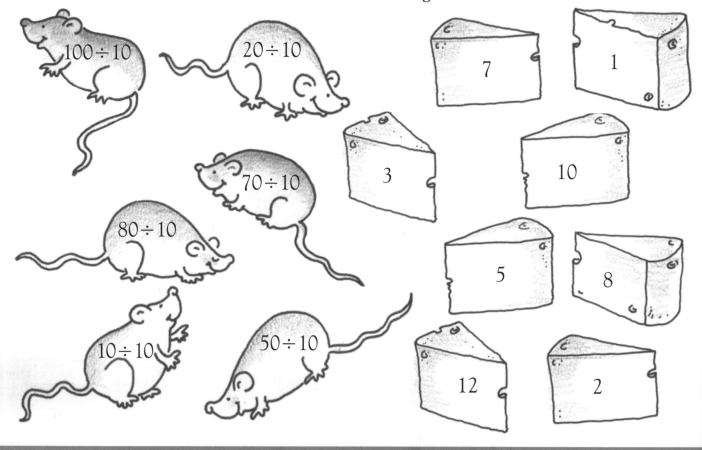

Using the 10 times table

Write in the missing numbers.

3	x	10	=	30
10	x	3	=	30
30	÷	3	=	10
30	÷	10	=	3

5	x	10	=	50
	x		=	50
50	÷		=	5
50	÷		=	10

7	x	10	=	70
	x		=	
	÷		=	
	÷		=	

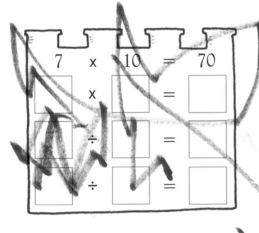

9	x	10	=	90
	x		=	
	÷		=	
	÷		=	

2	x	10	=	20
	x		=	
	÷		=	
	÷		=	

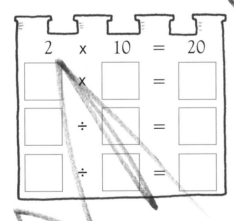

4	x	10	=	40
	x		=	
	÷		=	
	÷		=	

8	x	10	=	80
	x		=	
	÷		=	
	÷		=	

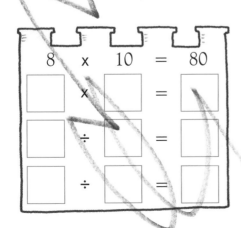

6	x	10	=	60
	x		=	
	÷		=	
	÷		=	

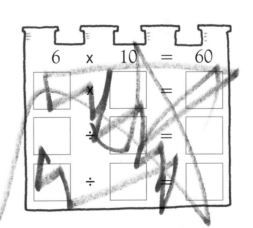
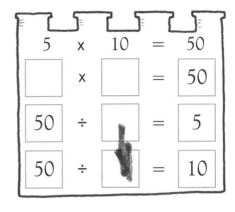

3 times table

Count in 3s, colour, and find a pattern.

1	2	3	4	5
6	7	8	9	10
11	12	13	14	15
16	17	18	19	20
21	22	23	24	25

Write the answers.

1 x 3 = 3   2 x 3 = ☐   3 x 3 = ☐   4 x 3 = ☐   5 x 3 = ☐

How many flowers?

   2 sets of 3   2 x 3 = 6

   3 sets of 3   3 x 3 = 9

   4 sets of 3   4 x 3 = 12

   5 sets of 3   5 x 3 = 15

Multiplying by 3

Today

Write the number sentences to match the pictures.

 3 sets of 3 = 9

3 × 3 = 9

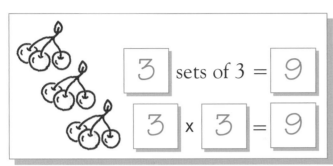 4 sets of 3 = 12

4 × 3 = 12

 2 sets of 3 = 6

2 × 3 = 6

 5 sets of 3 = 12

5 × 3 = 12

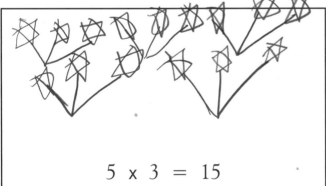 3 sets of 3 = 9

3 × 3 = 9

 1 set of 3 = 3

1 × 3 = 3

Draw your own pictures to match these number sentences.

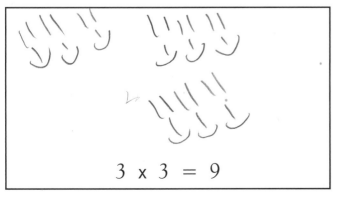

5 × 3 = 15

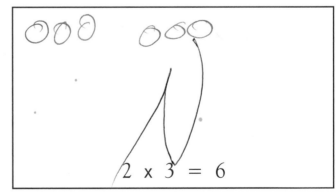

2 × 3 = 6

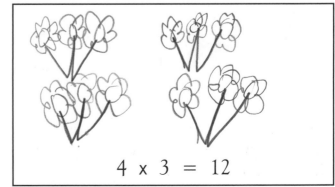

3 × 3 = 9

4 × 3 = 12

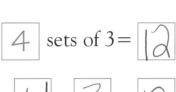

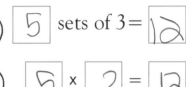

Dividing by 3

Divide the money equally among the purses.
Write a problem to show what you have done.
You might find it easier to change all the money into 1¢ coins.

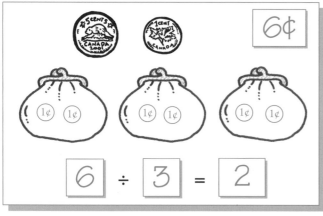

6¢

6 ÷ 3 = 2

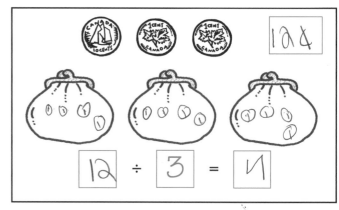

12¢

12 ÷ 3 = 4

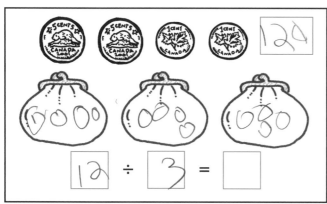

12¢

12 ÷ 3 =

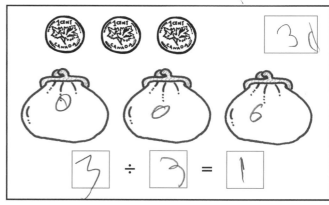

3¢

3 ÷ 3 = 1

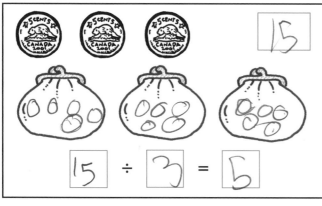

15

15 ÷ 3 = 5

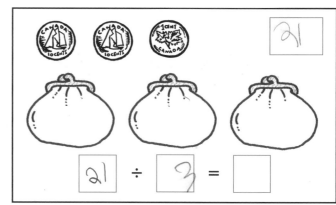

21

21 ÷ 3 =

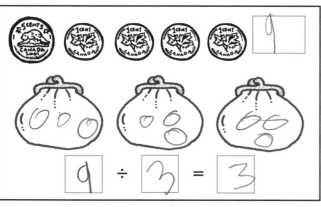

9

9 ÷ 3 = 3

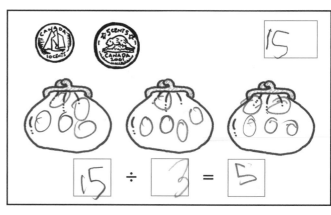

15

15 ÷ 3 = 5

4 times table

Count in 4s, colour, and find a pattern.

1	2	3	4	5
6	7	8	9	10
11	12	13	14	15
16	17	18	19	20
21	22	23	24	25

Write the answers.

1 x 4 = ☐   2 x 4 = ☐   3 x 4 = ☐   4 x 4 = ☐   5 x 4 = ☐

How many flowers?

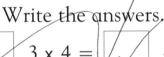

4 sets of 4   4 x 4 = 16

☐ sets of 4   ☐ x ☐ = ☐

☐ sets of 4   ☐ x ☐ = ☐

☐ sets of 4   ☐ x ☐ = ☐

Multiplying by 4

Write number sentences to match the pictures.

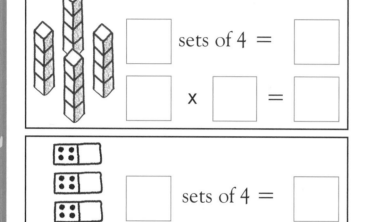

3 sets of 4 = 12

3 x 4 = 12

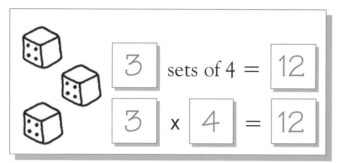

2 sets of 4 =

☐ x ☐ = ☐

☐ sets of 4 = ☐

☐ x ☐ = ☐

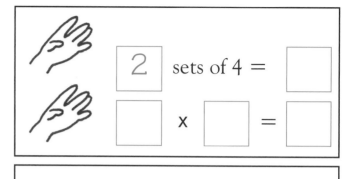

☐ set of 4 = ☐

☐ x ☐ = ☐

☐ sets of 4 = ☐

☐ x ☐ = ☐

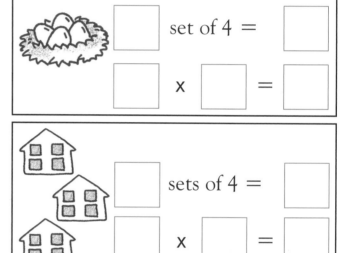

☐ sets of 4 = ☐

☐ x ☐ = ☐

Draw different pictures to match these number sentences.

2 x 4 = 8

4 x 4 = 16

5 x 4 = 20

3 x 4 = 12

Dividing by 4

How many on each plate?

There are 4 children. How many things will each child have?
Draw the objects in the circles.

8 sandwiches

$$\boxed{8} \div \boxed{4} = \boxed{2} \text{ each}$$

12 cookies

$$\boxed{} \div \boxed{4} = \boxed{} \text{ each}$$

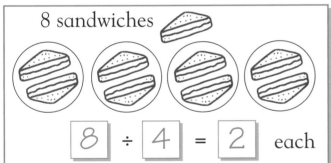

4 drinks

$$\boxed{} \div \boxed{} = \boxed{} \text{ each}$$

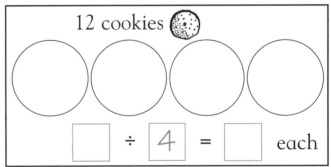

20 cherries

$$\boxed{} \div \boxed{} = \boxed{} \text{ each}$$

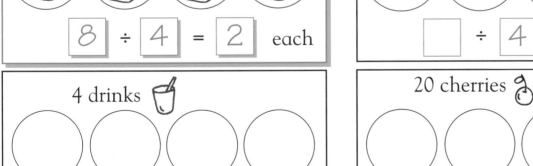

16 cupcakes

$$\boxed{} \div \boxed{} = \boxed{} \text{ each}$$

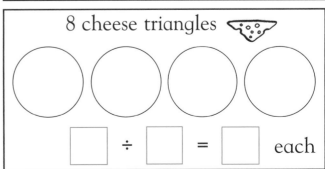

8 cheese triangles

$$\boxed{} \div \boxed{} = \boxed{} \text{ each}$$

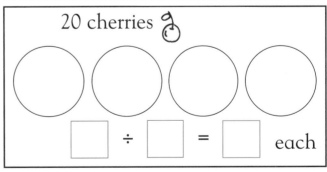

Mixed tables

How many pegs are there in each pegboard?

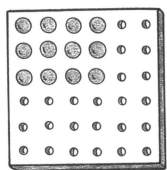

$\boxed{3}$ rows of $\boxed{4}$

$\boxed{3}$ x $\boxed{4}$ = $\boxed{12}$

How many pegs are there in each pegboard?

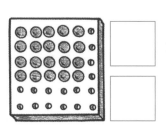 $\square$ rows of $\square$

$\square$ x $\square$ = $\square$

 $\square$ rows of $\square$

$\square$ x $\square$ = $\square$

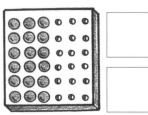 $\square$ rows of $\square$

$\square$ x $\square$ = $\square$

 $\square$ rows of $\square$

$\square$ x $\square$ = $\square$

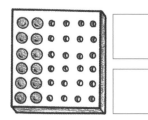 $\square$ rows of $\square$

$\square$ x $\square$ = $\square$

 $\square$ row of $\square$

$\square$ x $\square$ = $\square$

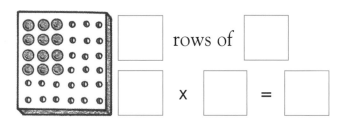 $\square$ rows of $\square$

$\square$ x $\square$ = $\square$

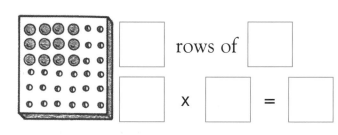 $\square$ rows of $\square$

$\square$ x $\square$ = $\square$

Mixed tables

Divide the 12 pennies equally. Draw the coins
and write the problem to show how many each person gets.

12 ÷ 3 = 4

4 ¢ each

☐ ÷ ☐ = ☐

☐ ¢ each

☐ ÷ ☐ = ☐

☐ ¢ each

☐ ÷ ☐ = ☐

☐ ¢ each

☐ ÷ ☐ = ☐

☐ ¢ each

Mixed tables

How much will they get paid?

Price List for Jobs	
Dust bedroom	3¢
Feed rabbit	2¢
Put toys away	6¢
Fetch newspaper	5¢
Walk dog	10¢

Write a problem to show how much money
Joe and Jasmine will get for these jobs.

Feed 4 rabbits  4 x 2¢ = 8¢

Dust 2 bedrooms  ☐ x ☐ = ☐ ¢

Walk the dog 4 times ☐ x ☐ = ☐ ¢

Put the toys away 3 times 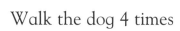   ☐ x ☐ = ☐ ¢

Fetch the newspaper 5 times ☐ x ☐ = ☐ ¢

How much will they get for these jobs?
Use the space to work out the problems.

Dust 3 bedrooms and walk
the dog twice

☐ + ☐ = ☐ ¢

Feed the rabbit 10 times and
put the toys away twice

☐ + ☐ = ☐ ¢

Mixed tables

Write the numbers that the raindrops are hiding.

4 x (5) = 20

20 ÷ 4 = (5)

2 x 4 = (8)

÷ 2 = 4

1 x (3) = 3

(3) x 3 = 6

6 ÷ 3 = ( )

3 x (1) = 3

45 ÷ 5 = ( )

5 x ( ) = 45

8 x 2 = ( )

16 ÷ 2 = ( )

60 ÷ (10) = 6

10 x (6) = 60

( ) x 4 = 12

12 ÷ 4 = ( )

7 x 5 = (35)

( ) ÷ 5 = 7

5 x ( ) = 50

50 ÷ ( ) = 5

Mixed tables

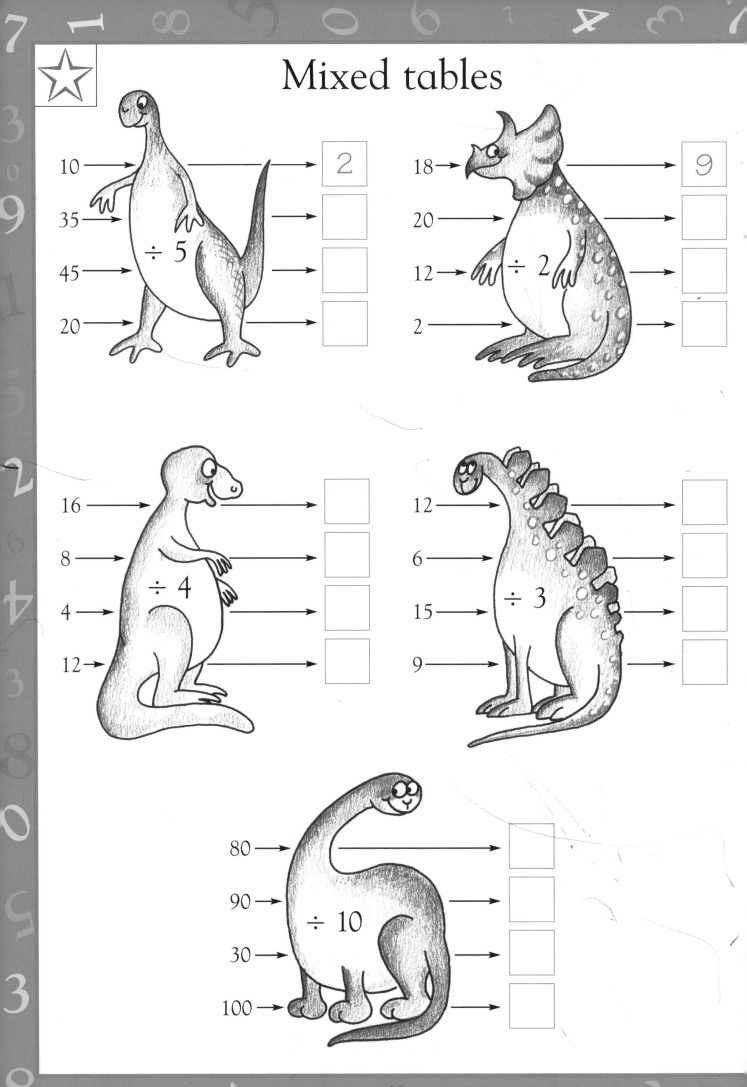

10 → → → 2

35 → →

45 → ÷ 5 →

20 → →

18 → → → 9

20 → →

12 → ÷ 2 →

2 → →

16 → →

8 → →

4 → ÷ 4 →

12 → →

12 → →

6 → →

15 → ÷ 3 →

9 → →

80 → →

90 → →

30 → ÷ 10 →

100 → →

Mixed tables

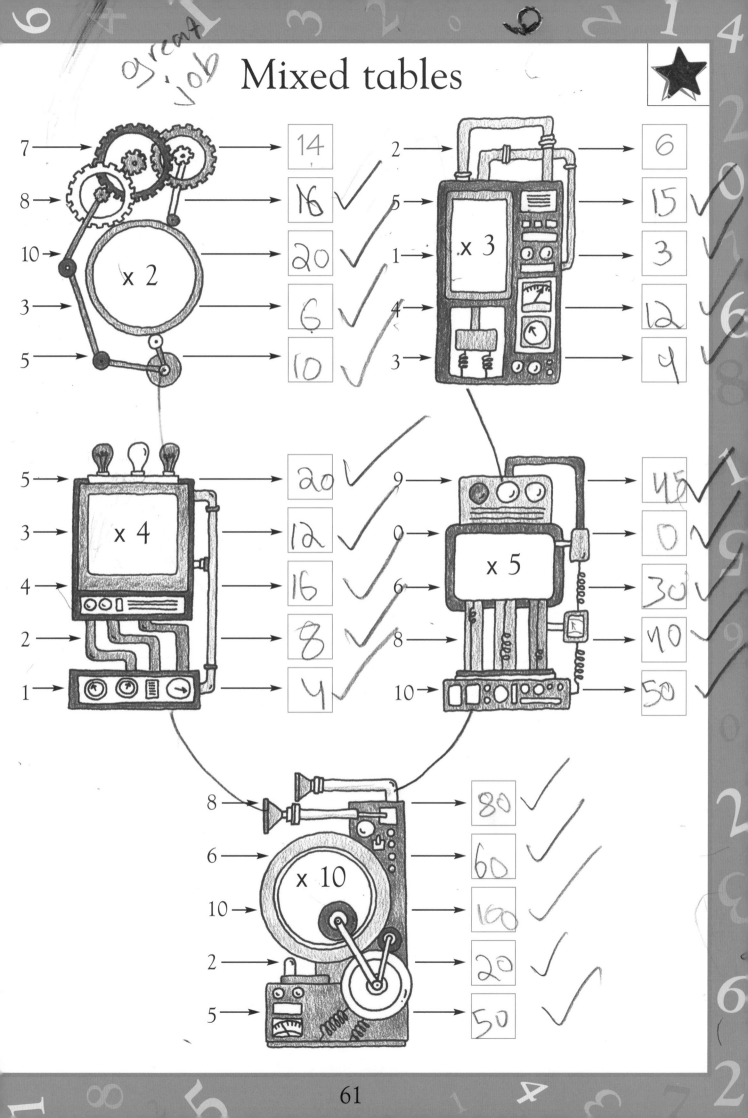

great job

x 2
7 → 14
8 → 16 ✓
10 → 20 ✓
3 → 6 ✓
5 → 10 ✓

x 3
2 → 6
5 → 15 ✓
1 → 3
4 → 12
3 → 4

x 4
5 → 20 ✓
3 → 12 ✓
4 → 16 ✓
2 → 8 ✓
1 → 4 ✓

x 5
9 → 45 ✓
0 → 0
6 → 30 ✓
8 → 40 ✓
10 → 50 ✓

x 10
8 → 80 ✓
6 → 60 ✓
10 → 100 ✓
2 → 20 ✓
5 → 50 ✓

Mixed tables

Work out how many.

Legs on 1 monster $\boxed{1}$ x $\boxed{3}$ = $\boxed{3}$ legs

Work out how many.

Buttons on 6 monsters   ☐ x ☐ = ☐ buttons

Eyes on 6 monsters   ☐ x ☐ = ☐ eyes

Hands on 9 monsters   ☐ x ☐ = ☐ hands

Noses on 7 monsters   ☐ x ☐ = ☐ noses

Legs on 4 monsters   ☐ x ☐ = ☐ legs

Eyes on 3 monsters   ☐ x ☐ = ☐ eyes

Arms on 8 monsters   ☐ x ☐ = ☐ arms

Buttons on 10 monsters   ☐ x ☐ = ☐ buttons

Number pairs

Put an X at (3,2).

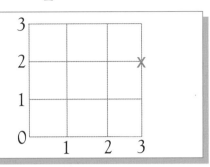

Put an X on this grid at each of these number pairs:

(1,1)   (1,9)   (3,9)   (3,6)   (7,6)   (7,9)   (9,9)   (9,1)   (7,1)   (7,4)   (3,4)   (3,1)   (1,1)

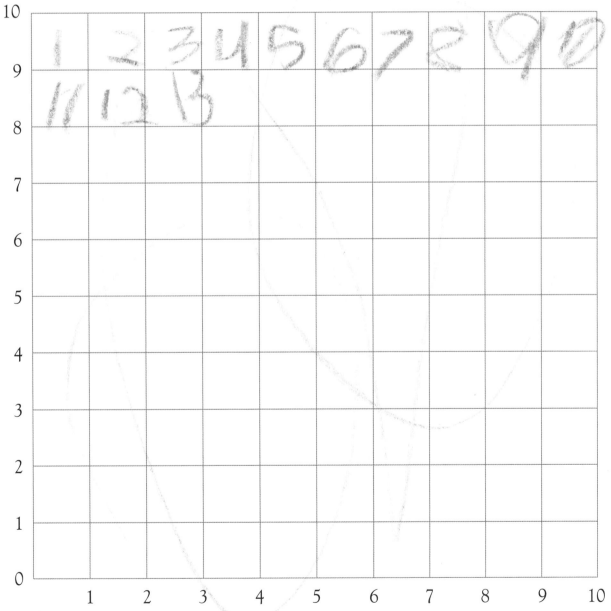

Join the Xs in the same order.

Which capital letter have you drawn?

Logic problems

Read the clues to find the secret number.

| 3 | 4 | 5 | 6 | 7 | 8 |

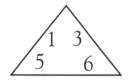

It is in both the rectangle and the circle.
It is not in the triangle. It is greater than 5.
What number is it?   7

Read the clues to find the secret number.

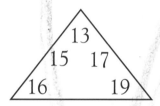

12		15
11		14
	13	

21	20	16
12	14	18

It is not in the square. It is an even number.
It is greater than any number in the triangle.
What number is it?

10	11
16	18
12	13

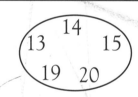

16	18	19
	20	21

It is in the square and the circle.
It is greater than 10 and less than 16. It is an odd number.
What number is it?

It is in the triangle.
It is not an even number.
It is in the rectangle and the square.
What number is it?

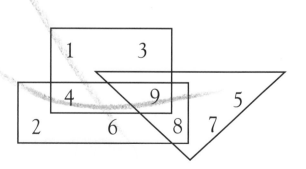

Dividing

Write the answer in the box.

$60 \div 10 =$ 6

8
10) 80

$20 \div 10 =$ 2

Write the answer in the box.

$50 \div 10 =$ ___ $80 \div 10 =$ ___ $10 \div 10 =$ ___

$120 \div 10 =$ ___ $60 \div 10 =$ ___ $190 \div 10 =$ ___

$230 \div 10 =$ ___ $40 \div 10 =$ ___ $160 \div 10 =$ ___

$30 \div 10 =$ ___ $300 \div 10 =$ ___ $330 \div 10 =$ ___

$70 \div 10 =$ ___ $390 \div 10 =$ ___ $560 \div 10 =$ ___

$90 \div 10 =$ ___ $420 \div 10 =$ ___ $850 \div 10 =$ ___

Write the answer in the box.

10) 60   10) 90   10) 120   10) 70

10) 10   10) 200   10) 40   10) 260

10) 370   10) 410   10) 560   10) 630

10) 690   10) 800   10) 850   10) 900

Write the answer in the box.

$630 \div 10 =$ ___ $480 \div 10 =$ ___ $170 \div 10 =$ ___

$100 \div 10 =$ ___ $130 \div 10 =$ ___ $200 \div 10 =$ ___

$500 \div 10 =$ ___ $140 \div 10 =$ ___ $400 \div 10 =$ ___

$320 \div 10 =$ ___ $150 \div 10 =$ ___ $800 \div 10 =$ ___

Rounding

...mount to the nearest tens.

17	28	89	42
20	30	90	40

Round each amount to the nearest tens.

46	50	36	40	72	70	28	30
41	40	48	50	83	80	67	70
57	60	82	70	64	60	32	30
28	30	63	66	13	10	56	60
61	60	87	90	77	80	54	50

Round each amount to the nearest hundreds.

145	100	260	300	115	100	565	600
335	300	770	800	835	800	225	200
470	500	290	300	605	600	245	200
730	700	405	400	655	600	380	400
295	300	160	200	925	900	645	600
350	300	450	400	280	300	860	900
659	700	510	500	150	100	333	300
250	200	750	700	740	700	650	600

Congruency

Figures that are the same size and shape are congruent.
Are these figures congruent?

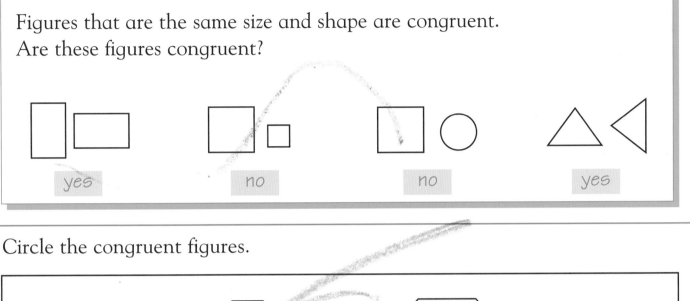

yes   no   no   yes

Circle the congruent figures.

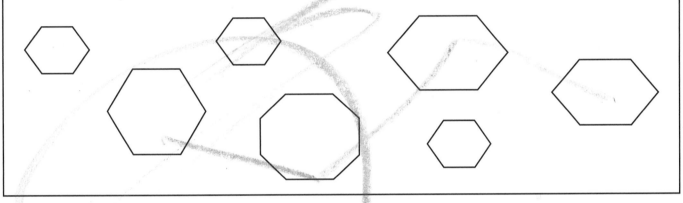

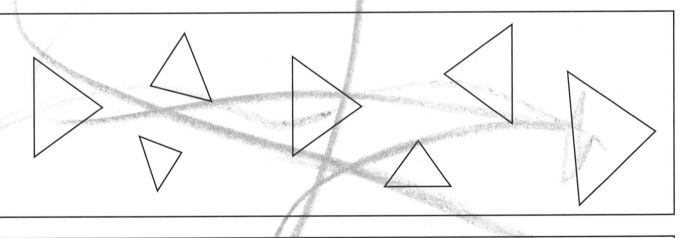

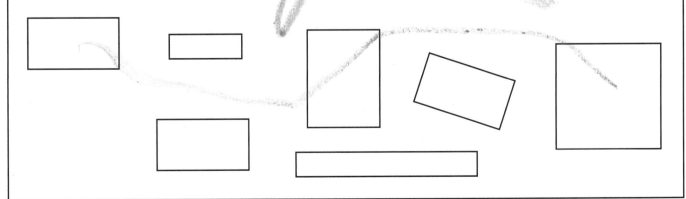

Identifying patterns

Complete each pattern.

48	42	36	30	24	18	12	6
44	41	38	35	32	29	26	23

Complete each pattern.

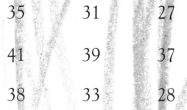
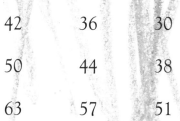

21	19	17
38	34	30
36	31	26
55	50	45
42	37	32
52	48	44
62	57	52
35	31	27
41	39	37
38	33	28
42	36	30
50	44	38
63	57	51
37	34	31
58	53	48
78	70	62
67	60	53

Odds and evens

Write the answer in the box.

3 + 3 = 6   4 + 6 = 10   7 + 3 = 10   2 + 6 = 8

Add the even numbers to the even numbers.

4 + 8 =   12 + 6 =   10 + 6 =   8 + 14 =

20 + 14 =   14 + 12 =   16 + 10 =   30 + 20 =

14 + 16 =   18 + 6 =   22 + 8 =   20 + 40 =

What do you notice about each answer? _____

Add the odd numbers to the odd numbers.

7 + 9 =   5 + 7 =   11 + 5 =   9 + 5 =

7 + 7 =   9 + 3 =   15 + 5 =   13 + 7 =

11 + 3 =   17 + 9 =   15 + 9 =   13 + 15 =

What do you notice about each answer? _____

Add the odd numbers to the even numbers.

3 + 8 =   9 + 12 =   5 + 18 =   7 + 14 =

11 + 4 =   13 + 10 =   15 + 6 =   21 + 4 =

7 + 20 =   13 + 30 =   11 + 12 =   17 + 6 =

What do you notice about each answer? _____

Add the even numbers to the odd numbers.

6 + 7 =   8 + 5 =   10 + 9 =   2 + 17 =

10 + 29 =   14 + 3 =   8 + 13 =   12 + 5 =

14 + 7 =   8 + 51 =   16 + 9 =   30 + 17 =

What do you notice about each answer? _____

Probability

Look at the marbles in the bag.

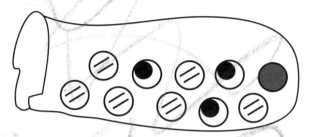

● This kind of marble is *least* likely to be picked from the bag.

⊘ This kind of marble is *most* likely to be picked from the bag.

Look at this table.

Kinds of beads in grab bag

metal	glass	clay	wood	plastic
9	12	2	5	1

Which kind of bead is the least likely to be picked?

Which kind of bead is the most likely to be picked?

Look at the chart.

Marbles in the bag

COLOUR	TALLIES
Red	卌
Blue	|||
Purple	卌 ||
Green	卌

Which colour marble is most likely to be picked?

Which colour marble is least likely to be picked?

Which colour marble is as likely to be picked as a green marble?

Place value

What is the value of each of the numbers in 573?

The value of 5 in 573 is 500 or five hundred

The value of 7 in 573 is 70 or seventy

The value of 3 in 573 is 3 or three

What is the value of 4 in these numbers? Write using number and words.

34

142

406

412

942

462

34

140

Circle each number with a 5 having the value of fifty.

685   954   534   555

Circle each number with a 4 having the value of four hundred.

482   954   434   984

Write increases or decreases and by how much.

Change the 2 in 24 to 3. The value of the number 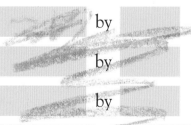 by

Change the 6 in 86 to 3. The value of the number 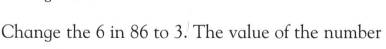 by

Change the 1 in 17 to 9. The value of the number 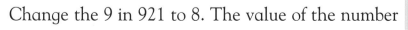 by

Change the 9 in 921 to 8. The value of the number 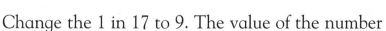 by

Change the 7 in 276 to 9. The value of the number 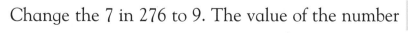 by

Change the 5 in 547 to 1. The value of the number 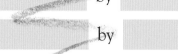 by

Coins and bills

Draw the coins and bills to equal $14.25.

 + + = $14.25

Draw the coins and bills to equal $17.52.

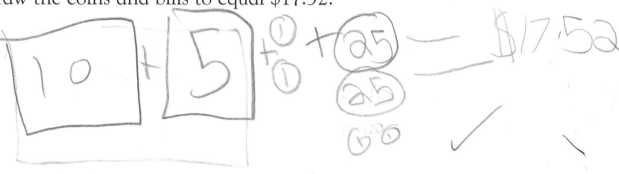

Draw the coins and bills to equal $43.75.

Draw the coins and bills to equal $70.14.

Part of a whole

Write the fraction that shows the shaded part.

How many parts are shaded?   3 parts

How many parts in all?   4 parts

The shaded part is $\frac{3}{4}$

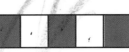

Circle the fraction that shows the shaded part.

   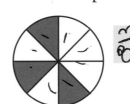   

$\frac{1}{2}$ $\frac{1}{3}$ $\frac{1}{4}$ $\frac{2}{5}$ $\frac{3}{4}$ $\frac{3}{5}$ $\frac{7}{8}$ $\frac{1}{6}$ $\frac{4}{5}$

Write the fraction that shows the shaded part.

 $\frac{1}{6}$  $\frac{3}{8}$

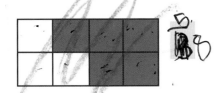 $\frac{5}{8}$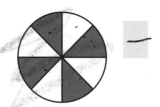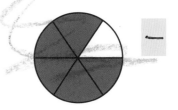

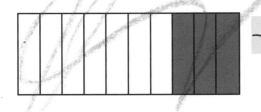   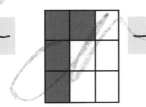   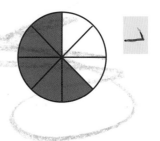

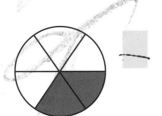   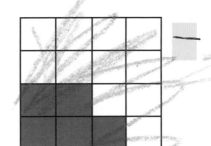

Creating patterns

What are the next two shapes?

  ◯   ◯

What are the next two numbers or letters?

0	1	1	0	1	1	0	1		
0	1	2	3	0	1	2	3		
0	4	0	4	0	4	0	4		
a	b	b	a	a	b	b	a		
a	b	c	a	b	c	a	b		
2	4	6	8	2	4	6	8		
1	3	5	7	1	3	5	7		
0	1	2	0	1	2	0	1		

Create your own patterns.

Number order

Put each group of numbers in order from least to greatest.

| 7240 | 3527 | 989 | | 989 | 3527 | 7240 |
| 1588 | 298 | 4726 | | 298 | 1588 | 4726 |

Put each group of numbers in order from least to greatest. Use drawings to help.

$2\frac{1}{2}$	$1\frac{1}{2}$	$3\frac{1}{2}$
$\frac{7}{10}$	$\frac{3}{10}$	$\frac{5}{10}$
$\frac{3}{4}$	$\frac{2}{4}$	$1\frac{1}{4}$
$1\frac{2}{3}$	$\frac{1}{3}$	$2\frac{1}{3}$
$\frac{6}{6}$	$\frac{2}{6}$	$\frac{4}{6}$
$\frac{5}{8}$	$1\frac{1}{8}$	$1\frac{5}{8}$
$1\frac{2}{5}$	$\frac{3}{5}$	$\frac{4}{5}$
$\frac{3}{10}$	$\frac{2}{10}$	$1\frac{1}{10}$
$\frac{9}{12}$	$\frac{15}{12}$	$\frac{5}{12}$
$\frac{5}{10}$	$\frac{2}{10}$	$\frac{3}{10}$
$\frac{5}{6}$	$\frac{3}{6}$	$1\frac{1}{6}$

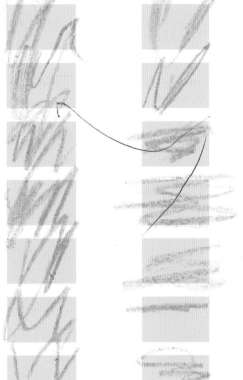

Adding

Write the answer between the lines.

```
    1           1           1
  46          57          48
+ 25        + 24        + 24
─────       ─────       ─────
  71          81          72
```

Write the answer between the lines.

```
  26          37          48          59          25
+ 15        + 16        + 14        + 12        + 15
─────       ─────       ─────       ─────       ─────
```

```
  38          25          36          43          27
+ 15        + 16        + 17        + 19        + 15
─────       ─────       ─────       ─────       ─────
```

```
  56          18          28          47          58
+ 17        + 14        + 14        + 26        + 15
─────       ─────       ─────       ─────       ─────
```

```
  27          19          23          57          68
+ 14        + 14        + 16        + 15        + 13
─────       ─────       ─────       ─────       ─────
```

```
  26          34          13          18          25
+ 35        + 48        + 27        + 32        + 45
─────       ─────       ─────       ─────       ─────
```

```
  17          33          29          32          23
+ 44        + 58        + 53        + 53        + 48
─────       ─────       ─────       ─────       ─────
```

Adding

Write the answer between the lines.

```
    1
   45          66          1
 + 15        + 23         43
 ┌────┐      ┌────┐      + 18
 │ 60 │      │ 89 │      ┌────┐
 └────┘      └────┘      │ 61 │
                         └────┘
```

Write the answer between the lines.

```
   17          23          45          62          38
 + 13        + 17        + 25        + 18        + 12
 ┌────┐      ┌────┐      ┌────┐      ┌────┐      ┌────┐
 └────┘      └────┘      └────┘      └────┘      └────┘


   25          37          42          50          30
 + 25        + 23        + 28        + 37        + 48
 ┌────┐      ┌────┐      ┌────┐      ┌────┐      ┌────┐
 └────┘      └────┘      └────┘      └────┘      └────┘


   46          74          42          67          37
 + 34        + 16        + 38        + 23        + 43
 ┌────┐      ┌────┐      ┌────┐      ┌────┐      ┌────┐
 └────┘      └────┘      └────┘      └────┘      └────┘


   54          38          47          83          31
 + 46        + 32        + 43        + 17        + 39
 ┌────┐      ┌────┐      ┌────┐      ┌────┐      ┌────┐
 └────┘      └────┘      └────┘      └────┘      └────┘


   76          68          73          55          74
 + 24        + 32        + 27        + 45        + 26
 ┌────┐      ┌────┐      ┌────┐      ┌────┐      ┌────┐
 └────┘      └────┘      └────┘      └────┘      └────┘


   73          48          49          28          65
 + 16        + 33        + 42        + 26        + 45
 ┌────┐      ┌────┐      ┌────┐      ┌────┐      ┌────┐
 └────┘      └────┘      └────┘      └────┘      └────┘
```

Subtracting

Write the answer between the lines.

38	42	64
− 23	− 20	− 34
15	22	30

Write the answer between the lines.

45	27	53	85	47
− 23	− 14	− 20	− 41	− 25

29	53	82	37	44
− 16	− 12	− 40	− 26	− 31

63	74	47	63	76
− 21	− 32	− 36	− 42	− 35

85	83	95	67	86
− 42	− 41	− 35	− 53	− 45

65	74	86	96	67
− 35	− 54	− 66	− 86	− 17

59	48	46	78	67
− 39	− 27	− 32	− 47	− 56

Subtracting

Write the answer between the lines.

```
  3 13          4 14          5 11
  4̶3̶           5̶4̶           6̶1̶
-  27        -  28        -  43
  ‾‾‾‾         ‾‾‾‾         ‾‾‾‾
   16           26           18
```

Write the answer between the lines.

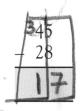

```
  3 4̶5          2̶ 1̶6         3 1 2         50            5 1 2
                              3̶ 4̶2̶                        6̶2̶
-  28        -  18        -  17        -  45        -  17
  ‾‾‾‾         ‾‾‾‾         ‾‾‾‾         ‾‾‾‾         ‾‾‾‾
   17           18           25           10           45
```

```
  43           74           90           65           63
-  29        -  47        -  37        -  48        -  49
  ‾‾‾‾         ‾‾‾‾         ‾‾‾‾         ‾‾‾‾         ‾‾‾‾
```

```
  57           64           62           78           36
-  39        -  48        -  34        -  69        -  27
  ‾‾‾‾         ‾‾‾‾         ‾‾‾‾         ‾‾‾‾         ‾‾‾‾
```

```
  54           68           50           38           44
-  26        -  39        -  27        -  28        -  36
  ‾‾‾‾         ‾‾‾‾         ‾‾‾‾         ‾‾‾‾         ‾‾‾‾
```

```
  31           43           70           53           46
-  16        -  28        -  36        -  37        -  28
  ‾‾‾‾         ‾‾‾‾         ‾‾‾‾         ‾‾‾‾         ‾‾‾‾
```

```
  90           50           54           66           90
-  46        -  26        -  35        -  48        -  44
  ‾‾‾‾         ‾‾‾‾         ‾‾‾‾         ‾‾‾‾         ‾‾‾‾
```

Real-life problems

Write the answer in the box.

Sarah has eight wrenches and is given six more.
How many wrenches does she have now?

$8 + 6 = 14$

Write the answer in the box.

Karl has 20 marbles but loses 12 in a game of marbles
contest. How many marbles does he have left?

$$\begin{array}{r} 20 \\ -12 \\ \hline \end{array}$$

10

After buying some candy for 30¢, Naomi still has
65¢ left. How much did she have to begin with?

45¢

Billy takes 20 balls out of a barrel
and leaves 15 in the barrel.
How many balls are
there altogether?

35 balls

June collected 150 stamps and her father gave her
60 more. How many stamps does June have now?

150

Angela puts 40 toys in a box that already has 35 toys in it.
How many toys are in the box now?

75

Patrick leaves 45¢ at home and takes 50¢ with him. How much
money does Patrick have altogether?

95¢

Don gives some of his allowance to his sister. He gives his sister
80¢ and has 60¢ left. How much allowance did Don have in the
first place?

140

Five letters of the alphabet are vowels. How many letters of the
alphabet are not vowels?

50

Multiplying

Write the answer between the lines.

```
      4              1              6
  x   3          x   6          x   3
  _____        _____        _____
    12             6              18
```

Write the answer between the lines.

```
      6              8              2              5              5
  x   2          x   2          x   2          x   2          x   6
  _____        _____        _____        _____        _____


      3              5              4              9              6
  x   3          x   3          x   3          x   3          x   3
  _____        _____        _____        _____        _____


      7              8              4              5              2
  x   4          x   4          x   4          x   4          x   4
  _____        _____        _____        _____        _____


      5              2              4              8             10
  x   5          x   5          x   5          x   5          x   5
  _____        _____        _____        _____        _____


      6              3              2              8              4
  x   6          x   6          x   6          x   6          x   6
  _____        _____        _____        _____        _____


      5              8              3              7              7
  x   7          x   7          x   7          x   7          x   5
  _____        _____        _____        _____        _____
```

81

Multiplying

$$\begin{array}{r} 5 \\ \times\ 7 \\ \hline 35 \end{array} \qquad \begin{array}{r} 7 \\ \times\ 4 \\ \hline 28 \end{array} \qquad \begin{array}{r} 2 \\ \times\ 6 \\ \hline 12 \end{array}$$

Write the answer between the lines.

$$\begin{array}{r} 8 \\ \times\ 2 \\ \hline 16 \end{array} \qquad \begin{array}{r} 4 \\ \times\ 8 \\ \hline 11 \end{array} \qquad \begin{array}{r} 5 \\ \times\ 8 \\ \hline 10 \end{array} \qquad \begin{array}{r} 8 \\ \times\ 3 \\ \hline 13 \end{array} \qquad \begin{array}{r} 3 \\ \times\ 8 \\ \hline \end{array}$$

$$\begin{array}{r} 9 \\ \times\ 3 \\ \hline 14 \end{array} \qquad \begin{array}{r} 4 \\ \times\ 9 \\ \hline 10 \end{array} \qquad \begin{array}{r} 2 \\ \times\ 9 \\ \hline \end{array} \qquad \begin{array}{r} 3 \\ \times\ 9 \\ \hline \end{array} \qquad \begin{array}{r} 6 \\ \times\ 9 \\ \hline \end{array}$$

$$\begin{array}{r} 3 \\ \times\ 4 \\ \hline \end{array} \qquad \begin{array}{r} 4 \\ \times\ 5 \\ \hline \end{array} \qquad \begin{array}{r} 4 \\ \times\ 4 \\ \hline \end{array} \qquad \begin{array}{r} 3 \\ \times\ 5 \\ \hline \end{array} \qquad \begin{array}{r} 9 \\ \times\ 4 \\ \hline \end{array}$$

$$\begin{array}{r} 9 \\ \times\ 5 \\ \hline \end{array} \qquad \begin{array}{r} 8 \\ \times\ 5 \\ \hline \end{array} \qquad \begin{array}{r} 10 \\ \times\ 5 \\ \hline \end{array} \qquad \begin{array}{r} 7 \\ \times\ 5 \\ \hline \end{array} \qquad \begin{array}{r} 10 \\ \times\ 6 \\ \hline \end{array}$$

$$\begin{array}{r} 9 \\ \times\ 4 \\ \hline \end{array} \qquad \begin{array}{r} 10 \\ \times\ 7 \\ \hline \end{array} \qquad \begin{array}{r} 9 \\ \times\ 6 \\ \hline \end{array} \qquad \begin{array}{r} 7 \\ \times\ 7 \\ \hline \end{array} \qquad \begin{array}{r} 7 \\ \times\ 8 \\ \hline \end{array}$$

$$\begin{array}{r} 6 \\ \times\ 4 \\ \hline \end{array} \qquad \begin{array}{r} 6 \\ \times\ 5 \\ \hline \end{array} \qquad \begin{array}{r} 6 \\ \times\ 6 \\ \hline \end{array} \qquad \begin{array}{r} 6 \\ \times\ 7 \\ \hline \end{array} \qquad \begin{array}{r} 6 \\ \times\ 8 \\ \hline \end{array}$$

Dividing

Write the answer in the box.

26 ÷ 6 =	34 ÷ 6 =	36 ÷ 6 =
42 ÷ 6 =	38 ÷ 6 =	54 ÷ 6 =
19 ÷ 6 =	25 ÷ 6 =	30 ÷ 6 =
21 ÷ 6 =	33 ÷ 6 =	42 ÷ 6 =
36 ÷ 7 =	46 ÷ 7 =	52 ÷ 7 =
38 ÷ 7 =	28 ÷ 7 =	50 ÷ 7 =
39 ÷ 7 =	35 ÷ 7 =	24 ÷ 7 =
49 ÷ 7 =	30 ÷ 7 =	53 ÷ 7 =
40 ÷ 8 =	53 ÷ 8 =	48 ÷ 8 =
40 ÷ 5 =	55 ÷ 8 =	46 ÷ 8 =
56 ÷ 7 =	32 ÷ 8 =	51 ÷ 8 =
56 ÷ 8 =	37 ÷ 8 =	44 ÷ 8 =
63 ÷ 7 =	70 ÷ 7 =	36 ÷ 9 =
63 ÷ 9 =	37 ÷ 9 =	36 ÷ 4 =
45 ÷ 9 =	22 ÷ 9 =	24 ÷ 6 =
45 ÷ 5 =	23 ÷ 9 =	50 ÷ 5 =

Dividing

Write the answer above the line.

$$5 r 2$$
$$6 \overline{)\ 32}$$
$$\underline{30}$$
$$2$$

$$4 r 1$$
$$7 \overline{)\ 29}$$
$$\underline{28}$$
$$1$$

$$6 r 2$$
$$9 \overline{)\ 56}$$
$$\underline{54}$$
$$2$$

Write the answer in the box above the line.

1	5	5	7	9
$6 \overline{)\ 45}$	$6 \overline{)\ 37}$	$6 \overline{)\ 27}$	$6 \overline{)\ 41}$	$6 \overline{)\ 38}$
$\underline{42}$	$\underline{36}$	$\underline{24}$	$\underline{36}$	$\underline{36}$
3	1	3	5	2

11	13	15	17	19
$7 \overline{)\ 34}$	$7 \overline{)\ 42}$	$7 \overline{)\ 74}$	$7 \overline{)\ 36}$	$7 \overline{)\ 41}$
$\underline{28}$	$\underline{42}$	$\underline{70}$	$\underline{35}$	$\underline{35}$
6	0	4	1	6

21	24	25	27	29
$8 \overline{)\ 37}$	$8 \overline{)\ 29}$	$8 \overline{)\ 44}$	$8 \overline{)\ 73}$	$8 \overline{)\ 39}$
$\underline{32}$	$\underline{24}$	$\underline{40}$	$\underline{72}$	$\underline{32}$
5	5	4	1	7

31	33	35	37	39
$9 \overline{)\ 20}$	$9 \overline{)\ 34}$	$9 \overline{)\ 44}$	$9 \overline{)\ 74}$	$9 \overline{)\ 38}$
$\underline{18}$	$\underline{27}$	$\underline{36}$	$\underline{72}$	$\underline{36}$
2	7	8	2	2

Choosing the operation

Write either x or ÷ in the box.

4 ⊠ 9 = 36   24 ÷ 4 = 6   80 ÷ 8 = 10

Write either x or ÷ in the box.

9 ÷ 7 = 63	8 x 6 = 48	54 ÷ 9 = 6
5 x 8 = 40	30 ÷ 6 = 5	49 ÷ 7 = 7
36 ÷ 4 = 9	45 ÷ 9 = 5	7 x 8 = 56
48 ÷ 6 = 8	7 x 9 = 63	27 ÷ 3 = 9
4 x 6 = 24	24 ÷ 8 = 3	81 ÷ 9 = 9
8 x 8 = 64	28 ÷ 7 = 4	48 ÷ 8 = 6
63 ÷ 7 = 9	30 ÷ 5 = 6	3 x 8 = 24
6 x 8 = 48	40 ÷ 8 = 5	56 ÷ 7 = 8
54 ÷ 6 = 9	18 ÷ 3 = 6	64 ÷ 8 = 8
16 ÷ 8 = 2	21 ÷ 7 = 3	28 ÷ 4 = 7
27 ÷ 9 = 3	50 ÷ 10 = 5	70 ÷ 7 = 10
8 x 7 = 56	4 x 9 = 36	5 x 9 = 45
2 x 6 = 12	70 ÷ 7 = 10	8 ÷ 8 = 1
10 ÷ 5 = 2	40 ÷ 8 = 5	14 ÷ 7 = 2
42 ÷ 6 = 7	60 ÷ 10 = 6	9 ÷ 9 = 1
5 x 5 = 25	100 ÷ 10 = 10	6 ÷ 6 = 1

Real-life problems

Write the answer in the box.
A number multiplied by 8 is 56.
What is the number?

I divide a number by 9 and the result is 6.
What is the number?

Write the answer in the box.

A number multiplied by 6 is 42.
What is the number?

I divide a number by 4 and the
result is 7. What is the number?

I divide a number by 8 and the
result is 6. What number did I
begin with?

A number multiplied by itself
gives the answer 25. What is
the number?

I divide a number by 7 and the
result is 7. What number did I
begin with?

A number multiplied by itself
gives the answer 49. What is
the number?

I multiply a number by 7 and
I end up with 56. What number
did I begin with?

Seven times a number is 63.
What is the number?

What do I have to multiply 8
by to get the result 32?

Six times a number is 36.
What is the number?

When 6 is multiplied by a
number the result is 42. What
number was 6 multiplied by?

A number divided by 5 gives
the answer 10. What was the
starting number?

I multiply a number by 9 and
end up with 45. What number
did I multiply?

I multiply a number by 7 and
the result is 49. What number
did I begin with?

Real-life problems

Solve the problem. Write the answer in the box.

A jump rope is supposed to be 130 cm long but 35 cm has been cut off. How much of the skipping rope is left?

95 cm

$$\begin{array}{r} \overset{12}{\cancel{0}}\ \overset{2}{\cancel{3}}\ 10 \\ \cancel{130} \\ -\ \ 35 \\ \hline 95 \end{array}$$

Solve the problem. Write the answer in the box.

Mario is given three cans of juice. Each can contains 425 ml. How much does Mario have altogether?

Trang sees these toys on sale in a store window. She buys two of the toys and pays $10.10. Which toys does Trang buy?

$4.30 $6.40 $7.50 $3.70

A school playground is 145 m long. 68 m are used by the 3rd grade children and the rest by the 4th grade children. How much space is used by the 4th grade children?

Mary buys a box of chocolates that costs $7.85. She pays for the chocolates with a ten dollar bill. How much change should she receive?

A box of tea contains 350 grams. Half of the tea has been used. How much of the tea is left?

Real-life problems

Solve the problem. Write the answer in the box.

A boy weighs 7 kg more than his sister.
His sister weighs 36 kg. How much does the brother weigh?

43 kg

```
  36
+  7
────
  43
```

Solve the problem. Write the answer in the box.

Two bags of cement have a total mass
of 150 kg. One bag weighs 80 kg. How
much does the other bag weigh?

There are 4 bars of chocolate in
each box. How many bars will
there be in 7 boxes?

One box contains 186 tissues.
How many tissues will there be
in 2 boxes?

Dean's older sister weighs 50 kg,
and he is 8 kg lighter than her.
How much does Dean weigh?

A boy has a bottle of lemonade that
contains 2 litres. He drinks 465 ml.
How much lemonade is left?

Kitchen countertops can be
measured in centimetres.
How long is 1.50 m in cm?

Problems using time

Write the answer in the box.

What time will it be in 15 minutes?

5:50

Write the answer in the box.

What time will it be in 45 minutes?

8:45

What time was it 2 hours ago?

5:45

What time was it ten minutes ago?

7:35

Write the answer in the box.

What time will it be in half an hour?

What time will it be in 45 minutes?

What time was it half an hour ago?

Write the answer in the box.

What time was it half an hour ago?

How many hours until 12:30?

What time was it 45 minutes ago?

Charts

	Period 1	Period 2	Period 3	Period 4
Monday	Math	Reading	Social Studies	Design and Technology
Tuesday	Math	Reading	Writing	Gym
Wednesday	Math	Reading	Science	Science
Thursday	Math	Reading	Art	Art
Friday	Reading	Gym	Science	Music

A.M.   P.M.

Write the answer in the box.

What subject does the class have last period on Tuesday?

How many periods of Math does the class have?

When does the class have an afternoon of Art?

How many periods of Reading does the class have?

What subject comes before Music?

Which day is the Writing lesson?

Which subject is taught third period on Monday?

What is the last lesson on Friday morning?

When is Science?

What subject is taught second period on Thursday?

Symmetry

The dotted line is a mirror line. Complete each shape.

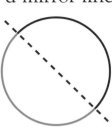 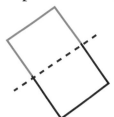

Complete each shape.

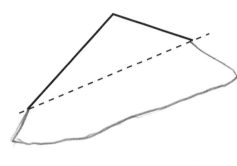

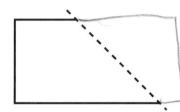

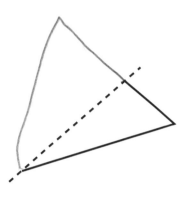 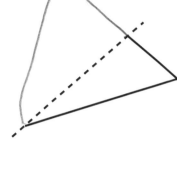

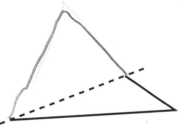

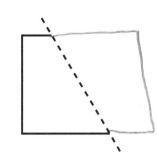

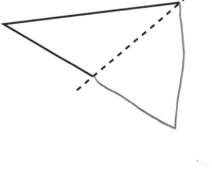

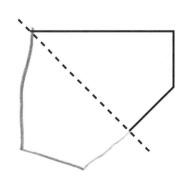

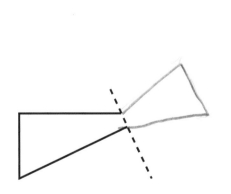

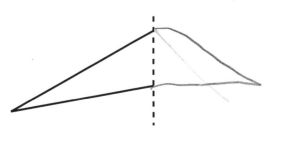 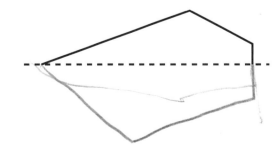

3-dimensional shapes

Draw a small circle around each vertex in this shape.

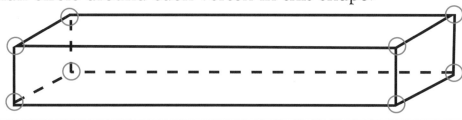

Draw a small circle around each vertex in these shapes.

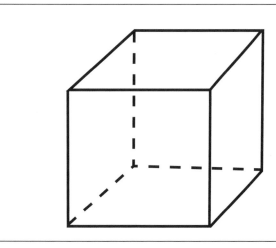

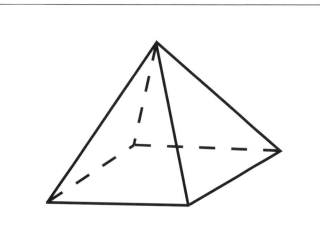

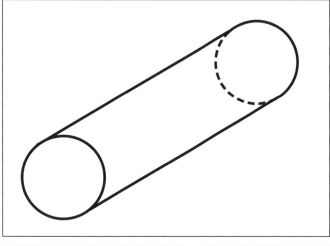

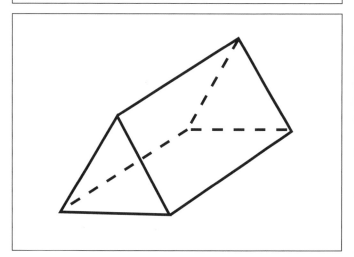

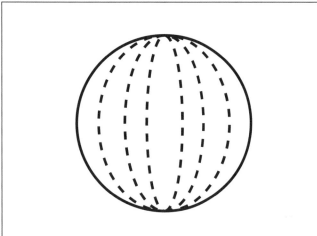

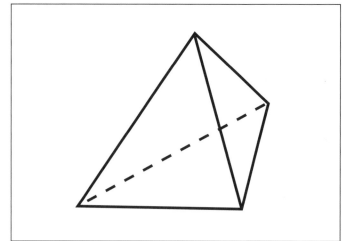

Number pairs

Look at this grid.

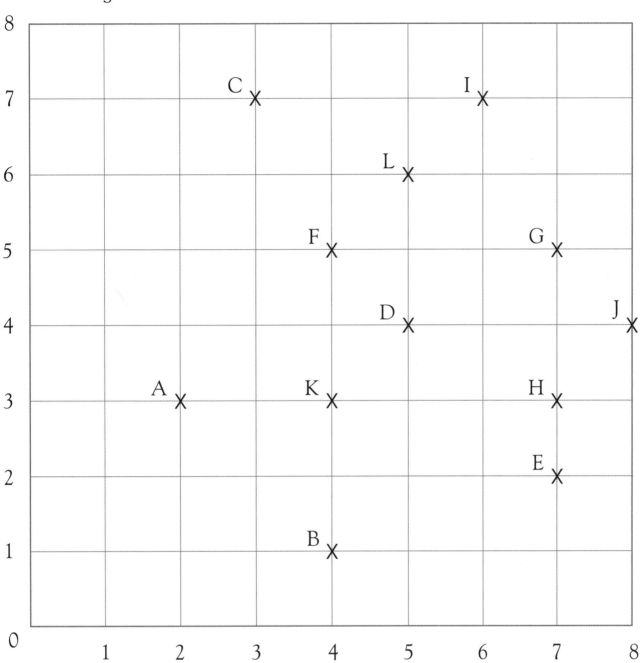

Write the number pairs of the X by each letter.

A = 2, 3   D =   G =   J =

B =   E =   H =   K =

C =   F =   I =   L =

Adding and subtracting

Add 100 to 356.

456

Add 100 to 376.

476

Subtract 100 from 324.

224

Subtract 100 from 296.

196

Add 100 to each number.

376		795		646		585	
286		57		312		634	
12		789		724		803	

Add 100 to each number.

485		607		37		843	
587		56		45		707	
897		564		499		1	

Subtract 100 from each number.

364		729		477		765	
103		146		203		599	
100		745		178		107	

Subtract 100 from each number.

734		610		307		362	
675		907		445		401	
400		638		832		256	

Dividing by 10

Divide 90 by 10.

9

Divide 400 by 10.

40

Divide each number by 10.

60		80		10		50	
100		150		230		800	
210		170		20		260	
40		360		590		730	
420		380		820		540	

Multiply each number by 10.

30		70		90		10	
60		80		11		14	
17		19		23		28	
38		41		84		94	
60		100		75		56	

Divide each number by 10.

700		310		100		650	
480		280		540		130	
30		670		320		400	
300		900		120		660	
220		180		600		890	

95

Length

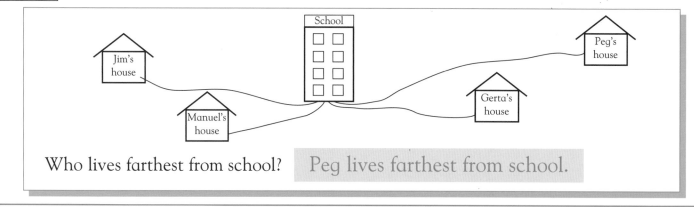

Who lives farthest from school? Peg lives farthest from school.

Look at this map.

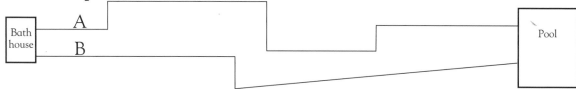

Which route between the bath house and the pool is shorter, A or B?

Look at this map.

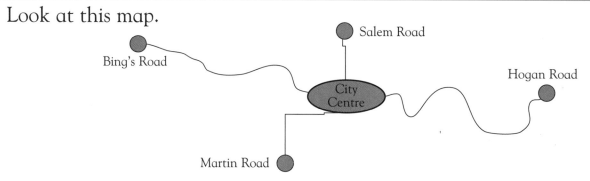

Is the Bing's Road to City Centre
longer or shorter than the Martin Road?

Which road to City Centre is longest?

Which road to City Centre is shorter than the Martin Road?

Look at this picture.

Whose ribbon is longest?

Whose ribbon is shorter than Tim's ribbon?

Whose ribbon is about the same length as Tim's ribbon?

Identifying patterns

Continue each pattern.

11	22	33	44	55	66	77	88
12	24	36	48	60	72	84	96

Continue each pattern.

12	23	34	45	56	67	78	89
9	21	33	45	57			
32	43	54	65	76			
2	14	26	38	50			
2	13	24	35	46			
6	18	30	42	54			
3	8	13	18	23			
12	24	36	48	60			

Continue each pattern.

78	67	56	45	34			
94	82	70	58	46			
88	77	66	55	44			
96	84	72	60	48			
7	18	29	40	51			
14	26	38	50	62			
8	19	30	41	52			
10	22	34	46	58			

Properties of polygons

Circle the polygon that has 4 sides of the same length.

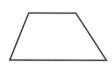

Circle the polygon described.

The 3 sides are all the same length.

 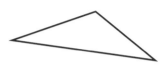

Exactly 2 pairs of sides are parallel.

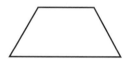

Exactly 1 pair of sides is parallel.

 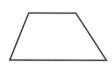

All the sides are of equal length and each side is parallel to one other side.

Each of the sides is a different length.

   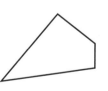

Has 6 sides of equal length.

Square numbers

> • •   This square has two rows
> and two columns. It is 2 x 2.
> • •   How many dots are there?   4

Draw a picture like the one above to show each of these numbers.

3 x 3

How many
dots are there?

4 x 4

How many
dots are there?

5 x 5

How many
dots are there?

6 x 6

How many
dots are there?

7 x 7

How many
dots are there?

8 x 8

How many
dots are there?

9 x 9

How many dots are there?

10 x 10

How many dots are there?

Mixed numbers

A mixed number is a whole number and a fraction.

Write the number and the fraction to represent each figure.

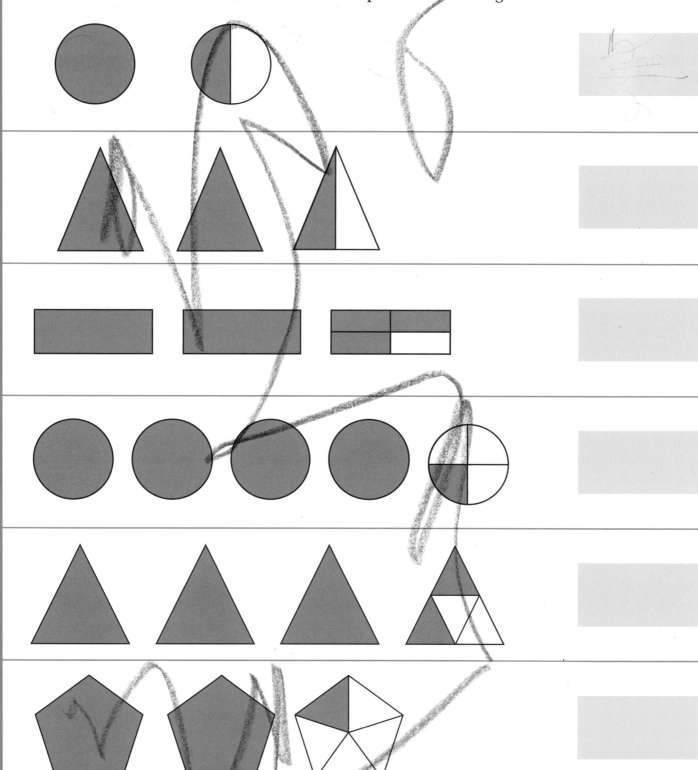

Fractions of shapes

Shade $\frac{3}{5}$ of each shape.

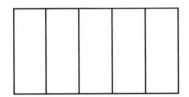

Shade $\frac{4}{5}$ of each shape.

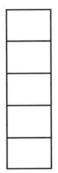

Shade $\frac{8}{10}$ of each shape.

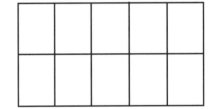

Shade the fraction of each shape.

$\frac{4}{10}$

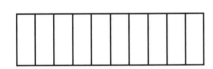

$\frac{8}{10}$

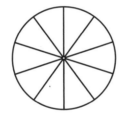

$\frac{3}{10}$

$\frac{7}{10}$

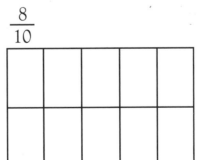

$\frac{6}{10}$

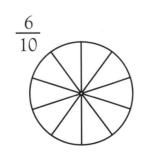

$\frac{9}{10}$

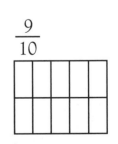

101

Comparing fractions

In each pair, circle the fraction with the greater value.

$\left(\dfrac{1}{2}\right)$ or $\dfrac{1}{5}$

$\dfrac{3}{8}$ or $\left(\dfrac{5}{8}\right)$

In each pair, circle the fraction with the greater value.

$\dfrac{1}{4}$ or $\dfrac{1}{3}$

$\dfrac{1}{5}$ or $\dfrac{1}{6}$

$\dfrac{1}{8}$ or $\dfrac{1}{3}$

$\dfrac{1}{4}$ or $\dfrac{1}{7}$

$\dfrac{1}{2}$ or $\dfrac{1}{3}$

$\dfrac{1}{12}$ or $\dfrac{1}{2}$

$\dfrac{1}{3}$ or $\dfrac{1}{9}$

$\dfrac{1}{10}$ or $\dfrac{1}{100}$

$\dfrac{1}{3}$ or $\dfrac{2}{3}$

$\dfrac{3}{7}$ or $\dfrac{5}{7}$

$\dfrac{2}{5}$ or $\dfrac{1}{5}$

$\dfrac{1}{4}$ or $\dfrac{3}{4}$

$\dfrac{4}{9}$ or $\dfrac{3}{9}$

$\dfrac{1}{12}$ or $\dfrac{2}{12}$

$\dfrac{6}{10}$ or $\dfrac{3}{10}$

$\dfrac{1}{6}$ or $\dfrac{5}{6}$

In each pair, circle the fraction with the greater value.

$1\dfrac{3}{4}$ or $1\dfrac{2}{5}$

$1\dfrac{1}{2}$ or $1\dfrac{1}{3}$

$3\dfrac{1}{6}$ or $2\dfrac{1}{3}$

$2\dfrac{1}{4}$ or $2\dfrac{3}{4}$

$2\dfrac{5}{8}$ or $2\dfrac{3}{8}$

$1\dfrac{1}{4}$ or $1\dfrac{1}{9}$

$6\dfrac{2}{3}$ or $4\dfrac{2}{3}$

$5\dfrac{1}{10}$ or $5\dfrac{3}{10}$

$\dfrac{3}{4}$ or $\dfrac{1}{3}$

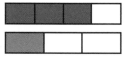

$\dfrac{3}{5}$ or $\dfrac{2}{3}$

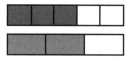

$\dfrac{5}{6}$ or $\dfrac{3}{4}$

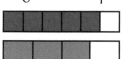

$3\dfrac{1}{2}$ or $3\dfrac{2}{3}$

$4\dfrac{2}{5}$ or $4\dfrac{5}{6}$

$2\dfrac{6}{10}$ or $2\dfrac{4}{5}$

$1\dfrac{4}{5}$ or $1\dfrac{4}{6}$

Rounding

Write each amount to the nearest dollar.

$1.67	$2.83	$1.23	$3.28
$2.00	$3.00	$1.00	$3.00

Write each amount to the nearest dollar.

$2.67		$3.18		$6.75		$7.43	
$8.28		$8.67		$4.97		$2.43	
$4.66		$8.12		$6.08		$5.40	
$7.02		$6.74		$7.83		$2.78	
$1.64		$8.64		$5.67		$1.37	

Write each number to the nearest ten.

75		32		67		35	
74		81		73		63	
54		28		59		19	
58		66		71		46	
64		19		51		77	

Write each number to the nearest hundred.

346		540		729	
125		177		290	
350		501		88	
467		750		345	
838		550		545	

Adding

Write the answer between the lines.

$$
\begin{array}{r} 67 \\ +\ 32 \\ \hline 99 \end{array}
\qquad
\begin{array}{r} {\scriptstyle 1} \\ 39 \\ +\ 43 \\ \hline 82 \end{array}
\qquad
\begin{array}{r} {\scriptstyle 1} \\ 45 \\ +\ 26 \\ \hline 71 \end{array}
$$

Write the answer between the lines.

$$
\begin{array}{r} 43 \\ +\ 25 \\ \hline \end{array}
\quad
\begin{array}{r} 72 \\ +\ 16 \\ \hline \end{array}
\quad
\begin{array}{r} 56 \\ +\ 14 \\ \hline \end{array}
\quad
\begin{array}{r} 28 \\ +\ 15 \\ \hline \end{array}
\quad
\begin{array}{r} 47 \\ +\ 13 \\ \hline \end{array}
$$

$$
\begin{array}{r} 36 \\ +\ 15 \\ \hline \end{array}
\quad
\begin{array}{r} 54 \\ +\ 17 \\ \hline \end{array}
\quad
\begin{array}{r} 84 \\ +\ 13 \\ \hline \end{array}
\quad
\begin{array}{r} 47 \\ +\ 16 \\ \hline \end{array}
\quad
\begin{array}{r} 54 \\ +\ 19 \\ \hline \end{array}
$$

$$
\begin{array}{r} 45 \\ +\ 15 \\ \hline \end{array}
\quad
\begin{array}{r} 48 \\ +\ 14 \\ \hline \end{array}
\quad
\begin{array}{r} 64 \\ +\ 19 \\ \hline \end{array}
\quad
\begin{array}{r} 70 \\ +\ 14 \\ \hline \end{array}
\quad
\begin{array}{r} 45 \\ +\ 17 \\ \hline \end{array}
$$

$$
\begin{array}{r} 18 \\ +\ 33 \\ \hline \end{array}
\quad
\begin{array}{r} 17 \\ +\ 44 \\ \hline \end{array}
\quad
\begin{array}{r} 14 \\ +\ 56 \\ \hline \end{array}
\quad
\begin{array}{r} 18 \\ +\ 44 \\ \hline \end{array}
\quad
\begin{array}{r} 14 \\ +\ 54 \\ \hline \end{array}
$$

$$
\begin{array}{r} 26 \\ +\ 36 \\ \hline \end{array}
\quad
\begin{array}{r} 45 \\ +\ 34 \\ \hline \end{array}
\quad
\begin{array}{r} 74 \\ +\ 18 \\ \hline \end{array}
\quad
\begin{array}{r} 36 \\ +\ 17 \\ \hline \end{array}
\quad
\begin{array}{r} 81 \\ +\ 8 \\ \hline \end{array}
$$

$$
\begin{array}{r} 45 \\ +\ 35 \\ \hline \end{array}
\quad
\begin{array}{r} 43 \\ +\ 28 \\ \hline \end{array}
\quad
\begin{array}{r} 57 \\ +\ 44 \\ \hline \end{array}
\quad
\begin{array}{r} 49 \\ +\ 37 \\ \hline \end{array}
\quad
\begin{array}{r} 37 \\ +\ 46 \\ \hline \end{array}
$$

Adding

Write the answer between the lines.

	¹	¹
35 cm	74 cm	46 cm
+25 cm	+18 cm	+36 cm
60 cm	92 cm	82 cm

Write the answer between the lines.

37 cm	56 cm	68 cm	49 cm	28 cm
+ 46 cm	+ 36 cm	+ 45 cm	+ 27 cm	+ 36 cm

47 km	29 km	56 km	55 km	38 km
+ 44 km	+ 34 km	+ 35 km	+ 37 km	+ 44 km

65 kg	43 kg	52 kg	47 kg	36 kg
+ 27 kg	+ 18 kg	+ 17 kg	+ 27 kg	+ 17 kg

57 ml	48 ml	44 ml	66 ml	43 ml
+ 42 ml	+ 24 ml	+ 18 ml	+ 27 ml	+ 29 ml

Write the answer between the lines.

$23.00	$36.00	$75.00	$27.00
+ $18.00	+ $43.00	+ $16.00	+ $38.00

Adding

Write the answer between the lines.

```
  ¹              ¹              ¹
  35             18             24
  17             14             16
+ 16           + 17           + 19
────           ────           ────
  68             49             59
```

Write the answer between the lines.

```
   12            17            15            12            18
   13            10            13            14            10
 + 13          + 11          + 11          + 12          + 11
 ────          ────          ────          ────          ────
   38
```

```
   17            19            16            12            19
   26            13            21            25            32
 + 12          + 14          + 31          + 33          + 12
 ────          ────          ────          ────          ────
                 46            68            70
```

```
   20            30            40            50            60
   32            26            42            21            14
 + 16          + 25          + 25          + 21          +  8
 ────          ────          ────          ────          ────
                 81           107            92
```

```
   25            35            45            55            65
   15            25            15            35            15
 +  5          +  5          +  5          +  5          +  5
 ────          ────          ────          ────          ────
```

```
   23            34            45            56            67
   45            32            16            16            12
 + 32          + 13          +  9          +  7          +  8
 ────          ────          ────          ────          ────
```

Subtracting

Write the answer between the lines.

	3 12	2 16
57	4̸2̸	3̸6̸
− 15	− 16	− 29
42	**26**	**7**

Write the answer between the lines.

40	60	70	4̸5̸0̸ ¹⁰	90
− 18	− 23	− 37	− 18	− 27
			32	

41	62	7 8̸5̸ ¹⁵	64	6 7̸1̸ ¹¹
− 14	− 15	− 37	− 45	− 36
		48		**35**

45	65	6 7̸5̸ ¹⁵	95	85
− 18	− 34	− 69	− 49	− 38
		06		

73	7 8̸2̸ ¹²	6 7̸4̸ ¹⁴	8 1̸1̸ ⁷	64
− 27	− 38	− 47	− 39	− 47
	44	**27**	**42**	

61	52	5 6̸1̸1	53	6 7̸3̸ ¹³
− 14	− 17	− 19	− 23	− 44
		42		**29**

70	63	83	53	47
− 26	− 7	− 56	− 36	− 43

Subtracting

Write the answer between the lines.

$$\begin{array}{c} \overset{4\ 16}{\cancel{56}} \text{ cm} \\ -\ 18 \text{ cm} \\ \hline 38 \text{ cm} \end{array} \qquad \begin{array}{c} \overset{2\ 17}{\cancel{37}} \text{ km} \\ -\ 19 \text{ km} \\ \hline 18 \text{ km} \end{array} \qquad \begin{array}{c} \overset{4\ 18}{\cancel{58}} \text{ kg} \\ -\ 19 \text{ kg} \\ \hline 39 \text{ kg} \end{array}$$

Write the answer between the lines.

45 cm − 23 cm	63 cm − 44 cm	74 cm − 38 cm	82 cm − 29 cm	40 cm − 17 cm
61 cm − 27 cm	81 cm − 36 cm	62 cm − 27 cm	83 cm − 36 cm	43 cm − 17 cm
45 cm − 26 cm	60 cm − 47 cm	73 cm − 48 cm	74 cm − 39 cm	85 cm − 47 cm

Write the answer between the lines.

50 km − 28 km	37 km − 18 km	75 km − 39 km	84 km − 29 km	90 km − 37 km

Write the answer between the lines.

68 kg − 39 kg	47 kg − 38 kg	64 kg − 27 kg	79 kg − 27 kg	56 kg − 45 kg

Real-life problems

Solve the problem and then write the answer.

Tuhil is reading a book that
has 72 pages. He has read 38 pages.
How many more pages does
Tuhil have to read?

34 pages

$$\begin{array}{r} {}^{6}\cancel{7}{}^{12}\cancel{2} \\ -\ 38 \\ \hline 34 \end{array}$$

Solve the problem and then write the answer in the box.

Eric has 37 marbles and plays two
games. He wins another 24 marbles
in the first game but then loses 18 in
the second game. How many marbles
does Eric have now?

Angie has 70 felt-tip pens and gives
26 of them to Abir. She buys 12 new
pens to replace the ones she has
given away. How many pens does
Angie have now?

Edwin empties his trouser pockets
and finds 26¢ in one pocket, 13¢ in
another pocket, and 37¢ in another
one. How much money has Edwin
found altogether?

Isabelle has 64 french fries with her
burger. She eats 16 fries and gives 6
to her baby brother. How many fries
does Isabelle have left?

Multiplying

Write the answer between the lines.

7	3	6	9
x 5	x 4	x 3	x 4
35	12	18	36

Write the answer between the lines.

6	10	7	8	4
x 4	x 4	x 4	x 4	x 4

9	1	8	2	4
x 3	x 3	x 3	x 3	x 3

3	9	10	8	10
x 5	x 5	x 5	x 5	x 3

4	5	4	7	8
x 2	x 2	x 2	x 2	x 2

5	3	4	10	2
x 6	x 6	x 6	x 6	x 6

7	5	1	4	10
x 8	x 8	x 8	x 8	x 8

Multiplying

Write the answer between the lines.

4	5	8	7
x 4	x 6	x 4	x 5
16	30	32	35

Write the answer between the lines.

3	0	7	9	6
x 7	x 7	x 7	x 7	x 7

7	8	6	4	1
x 9	x 9	x 9	x 9	x 9

3	7	9	8	4
x 10	x 10	x 10	x 10	x 10

7	11	7	11	7
x 4	x 5	x 6	x 6	x 8

8	8	8	11	11
x 6	x 7	x 8	x 9	x 8

9	9	11	9	9
x 5	x 6	x 7	x 8	x 9

Dividing

Write the answer in the box.

$24 \div 7 =$ 「 $3\ r\ 3$ 」 　　　　「 $4\ r\ 1$ 」 　　　$43 \div 8 =$ 「 $5\ r\ 3$ 」

$$5\overline{)\,2\ 1}$$
$$\underline{-2\ 0}$$
$$1$$

$$8\overline{)\,4\ 3}$$
$$\underline{-4\ 0}$$
$$3$$

Write the answer in the box.

$27 \div 3 =$ 　　　　$14 \div 3 =$ 　　　　$23 \div 3 =$

$7 \div 3 =$ 　　　　$31 \div 4 =$ 　　　　$14 \div 4 =$

$38 \div 4 =$ 　　　　$4 \div 4 =$ 　　　　$42 \div 5 =$

$23 \div 5 =$ 　　　　$15 \div 5 =$ 　　　　$27 \div 5 =$

$47 \div 6 =$ 　　　　$35 \div 5 =$ 　　　　$46 \div 5 =$

Write the answer in the box.

$8\overline{)\,3\ 4}$ 　　　$8\overline{)\,4\ 6}$ 　　　$8\overline{)\,2\ 1}$ 　　　$8\overline{)\,5\ 6}$ 　　　$9\overline{)\,2\ 7}$

$2\overline{)\,3}$ 　　　$2\overline{)\,1\ 6}$ 　　　$3\overline{)\,1\ 7}$ 　　　$3\overline{)\,2\ 3}$ 　　　$3\overline{)\,3\ 0}$

Write the answer in the box.

$45 \div 8 =$ 　　　　$73 \div 8 =$ 　　　　$56 \div 8 =$

$73 \div 9 =$ 　　　　$41 \div 9 =$ 　　　　$50 \div 9 =$

$54 \div 10 =$ 　　　　$89 \div 10 =$ 　　　　$42 \div 10 =$

Dividing

Write the answer in the box.

$31 \div 4 =$ `7 r 3`

$$\begin{array}{r} 2\,r\,5 \\ 6\overline{)\,1\,7} \\ -1\,2 \\ \hline 5 \end{array}$$

$31 \div 9 =$ `3 r 4`

$$\begin{array}{r} 9\overline{)\,3\,1} \\ -2\,7 \\ \hline 4 \end{array}$$

Write the answer in the box.

$46 \div 9 =$ 　　　　$28 \div 7 =$ 　　　　$45 \div 9 =$

$74 \div 8 =$ 　　　　$32 \div 3 =$ 　　　　$45 \div 7 =$

$61 \div 7 =$ 　　　　$65 \div 9 =$ 　　　　$12 \div 9 =$

$17 \div 4 =$ 　　　　$24 \div 6 =$ 　　　　$36 \div 6 =$

$37 \div 8 =$ 　　　　$37 \div 9 =$ 　　　　$37 \div 10 =$

Write the answer in the box.

$7\overline{)\,4\,5}$ 　　$8\overline{)\,5\,6}$ 　　$9\overline{)\,4\,3}$ 　　$9\overline{)\,3\,0}$ 　　$9\overline{)\,3\,5}$

$9\overline{)\,5\,3}$ 　　$9\overline{)\,7\,6}$ 　　$9\overline{)\,5\,4}$ 　　$9\overline{)\,4\,3}$ 　　$9\overline{)\,2\,7}$

Write the answer in the box.

$8 \div 6 =$ 　　　　$12 \div 10 =$ 　　　　$11 \div 9 =$

$13 \div 10 =$ 　　　　$17 \div 7 =$ 　　　　$23 \div 8 =$

$70 \div 10 =$ 　　　　$70 \div 7 =$ 　　　　$54 \div 6 =$

Choosing the operation

Write either x or ÷ in the box to make the number sentence true.

6 × 7 = 42   24 ÷ 6 = 4   10 ÷ 2 = 5

Write either x or ÷ in the box to make the number sentence true.

35 ☐ 7 = 5	35 ☐ 5 = 7	7 ☐ 5 = 35
5 ☐ 7 = 35	6 ☐ 9 = 54	54 ☐ 6 = 9
9 ☐ 6 = 54	54 ☐ 9 = 6	32 ☐ 4 = 8
4 ☐ 8 = 32	8 ☐ 4 = 32	32 ☐ 8 = 4
4 ☐ 9 = 36	36 ☐ 4 = 9	9 ☐ 4 = 36
36 ☐ 9 = 4	80 ☐ 8 = 10	8 ☐ 10 = 80
7 ☐ 9 = 63	63 ☐ 7 = 9	63 ☐ 9 = 7
9 ☐ 7 = 63	9 ☐ 9 = 81	81 ☐ 9 = 9
64 ☐ 8 = 8	8 ☐ 8 = 64	25 ☐ 5 = 5
5 ☐ 5 = 25	16 ☐ 4 = 4	4 ☐ 4 = 16
7 ☐ 7 = 49	49 ☐ 7 = 7	3 ☐ 3 = 9
9 ☐ 3 = 3	100 ☐ 10 = 10	10 ☐ 10 = 100
50 ☐ 10 = 5	5 ☐ 8 = 40	40 ☐ 4 = 10
20 ☐ 5 = 4	4 ☐ 10 = 40	36 ☐ 6 = 6
3 ☐ 7 = 21	21 ☐ 3 = 7	7 ☐ 4 = 28
14 ☐ 10 = 140	140 ☐ 2 = 70	70 ☐ 10 = 7
42 ☐ 6 = 7	7 ☐ 10 = 70	72 ☐ 8 = 9
50 ☐ 5 = 10	20 ☐ 4 = 5	3 ☐ 8 = 24

Real-life problems

Write the answer in the box.

There are 8 ink cartridges in each pack.
How many cartridges will there
be in 6 packs?

48 cartridges

$8 \times 6 = 48$

Write the answer in the box.

Ian shares 50 oranges equally
among 6 elephants and gives the
remainder to the giraffes. How many
oranges do the giraffes receive?

There are 9 children at a birthday
party and each child has 4 chocolate
cupcakes. How many cupcakes
do the children have altogether?

Ben has 60 building blocks and puts
them in stacks of 7. How many stacks
of 7 can Ben make?

Katie has seven dimes, four
nickels, and four pennies.
How much does she have altogether?

The dog wants to bury four bones in
each hole. The dog has 36 bones.
How many holes must the dog dig?

Perimeter

Write the perimeter of this shape in the answer box.

2 cm

8 cm

8 cm
2 cm
8 cm
+ 2 cm

20 cm

Write the perimeter of each shape in the answer box.

5 cm
1 cm

4 cm
3 cm

8 cm
4 cm

6 cm
6 cm

2 cm
7 cm

8 cm
5 cm

4 cm
10 cm

12 cm
5 cm

9 cm
9 cm

20 cm
5 cm

Area

Write the area of the shape in the answer box.

1 cm

7 cm

$1 \times 7 = 7 \text{ cm}^2$
cm × cm
7 cm^2

cm²
m²
km²

Write the area of each shape in the answer box.

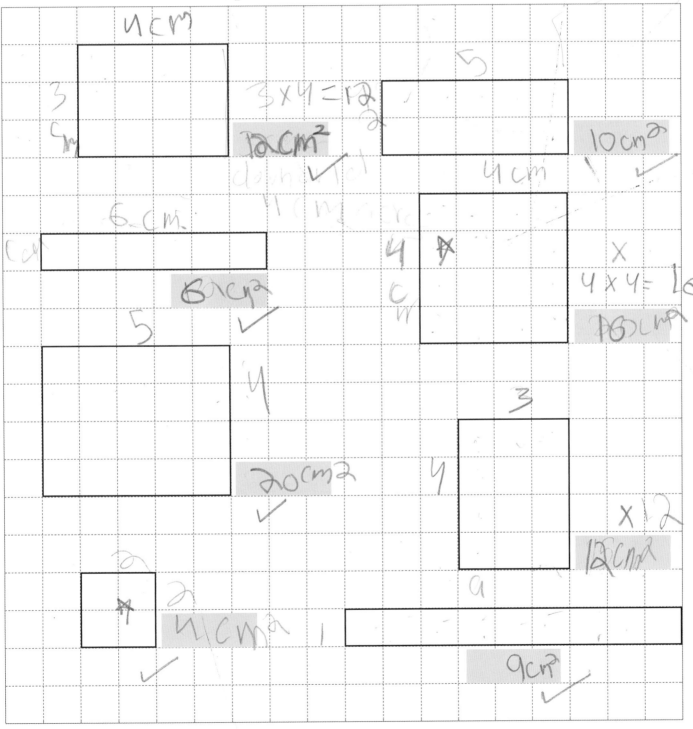

$3 \times 4 = 12$

12 cm²

10 cm²

6 cm²

$4 \times 4 = 16$

16 cm²

20 cm²

× 12

12 cm²

4 cm²

9 cm²

Area

Write the area of this shape in the answer box.

3 cm

8 cm

$3 \times 8 = 24$

24 cm²

Write the area of each shape in the answer box.

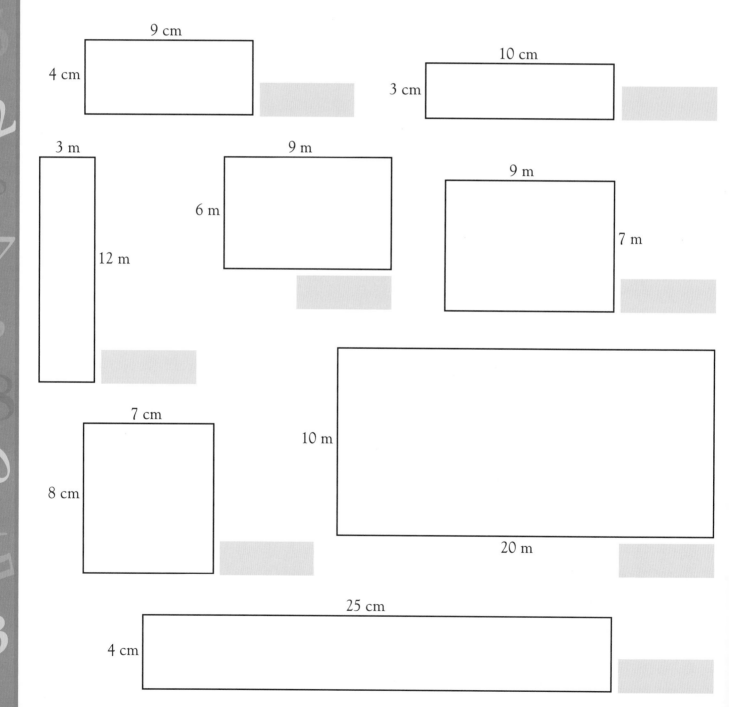

9 cm

4 cm

10 cm

3 cm

3 m

9 m

6 m

9 m

7 m

12 m

7 cm

8 cm

10 m

20 m

25 cm

4 cm

Problems using time

Write the answer in the box.

How many minutes until 12 o'clock?

90 minutes

Write the answer in the box.

What time will it be in half an hour?

What time was it ten minutes ago?

How many minutes until 10 o'clock?

The clock is 20 minutes fast. What is the real time?

Write the answer in the box.

What was the time half an hour ago?

How many minutes until 4 o'clock?

How long until a quarter to 4?

How many minutes since 2 o'clock?

Write the answer in the box.

How many minutes since 2:30?

How many minutes until 4 o'clock?

What time did the clock show half an hour ago?

How many hours until 8:15?

Reading timetables

	Frostburg	Elmhurst	Badger Farm	Winchester
Redline bus	8:00	8:05	8:15	8:25
Blueline bus	8:05	No stop	8:12	8:20
City taxi	8:30	8:35	8:45	8:55
Greenline bus	8:07	No stop	No stop	8:15

The timetable shows the times it takes to travel using different transport companies between Frostburg and Winchester.

Write the answer in the box.

How long does the Redline bus take between Frostburg and Winchester?

When does the Blueline bus arrive at Badger Farm?

Where does the Greenline bus not stop?

Where is City taxi at 8:35?

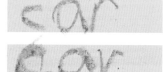

Does the Blueline bus stop at Elmhurst?

How long does the Redline bus take to travel between Badger Farm and Winchester?

Which is the fastest trip between Frostburg and Winchester?

Which service arrives at five minutes to nine?

How long does City taxi take between Frostburg and Badger Farm?

Where is the Blueline bus at twelve minutes past eight?

Averages

Write the average of this row in the box.

 4   2   2   2   6   3   2

The average is   3 .

Write the average of each row in the box.

2	3	7	4	2	7	2	5	5
7	4	5	4	8	5	3	4	4
5	3	5	3	5	2	4	5	5
7	5	9	7	2	4	8	6	6
4	3	4	3	4	3	4	7	7
1	4	2	7	3	8	2	5	5
3	2	1	2	2	3	2	1	1
8	3	6	3	8	2	8	2	3

Write the average of each row in the box.

4	8	6	3	9	6	6	6
5	9	2	6	9	1	3	3
6	3	8	6	1	5	6	6
3	8	6	7	5	9	4	1
1	8	3	4	2	6	4	4
9	5	8	7	4	7	9	9
1	3	2	3	1	2	2	2
6	3	7	4	5	4	6	6

Estimating

Estimate to find the answer.

One crate of apples sells for between $8 and $12. If Sam sold 10 crates of apples, about how much did he earn?

Sam earned about $100 .

Estimate to find the answer.

The river ferry makes 5 trips a day. There are between 40 and 60 people on each trip. About how many people ride the ferry every day?

About

Peter has 25 bean plants in his garden. Each plant produces 3 to 5 litres of beans. About how many litres of beans will Peter have?

About

Movie tickets cost between $6 and $10. If the theatre holds 200 people, about how much money is made in ticket sales when the theatre is full?

About

Luz can fit between 30 and 50 beads in a storage bag. If she has 12 bags, about how many beads will she be able to store?

About

Ahmed rides his bike 10 to 20 kilometres a day. About how many kilometres does he ride in five days?

About

Calculating change

Circle the correct change.

Carlo bought a ball.   He paid

How much change did he get?

Circle the correct change.

Snack Menu	
Banana	25¢
Pear	75¢
Apple	60¢

Kate bought an apple. She paid

How much change did she get?

Ali bought a banana. He paid

How much change did he get?

Dan bought a pear. He paid

How much change did he get?

Counting money

Count the coins. Write the total amount.

25¢   +   25¢   +   25¢   +   5¢   +   5¢   +   10¢   =   95¢

Count the coins. Write the total amount.

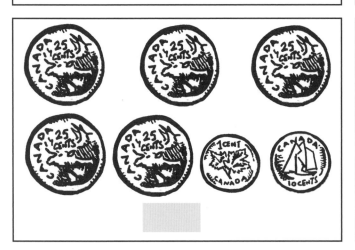

Number pairs

Look at the grid and then answer the questions below.

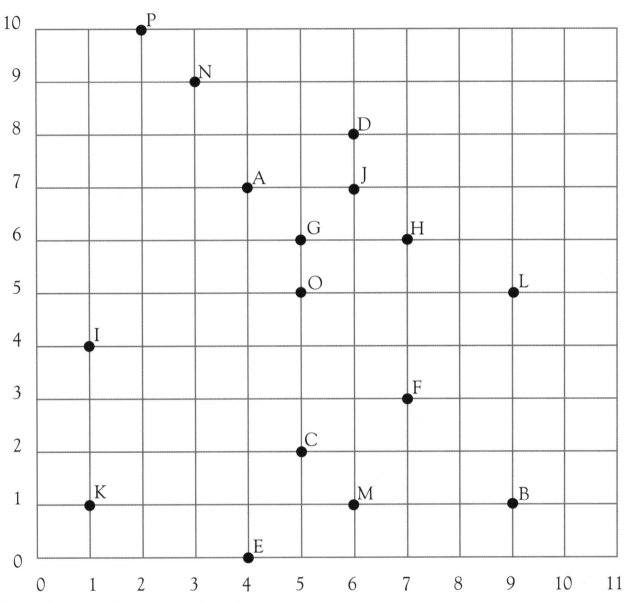

Give the number pair of each letter.

A =   B =   C =   D =

E =   F =   G =   H =

I =   J =   K =   L =

M =   N =   O =   P =

Multiply or divide?

Write + or – in the box.

6 ⊠ 5 = 30   18 ÷ 2 = 9   5 ⊠ 10 = 50

Write x or ÷ in the box.

7 ☐ 5 = 35   10 ☐ 2 = 5   12 ☐ 2 = 6

30 ☐ 5 = 6   30 ☐ 10 = 3   9 ☐ 2 = 18

14 ☐ 2 = 7   35 ☐ 5 = 7   6 ☐ 10 = 60

40 ☐ 10 = 4   20 ☐ 4 = 5   5 ☐ 3 = 15

5 ☐ 6 = 30   3 ☐ 10 = 30   90 ☐ 10 = 9

50 ☐ 5 = 10   18 ☐ 2 = 9   15 ☐ 3 = 5

Write the answers in the boxes.

A number divided by 4 is 10. What is the number?   ☐

I multiply a number by 6 and the answer is 30. What is the number?   ☐

A number multiplied by 10 gives the answer 10. What is the number?   ☐

I divide a number by 8 and the answer is 5. What is the number?   ☐

A number divided by 7 is 5. What is the number?   ☐

I multiply a number by 2 and the answer is 18. What is the number?   ☐

A number multiplied by 5 is 45. What is the number?   ☐

I divide a number by 2 and the answer is 1. What is the number?   ☐

Write x or ÷ in the box.

7 ☐ 10 = 70   5 ☐ 5 = 25   10 ☐ 10 = 1

5 ☐ 5 = 1   9 ☐ 2 = 18   2 ☐ 2 = 4

15 ☐ 5 = 3   10 ☐ 10 = 100   50 ☐ 5 = 10

100 ☐ 10 = 10   2 ☐ 2 = 1   20 ☐ 5 = 4

Lines of symmetry

Draw the line of symmetry on each shape.

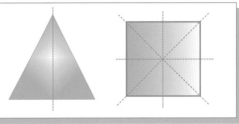

Draw the line of symmetry on each shape.

A   B   C

D   E   I

K   M   T

Half of each shape is drawn and the line of symmetry. Draw the other half.

U   V   V

Y   3   8

Counting by 2s, 5s, and 10s

Find the pattern. Continue each row.

Count by 2s.	9	11	13	15	17	19	21
Count by 5s.	8	13	18	23	28	33	38
Count by 10s.	65	55	45	35	25	15	5

Find the pattern. Continue each row.

0	2	4					
8	10	12					
38	43	48					
40	45	50					
63	73	83					
85	90	95					
6	8	10					
21	19	17					
68	66	64					
85	80	75					50
43	41	39					
49	44	39					
71	69	67					
83	78	73					48
39	34						4

Multiples

Circle the numbers in the
2 times table.

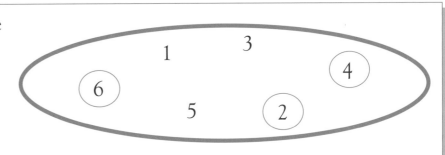

Circle the numbers in the
2 times table.

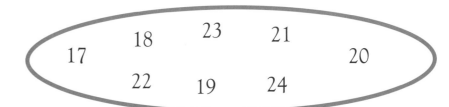

Circle the numbers in the
2 times table.

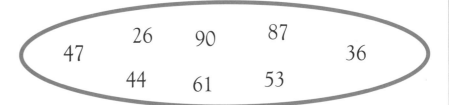

Circle the numbers in the
5 times table.

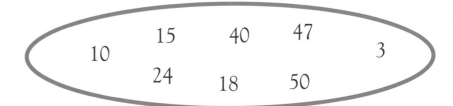

Circle the numbers in the
5 times table.

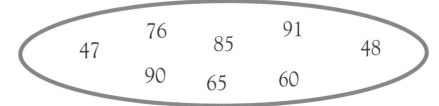

Circle the numbers in the
10 times table.

Circle the numbers in the
10 times table.

Comparing and ordering

Write these numbers in order, starting with the smallest.

431   678   273   586 | 273 | 431 | 586 | 678 |

Write these numbers in order, starting with the smallest.

267	931	374	740				
734	218	625	389				
836	590	374	669				
572	197	469	533				
948	385	846	289				
406	560	460	650				
738	837	378	783				
582	285	528	852				
206	620	602	260				
634	436	364	463				
47	740	74	704				
501	150	51	105				
290	92	209	29				
803	380	83	38				
504	450	54	45				

Rounding

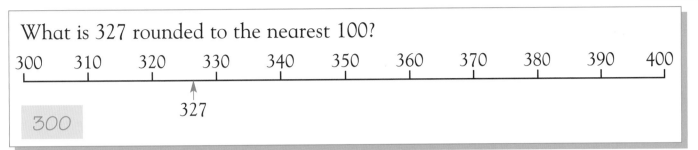

What is 327 rounded to the nearest 100?

300   310   320   330   340   350   360   370   380   390   400

327

300

What is each number rounded to the nearest 100?

478 ☐   231 ☐   147 ☐   687 ☐

342 ☐   812 ☐   973 ☐   439 ☐

639 ☐   108 ☐   374 ☐   752 ☐

418 ☐   639 ☐   523 ☐   446 ☐

857 ☐   560 ☐   299 ☐   809 ☐

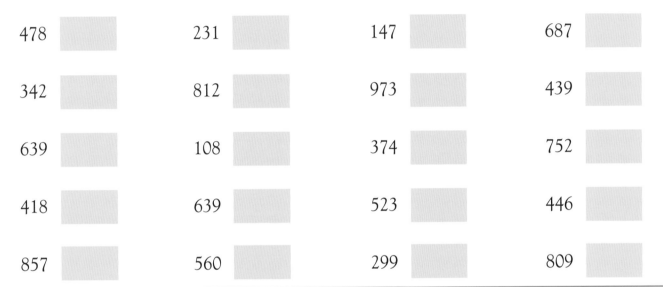

What is 250 rounded to the nearest 100?

200   210   220   230   240   250   260   270   280   290   300

250

300

What is each number rounded to the nearest 100?

450 ☐   850 ☐   650 ☐   87 ☐

21 ☐   405 ☐   150 ☐   950 ☐

655 ☐   540 ☐   980 ☐   50 ☐

750 ☐   250 ☐   90 ☐   59 ☐

550 ☐   105 ☐   955 ☐   350 ☐

Dividing by 2s, 5s, and 10s

$\frac{1}{2}$ of 12 is 6 $\frac{1}{5}$ of 10 is 2 $\frac{1}{10}$ of 20 is 2

What is $\frac{1}{2}$ of each number?

4		8		10		2
6		18		20		16
14		50		100		60

What is $\frac{1}{5}$ of each number?

5		25		40		70
50		65		20		30
45		60		35		75

What is $\frac{1}{10}$ of each number?

10		50		30		60
20		40		80		70

What is $\frac{1}{2}$ of each number?

22		30		24		28
32		26		36		34

What is $\frac{1}{10}$ of each number?

120		140		180		100
110		130		150		90

Multiplying

Write the answer in the box.

7 x 3 = 21   9 x 5 = 45   6 x 10 = 60

Write the answer in the box.

2 x 3 =   7 x 4 =   4 x 3 =   6 x 4 =

9 x 5 =   8 x 3 =   6 x 3 =   10 x 9 =

3 x 2 =   9 x 4 =   7 x 5 =   5 x 4 =

0 x 3 =   8 x 4 =   4 x 10 =   0 x 4 =

5 x 3 =   4 x 4 =   9 x 3 =   8 x 5 =

Write the answer in the box.

Three times a number is 18. What is the number?

A number multiplied by 4 is 36. What is the number?

A child draws 8 squares. How many sides have to be drawn?

Light bulbs come in packs of 3. Erin buys 6 packs. How many bulbs will she have?

Mari is given eight 5¢ coins. How much money is she given?

A box contains 4 cans of beans. A man buys 9 boxes. How many cans does he have?

A girl is given 3 stickers for every point she gains in a spelling test. How many will she receive if she gets 10 points?

Four times a number is 24. What is the number?

A bottle holds 4 litres of soda. How much will 7 bottles hold?

Six times a number is 30. What is the number?

Dividing

Work out each division problem.
Some will have remainders, some will not.

$15 \div 3 = \boxed{5}$

$17 \div 4 = \boxed{4 \, r \, 1}$

$$\begin{array}{r} 5\,r\,1 \\ 2\overline{)11} \\ -\,10 \\ \hline 1 \end{array} \qquad \begin{array}{r} 2\,r\,2 \\ 3\overline{)8} \\ -\,6 \\ \hline 2 \end{array}$$

Work out each division problem.

$24 \div 3 = $ $32 \div 4 = $ $18 \div 9 = $ $24 \div 6 = $

$16 \div 4 = $ $24 \div 4 = $ $40 \div 10 = $ $28 \div 4 = $

$40 \div 10 = $ $20 \div 4 = $ $40 \div 4 = $ $12 \div 6 = $

$9 \div 3 = $ $24 \div 3 = $ $35 \div 7 = $ $60 \div 10 = $

$3 \div 1 = $ $25 \div 5 = $ $36 \div 4 = $ $44 \div 4 = $

Work out each division problem. Some will have remainders, some will not.

$4\overline{)16} \qquad\qquad 5\overline{)32} \qquad\qquad 3\overline{)10} \qquad\qquad 5\overline{)13}$

$4\overline{)14} \qquad\qquad 3\overline{)21} \qquad\qquad 10\overline{)70} \qquad\qquad 3\overline{)19}$

Work out the answer to each problem.

23 carrots are shared equally by 4 rabbits.
How many carrots does each rabbit
receive and how many are left over?

36 apples are shared equally
between 5 horses. How many
apples does each horse receive
and how many are left over?

Bar graphs

Look at the bar graph. Then answer the question.

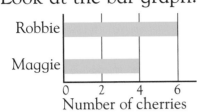

Number of cherries

How many cherries does
Robbie have?

6

Look at the bar graph. Then answer the questions.

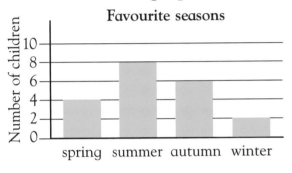

This graph shows the favourite seasons of a
group of children.

How many children were asked
which season they liked best?

How many children liked
autumn best?

Which season did four
children like?

Which was the favourite
season?

How many more children liked
autumn than liked winter?

Look at the bar graph. Then answer the questions.

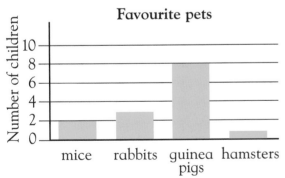

This graph shows the favourite pets of a
group of children.

How many children were asked
about which pets they liked?

Which pet did eight
children like?

How many children liked
rabbits?

How many children liked
hamsters?

How many more children liked
rabbits than liked hamsters?

Symmetry

Draw the lines of symmetry on each shape.

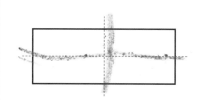
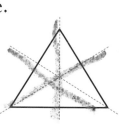

Draw the lines of symmetry on each shape. Some shapes may have no line of symmetry, and some shapes may have more than one line.

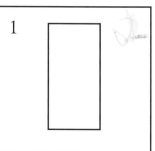
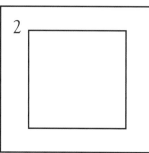
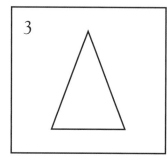
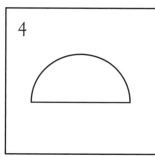

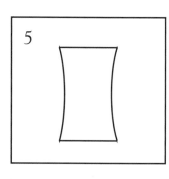
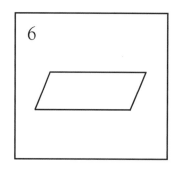
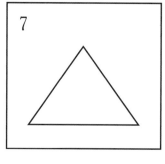
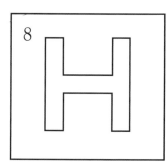

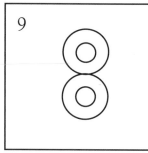
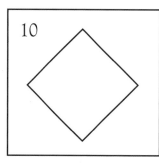
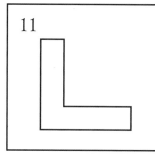
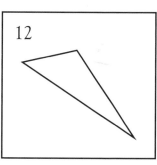

Half of each shape has been drawn as well as the line of symmetry (dotted line). Draw the other half of each shape.

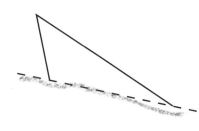

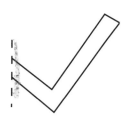

Ordering

Write these numbers in order starting with th...

670	760	607	706
607	670	706	760

Write these numbers in order starting with the smallest.

270	720	207	702
2	4	1	3

870	780	807	708
3	4	2	1

906	690	960	609
3	2	4	1

106	610	601	160
1	4	3	2

560	506	650	605
2	1	4	3

849	489	948	984
2	1	3	4

890	980	809	908
2	4	1	3

486	684	864	648
1	3	4	2

405	450	540	504
1	2	4	3

746	647	764	674
3	1	4	2

570	586	490	92
3	4	2	1

76	104	200	92
1	3	4	2

440	66	781	177
3	1	4	2

632	236	77	407
4	2	1	3

842	587	99	88
4	3	2	1

74	101	12	800
2	3	1	4

500	468	395	288
4	3	2	1

600	304	403	89
4	2	3	1

78	9	302	470
2	1	3	4

345	543	53	34
3	4	2	1

Fractions of shapes

 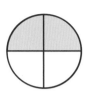

Shade half of each shape.

  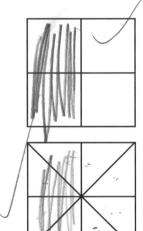

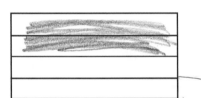  

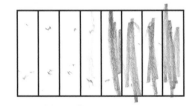 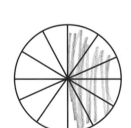 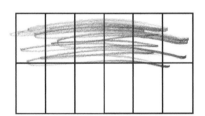

 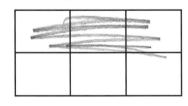 

Shade $\frac{1}{3}$ of each shape.

  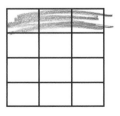

138

Choosing the operation

Write the answer in the box.

I add 25 to a number and the sum is 40. What number did I start with? 15

I subtract 13 and have 24 left. What number did I start with? 37

Write the answer in the box.

22 is added to a number and the sum is 30. What number did I begin with?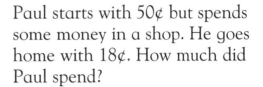

I subtract 14 from a number and end up with 17. What number did I start with?

I add 16 to a number and the total of the two numbers is 30. What number did I begin with?

When 26 is subtracted from a number, the difference is 14. What is the number?

After adding 22 to a number the total is 45. What is the number?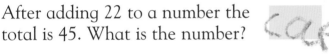

What number must you subtract from 19 to find a difference of 7?

I start with 29 and take away a number. The difference is 14. What number did I subtract?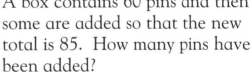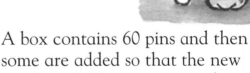

35 is added to a number and the total is 60. What is the number?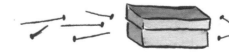

I increase a number by 14 and the total is 30. What number did I start with?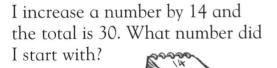

After taking 17 away from a number I am left with 3. What number did I start with?

Paul starts with 50¢ but spends some money in a shop. He goes home with 18¢. How much did Paul spend?

Sue starts out with 23¢ but is given some money by her aunt. Sue then has 50¢. How much was she given?

Alice gives 20¢ to charity. If she started with 95¢, how much has she have left?

Jane has a 500 millilitres bottle of orange soda. She drinks 350 millilitres. How many millilitres does she have left?

A box contains 60 pins and then some are added so that the new total is 85. How many pins have been added?

A tower is made up of 30 blocks. 45 more are put on the top. How many blocks are in the tower now?

Choosing the operation

Write the answer in the box.

A number is multiplied by 8 and the result is 24. What is the number? `3`

I divide a number by 4 and the answer is 9. What number did I begin with? `36`

Write the answer in the box.

A number is multiplied by 6 and the result is 30. What is the number?

When a number is divided by 7 the result is 4. What is the number?

I multiply a number by 10, and the final number is 70. What number did I multiply?

After dividing a number by 8, I am left with 4. What number did I divide?

When 20 is multiplied by a number the result is 100. What number is used to multiply?

I divide a number by 3 and the result is 9. What is the number?

After multiplying a number by 5, I have 40. What was the number I started with?

When a number is divided by 10 the result is 3. What number was divided?

I multiply a number by 4 and the result is 40. What number was multiplied?

After dividing a number by 2, I am left with 30. What number was divided?

45¢ is shared equally by some children. Each child receives 9¢. How many children are there?

Each box contains 7 markers. I have 28 markers altogether. How many boxes do I have?

I share 80¢ equally among some children. Each child is given 20¢. How many children have shared the money?

A bag contains 10 chocolate bars. In all I have 100 chocolate bars. How many bags do I have?

50 peanuts are shared equally between 2 squirrels. How many peanuts does each squirrel receive?

I give $25 to each charity. I give away $200. How many charities did I give money to?

Bar graphs and pictogr

Look at the bar graph and answer the question.

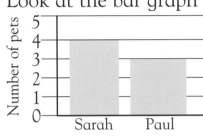

Which child has three pets?   Paul

Look at the bar graph and answer the questions.

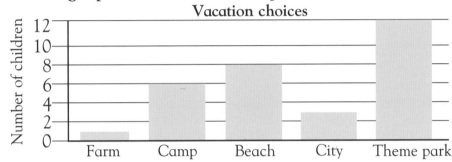

How many children went to camp on vacation?   6

Which place did three children go to?   city

Which place did fewer children go to than to the city?   Farm

Which was the most popular place for vacations?   Theme Park

How many children altogether went on vacation?   36

+ 3

Look at the pictograph and answer the questions.

Children's favourite hobbies

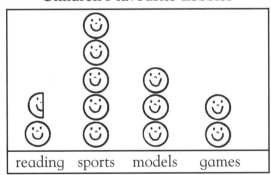

☺ each face stands for 2 children

How many children enjoy making models?   6

Which hobby is enjoyed by four children?   games

How many more children like games than like reading?   one

Which is the most popular hobby?   sports

Adding two numbers

Find each sum.

```
    2 7 1          ¹
  + 5 2 4        3 8 3
  ———————      + 5 7 1
    7 9 5      ———————
                 9 5 4
```

Remember to regroup if you need to.

Find each sum.

```
    3 3 4          3 5 2          6 2 3          5 4 3
  + 2 6 5        + 1 2 7        + 3 4 5        + 2 9 1
  ———————        ———————        ———————        ———————


    3 8 5          3 6 3          5 3 5          3 9 2
  + 6 0 6        + 1 4 7        + 1 8 7        + 4 8 8
  ———————        ———————        ———————        ———————
```

Write the answer in the box.

213 + 137 =   535 + 167 =

Write the missing number in the box.

```
    3 6 2          2 ■ 6          7 ■ 1          7 3 9
  + 4 1 9        + 5 8 1        + 2 6 4        + 2 4 ■
  ———————        ———————        ———————        ———————
    7 ■ 1          8 3 7          9 8 ■          ■ 7 9
```

Find each sum.

One jar contains 204 candies, and another contains 148 candies. How many candies are there altogether?

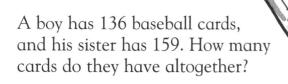

A boy has 136 baseball cards, and his sister has 159. How many cards do they have altogether?

Adding two numbers

Find each sum.

```
    3 2 1          ¹
  +   4 6 5        5 9 4
  ─────────      +   3 2 5
      786        ─────────
                    9 19
```

Remember to carry if you need to.

Find each sum.

```
    6 4 2          3 2 5          4 7 1
  +   2 4 1      +   6 5 3      +   2 3 8
  ─────────      ─────────      ─────────
```

```
    2 4 9          7 6 4          4 8 2
  +   4 7 1      +   2 1 5      +   3 4 9
  ─────────      ─────────      ─────────
```

Write the answer in the box.

342 +   264   =   531 +   236   =

13 +   642   =   338 +   261   =

Write the missing number in the box.

```
    2 4 1          6 5 2          3 4 2
  +   4 4█       +   2 █4       +   1 3█
  ─────────      ─────────      ─────────
    6 8 4          9 2 6          4 7 3
```

Find each sum.

621 people saw the local soccer team play on Saturday, and 246 people watched the midweek match. How many people saw the soccer team play that week?

214 people went to the rock concert on Saturday night, and 471 people went on Sunday night. How many people saw rock concerts that weekend?

Subtracting three-digit numbers

Write the difference between the lines.

$$\begin{array}{r} 364 \\ -\ 223 \\ \hline 141 \end{array}$$

$$\begin{array}{r} \overset{6\ 11}{4\cancel{7}\cancel{1}}\ \text{cm} \\ -\ 252\ \text{cm} \\ \hline 219\ \text{cm} \end{array}$$

Write the difference between the lines.

$$\begin{array}{r} 263 \\ -\ 151 \\ \hline \end{array}$$
$$\begin{array}{r} 478 \\ -\ 234 \\ \hline \end{array}$$
$$\begin{array}{r} 845 \\ -\ 624 \\ \hline \end{array}$$
$$\begin{array}{r} 793 \\ -\ 581 \\ \hline \end{array}$$

$$\begin{array}{r} 580\ \text{cm} \\ -230\ \text{cm} \\ \hline \end{array}$$
$$\begin{array}{r} 659\ \text{m} \\ -\ 318\ \text{m} \\ \hline \end{array}$$
$$\begin{array}{r} 850\ \text{cm} \\ -740\ \text{cm} \\ \hline \end{array}$$
$$\begin{array}{r} 372\ \text{m} \\ -262\ \text{m} \\ \hline \end{array}$$

Write the difference in the box.

365 − 123 =

799 − 354 =

$876 − $515 =

$940 − $730 =

$684 − $574 =

$220 − $120 =

Write the difference between the lines.

$$\begin{array}{r} 363 \\ -\ 145 \\ \hline \end{array}$$
$$\begin{array}{r} 484 \\ -\ 237 \\ \hline \end{array}$$
$$\begin{array}{r} 561 \\ -\ 342 \\ \hline \end{array}$$
$$\begin{array}{r} 394 \\ -\ 185 \\ \hline \end{array}$$

$$\begin{array}{r} 937 \\ -\ 719 \\ \hline \end{array}$$
$$\begin{array}{r} 568 \\ -\ 209 \\ \hline \end{array}$$
$$\begin{array}{r} 225 \\ -\ 116 \\ \hline \end{array}$$
$$\begin{array}{r} 752 \\ -\ 329 \\ \hline \end{array}$$

Find the answer to each problem.

A grocer has 234 apples. He sells 127.
How many apples does he have left?

A store has 860 movie videos to rent. 420
are rented. How many are left in the store?

There are 572 children in a school. 335 are
girls. How many are boys?

Subtracting three-digit numbers

Write the difference between the lines.

$$\begin{array}{r} {}^{3\ 11} \\ 4\!\!\!/1\,5 \\ -\ 1\,5\,2 \\ \hline 2\,6\,3 \end{array} \qquad \begin{array}{r} {}^{6\ 10\ 11} \\ 7\!\!\!/\,1\!\!\!/\,1\!\!\!/\ \text{m} \\ -\,3\,9\,2\ \text{m} \\ \hline 3\,1\,9\ \text{m} \end{array}$$

Write the difference between the lines.

$$\begin{array}{r} 524\ \text{m} \\ -\ 263\ \text{m} \\ \hline \end{array} \qquad \begin{array}{r} 319\ \text{m} \\ -\ 137\ \text{m} \\ \hline \end{array} \qquad \begin{array}{r} 647\ \text{cm} \\ -456\ \text{cm} \\ \hline \end{array} \qquad \begin{array}{r} 915\ \text{cm} \\ -\ 193\ \text{cm} \\ \hline \end{array}$$

$$\begin{array}{r} 714 \\ -\ 407 \\ \hline \end{array} \qquad \begin{array}{r} 926 \\ -\ 827 \\ \hline \end{array} \qquad \begin{array}{r} 421 \\ -\ 355 \\ \hline \end{array} \qquad \begin{array}{r} 815 \\ -\ 786 \\ \hline \end{array}$$

Write the difference in the box.

$$512 - 304 = \boxed{} \qquad\qquad 648 - 239 = \boxed{}$$

$$831 - 642 = \boxed{} \qquad\qquad 377 - 198 = \boxed{}$$

Write the difference between the lines.

$$\begin{array}{r} 423 \\ -\ 136 \\ \hline \end{array} \qquad \begin{array}{r} 615 \\ -\ 418 \\ \hline \end{array} \qquad \begin{array}{r} 312 \\ -\ 113 \\ \hline \end{array} \qquad \begin{array}{r} 924 \\ -\ 528 \\ \hline \end{array}$$

Write the missing number in the box.

$$\begin{array}{r} 7\ 2\ 3 \\ -\ 1\ 2\ \square \\ \hline 5\ 9\ 5 \end{array} \qquad \begin{array}{r} 5\ \square\ 2 \\ -\ 3\ 1\ 7 \\ \hline 2\ 4\ 5 \end{array} \qquad \begin{array}{r} 8\ 3\ \square \\ -\ 2\ 5\ 7 \\ \hline 5\ 7\ 7 \end{array} \qquad \begin{array}{r} 5\ 3\ 2 \\ -\ \square\ \square\ 5 \\ \hline 3\ 4\ 7 \end{array}$$

Find the answer to each problem.

A theatre holds 645 people. 257 people buy tickets. How many seats are empty?

There are 564 people in a park. 276 are boating on the lake. How many are taking part in other activities?

Multiplying by one-digit numbers

Find each product.

$$\begin{array}{r} 32 \\ \times\ 2 \\ \hline 64 \end{array}\qquad \overset{1}{\begin{array}{r} 26 \\ \times\ 3 \\ \hline 78 \end{array}}\qquad \overset{1}{\begin{array}{r} 34 \\ \times\ 4 \\ \hline 136 \end{array}}$$

Find each product.

$$\begin{array}{r} 27 \\ \times\ \ \ 2 \\ \hline \end{array}\qquad \begin{array}{r} 32 \\ \times\ \ \ 3 \\ \hline \end{array}\qquad \begin{array}{r} 16 \\ \times\ \ \ 4 \\ \hline \end{array}\qquad \begin{array}{r} 19 \\ \times\ \ \ 2 \\ \hline \end{array}$$

$$\begin{array}{r} 22 \\ \times\ \ \ 3 \\ \hline \end{array}\qquad \begin{array}{r} 25 \\ \times\ \ \ 4 \\ \hline \end{array}\qquad \begin{array}{r} 18 \\ \times\ \ \ 6 \\ \hline \end{array}\qquad \begin{array}{r} 33 \\ \times\ \ \ 5 \\ \hline \end{array}$$

$$\begin{array}{r} 39 \\ \times\ \ \ 2 \\ \hline \end{array}\qquad \begin{array}{r} 26 \\ \times\ \ \ 2 \\ \hline \end{array}\qquad \begin{array}{r} 41 \\ \times\ \ \ 2 \\ \hline \end{array}\qquad \begin{array}{r} 38 \\ \times\ \ \ 3 \\ \hline \end{array}$$

$$\begin{array}{r} 29 \\ \times\ \ \ 3 \\ \hline \end{array}\qquad \begin{array}{r} 45 \\ \times\ \ \ 2 \\ \hline \end{array}\qquad \begin{array}{r} 28 \\ \times\ \ \ 3 \\ \hline \end{array}\qquad \begin{array}{r} 16 \\ \times\ \ \ 6 \\ \hline \end{array}$$

$$\begin{array}{r} 10 \\ \times\ \ \ 5 \\ \hline \end{array}\qquad \begin{array}{r} 40 \\ \times\ \ \ 2 \\ \hline \end{array}\qquad \begin{array}{r} 20 \\ \times\ \ \ 4 \\ \hline \end{array}\qquad \begin{array}{r} 50 \\ \times\ \ \ 3 \\ \hline \end{array}$$

Find the answer to each problem.

Laura has 36 marbles, and
Sarah has twice as many.
How many marbles does
Sarah have?

A ruler is 30 cm long.
How long will 4 rulers be altogether?

Multiplying by one-digit numbers

Find each product.

```
      53          ³76          ³25
    x  3        x  6        x  7
   ┌─────┐     ┌─────┐     ┌─────┐
   │ 159 │     │ 456 │     │ 175 │
   └─────┘     └─────┘     └─────┘
```

Find each product.

```
    56          46          32          36          45
  x  8        x  7        x  6        x  9        x  4
  ─────       ─────       ─────       ─────       ─────
```

```
    73          96          58          33          48
  x  5        x  3        x  7        x  6        x  5
  ─────       ─────       ─────       ─────       ─────
```

```
    24          19          64          52          81
  x  9        x  8        x  4        x  6        x  3
  ─────       ─────       ─────       ─────       ─────
```

```
    37          40          50          30          20
  x  7        x  8        x  3        x  7        x  9
  ─────       ─────       ─────       ─────       ─────
```

Find the answer to each problem.

A school bus holds 36 children.
How many children can travel in
6 busloads?

Each of 28 children brings
7 drawings to school. How
many drawings do they
have altogether?

Division with remainders

Find each quotient.

$$5\ r\ 1$$
$$3\overline{)16}$$
$$\underline{15}$$
$$1$$

$$6\ r\ 2$$
$$4\overline{)26}$$
$$\underline{24}$$
$$2$$

Find each quotient.

$$2\overline{)35}$$ $$4\overline{)46}$$ $$3\overline{)22}$$ $$5\overline{)49}$$

$$4\overline{)58}$$ $$5\overline{)63}$$ $$5\overline{)37}$$ $$4\overline{)50}$$

$$3\overline{)76}$$ $$4\overline{)59}$$ $$5\overline{)94}$$ $$5\overline{)83}$$

$$2\overline{)99}$$ $$4\overline{)75}$$ $$5\overline{)77}$$ $$2\overline{)37}$$

Write the answer in the box.

What is 27 divided by 4?

Divide 78 by 5.

What is 46 divided by 3?

Divide 63 by 2.

Division with remainders

Find each quotient.

$$5\,r\,4$$

$$6\overline{)34}$$
$$\underline{30}$$
$$4$$

$$7\,r\,1$$

$$7\overline{)50}$$
$$\underline{49}$$
$$1$$

Find each quotient.

$$6\overline{)99}$$

$$6\overline{)43}$$

$$9\overline{)30}$$

$$8\overline{)76}$$

$$7\overline{)52}$$

$$7\overline{)83}$$

$$9\overline{)52}$$

$$6\overline{)91}$$

$$7\overline{)66}$$

$$8\overline{)63}$$

$$6\overline{)27}$$

$$8\overline{)46}$$

$$9\overline{)93}$$

$$7\overline{)85}$$

$$8\overline{)67}$$

$$7\overline{)26}$$

Write the answer in the box.

What is 87 divided by 7?

Divide 84 by 8.

What is 75 divided by 6?

Divide 73 by 9.

Appropriate units of measure

Choose the best units to measure the length of each item.

millimetres	centimetres	metres
desk	tooth	swimming pool
centimetres	millimetres	metres

Choose the best units to measure the length of each item.

centimetres	metres	kilometres

bed

bicycle

toothbrush

football field

shoe

driveway

sailboat

highway

The height of a door is about 2 _____ .

The length of a pencil is about 17 _____ .

The height of a flagpole is about 7 _____ .

Choose the best units to measure the mass of each item.

grams	kilograms	tonnes

train

kitten

watermelon

tennis ball

shoe

bag of potatoes

elephant

washing machine

The mass of a hamburger is about 26 _____ .

The mass of a bag of apples is about 1 _____ .

The mass of a truck is about 4 _____ .

Real-life problems

Find the answer to each problem.

Jacob spent $4.68 at the store and had $4.77 left.
How much did he have to start with?

$9.45

$$\begin{array}{r} 1\ \ 1 \\ 4.77 \\ +\ \ 4.68 \\ \hline 9.45 \end{array}$$

Tracy receives a weekly allowance of $3.00 a week.
How much will she have if she saves all of it for 8 weeks?

$24.00

$$\begin{array}{r} 3.00 \\ \times\ \ \ \ 8 \\ \hline 24.00 \end{array}$$

Find the answer to each problem.

A theatre charges $4 for each matinee
ticket. If it sells 360 tickets for a matinee
performance, how much does it take in?

David has saved $9.59. His sister
has $3.24 less. How much does
she have?

The cost for 9 children to go to a
theme park is $72. How much does
each child pay? If only 6 children
go, what will the cost be?

Paul has $3.69. His sister gives him
another $5.25, and he goes out and
buys a CD single for $3.99. How
much does he have left?

Ian has $20 in savings. He
decides to spend $\frac{1}{4}$ of it. How
much will he have left?

Perimeters of squares and rectangles

Find the perimeter of this rectangle.

To find the perimeter of a rectangle
or a square, add the lengths of the
four sides.
6 cm + 6 cm + 4 cm + 4 cm = 20 cm
You can also do this with multiplication.
(2 x 6) cm + (2 x 4) cm
= 12 cm + 8 cm = 20 cm

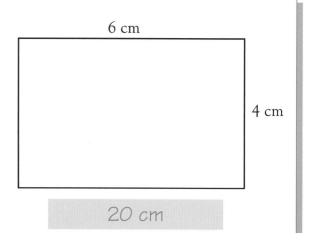

20 cm

Find the perimeters of these rectangles and squares.

4 cm
1 cm

cm

3 m
3 m

m

2 km
3 km

km

3 cm
2 cm

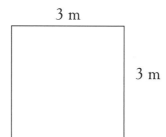

1 m
1 m

4 km
2 km

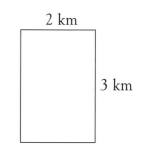

4 m
4 m

4 cm
3 cm

2 km
2 km

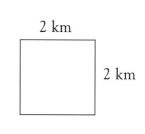

Comparing areas

Write how many units are in each figure.

18 units   16 units

Which figure has the greater area?

The figure on the left
has the greater area.

Write how many units are in each figure. Then circle the figure with the greatest area in each group.

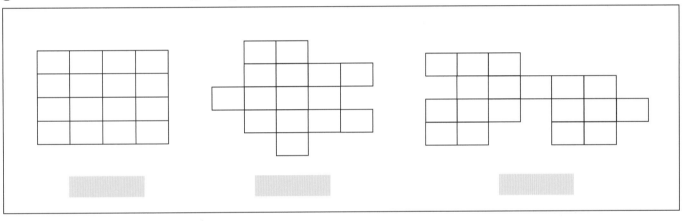

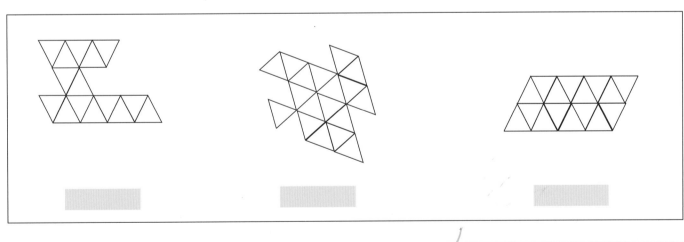

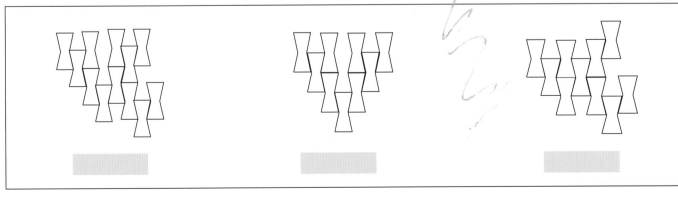

Adding fractions

Write the sum in the simplest form.

$\frac{1}{8} + \frac{3}{8} = \boxed{\frac{4}{8}} = \boxed{\frac{1}{2}}$ $\frac{3}{5} + \frac{3}{5} = \boxed{\frac{6}{5}} = \boxed{1}\,\boxed{\frac{1}{5}}$

Write the sum in the simplest form.

$\frac{1}{3} + \frac{1}{3} = \boxed{}$

$\frac{1}{4} + \frac{1}{4} = \boxed{} = \boxed{}$

$\frac{2}{3} + \frac{2}{3} = \boxed{} = \boxed{}\,\boxed{}$

$\frac{3}{7} + \frac{5}{7} = \boxed{} = \boxed{}\,\boxed{}$

$\frac{2}{5} + \frac{4}{5} = \boxed{} = \boxed{}\,\boxed{}$

$\frac{5}{16} + \frac{7}{16} = \boxed{} = \boxed{}$

$\frac{3}{8} + \frac{5}{8} = \boxed{} = \boxed{}$

$\frac{7}{13} + \frac{8}{13} = \boxed{} = \boxed{}\,\boxed{}$

$\frac{5}{16} + \frac{7}{16} = \boxed{} = \boxed{}$

$\frac{9}{10} + \frac{7}{10} = \boxed{} = \boxed{} = \boxed{}\,\boxed{}$

$\frac{4}{5} + \frac{3}{5} = \boxed{} = \boxed{}\,\boxed{}$

$\frac{7}{12} + \frac{5}{12} = \boxed{} = \boxed{}$

$\frac{3}{11} + \frac{5}{11} = \boxed{}$

$\frac{8}{14} + \frac{5}{14} = \boxed{}$

$\frac{2}{9} + \frac{4}{9} = \boxed{} = \boxed{}$

$\frac{5}{7} + \frac{1}{7} = \boxed{}$

$\frac{1}{12} + \frac{3}{12} = \boxed{} = \boxed{}$

$\frac{5}{11} + \frac{9}{11} = \boxed{} = \boxed{}\,\boxed{}$

$\frac{5}{18} + \frac{4}{18} = \boxed{} = \boxed{}$

$\frac{5}{9} + \frac{5}{9} = \boxed{} = \boxed{}\,\boxed{}$

$\frac{4}{15} + \frac{7}{15} = \boxed{}$

$\frac{2}{5} + \frac{1}{5} = \boxed{}$

$\frac{1}{6} + \frac{5}{6} = \boxed{} = \boxed{}$

$\frac{3}{4} + \frac{3}{4} = \boxed{} = \boxed{} = \boxed{}\,\boxed{}$

$\frac{1}{8} + \frac{5}{8} = \boxed{} = \boxed{}$

$\frac{3}{10} + \frac{9}{10} = \boxed{} = \boxed{} = \boxed{}\,\boxed{}$

$\frac{9}{15} + \frac{11}{15} = \boxed{} = \boxed{} = \boxed{}\,\boxed{}$

$\frac{1}{20} + \frac{6}{20} = \boxed{}$

Subtracting fractions

Write the sum in the simplest form.

$$\frac{5}{6} - \frac{4}{6} = \boxed{\frac{1}{6}}$$

$$\frac{5}{8} - \frac{3}{8} = \boxed{\frac{2}{8}} = \boxed{\frac{1}{4}}$$

Write the answer in the simplest form.

$$\frac{2}{3} - \frac{1}{3} = \boxed{}$$

$$\frac{7}{9} - \frac{4}{9} = \boxed{-} = \boxed{-}$$

$$\frac{1}{4} - \frac{1}{4} = \boxed{}$$

$$\frac{5}{7} - \frac{1}{7} = \boxed{-}$$

$$\frac{7}{12} - \frac{5}{12} = \boxed{-} = \boxed{-}$$

$$\frac{5}{11} - \frac{3}{11} = \boxed{-}$$

$$\frac{6}{7} - \frac{5}{7} = \boxed{-}$$

$$\frac{9}{12} - \frac{5}{12} = \boxed{-} = \boxed{-}$$

$$\frac{18}{30} - \frac{15}{30} = \boxed{-} = \boxed{-}$$

$$\frac{4}{5} - \frac{2}{5} = \boxed{-}$$

$$\frac{3}{6} - \frac{1}{6} = \boxed{-} = \boxed{-}$$

$$\frac{7}{8} - \frac{1}{8} = \boxed{-} = \boxed{-}$$

$$\frac{11}{16} - \frac{7}{16} = \boxed{-} = \boxed{-}$$

$$\frac{5}{9} - \frac{2}{9} = \boxed{-} = \boxed{-}$$

$$\frac{7}{13} - \frac{5}{13} = \boxed{-}$$

$$\frac{14}{15} - \frac{4}{15} = \boxed{-} = \boxed{-}$$

$$\frac{12}{13} - \frac{8}{13} = \boxed{-}$$

$$\frac{4}{5} - \frac{1}{5} = \boxed{-}$$

$$\frac{9}{10} - \frac{7}{10} = \boxed{-} = \boxed{-}$$

$$\frac{5}{6} - \frac{1}{6} = \boxed{-} = \boxed{-}$$

$$\frac{8}{17} - \frac{4}{17} = \boxed{-}$$

$$\frac{11}{18} - \frac{8}{18} = \boxed{-} = \boxed{-}$$

$$\frac{4}{5} - \frac{3}{5} = \boxed{-}$$

$$\frac{9}{11} - \frac{5}{11} = \boxed{-}$$

$$\frac{7}{8} - \frac{5}{8} = \boxed{-} = \boxed{-}$$

$$\frac{3}{16} - \frac{2}{16} = \boxed{-}$$

$$\frac{7}{12} - \frac{5}{12} = \boxed{-} = \boxed{-}$$

$$\frac{8}{14} - \frac{5}{14} = \boxed{-}$$

$$\frac{9}{10} - \frac{3}{10} = \boxed{-} = \boxed{-}$$

$$\frac{17}{20} - \frac{6}{20} = \boxed{-}$$

Volumes of cubes

This cube is 1 cm long,
1 cm high, and 1 cm wide.
We say it has a volume of
1 cubic centimetre (1 cm³).

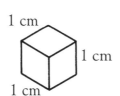

If we put 4 of these
cubes together the
new shape has a
volume of 4 cm³.

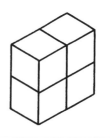

These shapes are made of 1 cm³ cubes. What are their volumes?

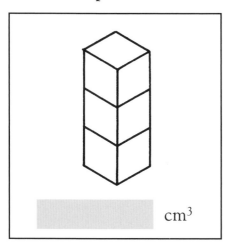

_____ cm³

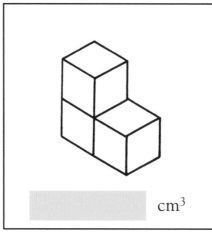

_____ cm³

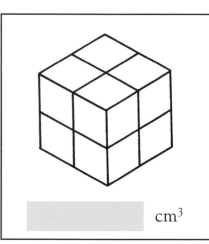

_____ cm³

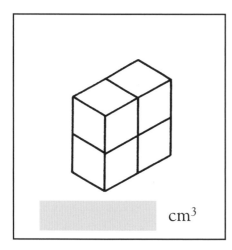

_____ cm³

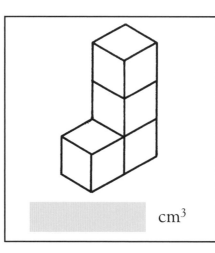

_____ cm³

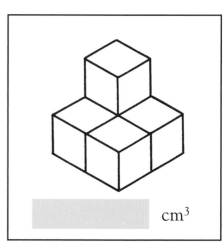

_____ cm³

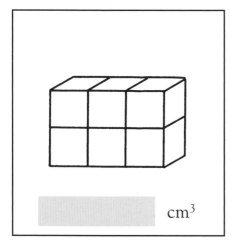

_____ cm³

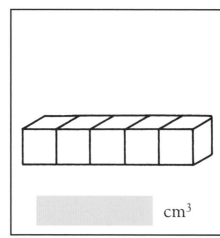

_____ cm³

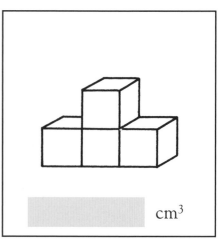

_____ cm³

Extra Practice

This section gives children a chance to further practise what they've learned, helping to reinforce the core skills developed while working through this book.

Contents
In this section, children will review:
- understanding place value of hundreds, tens, and ones
- representing, comparing, and ordering whole numbers up to 3 digits
- working with negative numbers
- rounding numbers to the nearest 10
- understanding strategies to add, subtract, multiply, and divide
- applying mathematics to solve problems in real-life situations
- solving money problems and telling time to the nearest 5 minutes
- the concept of fractions of objects and numbers
- recognizing angles
- using calculators
- representing and interpreting data
- reading metric units of measurement

The "Keeping skills sharp" pages can act as a test to see how well children are learning the material. Further parents' notes are found in the answer section at the back of the book.

When your child has completed this book, fill out the certificate of achievement and congratulate him or her on a job well done!

★ Place value

Circle the "ones" digit in each number.

4(5)   458   219   567   700

Circle the "tens" digit in each number.

184   365   456   786   200

Circle the "hundreds" digit in each number.

500   163   546   284   534

654 can be written as 600 + 50 + 4. This is called the **expanded form**. Write each number in its expanded form.

423

406

710

805

612

428

649

417

700 + 60 + 9 can be written as 769. This is called the **standard form**. Write each number in its standard form.

400 + 7   200 + 30 + 5

50 + 8   900 + 4

Look at this number line.

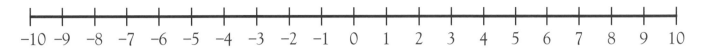

Add 1 to each number.
Note: When you add, you move to the right on the number line.

3 | 4 | 7 | | 9 | | 1 | | 0 | | −2 |

−10 | | 8 | | 4 | | 6 | | −3 | | −9 |

Subtract 1 from each number.
Note: When you subtract, you move left on the number line.

8 | | 5 | | 10 | | 1 | | −3 | | −9 |

2 | | 9 | | −5 | | 4 | | −8 | | −7 |

Add 3 to each number. **Hint**: Move to the right.

4 | | 7 | | 0 | | −7 | | −5 |

5 | | −3 | | −9 | | 6 | | −10 |

Subtract 4 from each number. **Hint**: Move to the left.

4 | | −5 | | 9 | | 10 | | −4 |

5 | | 2 | | 3 | | −1 | | −6 |

What is 2 more than these numbers?

7 [9]   28 [ ]   99 [ ]   80 [ ]   107 [ ]

What is 2 less than these numbers?

11 [ ]   70 [ ]   92 [ ]   48 [ ]   101 [ ]

What is 5 more than these numbers?

6 [ ]   17 [ ]   59 [ ]   31 [ ]   98 [ ]

What is 5 less than these numbers?

11 [ ]   34 [ ]   43 [ ]   98 [ ]   102 [ ]

Fill in the missing numbers.

90   95   100   105   110   115   120   125

110   120   130

25   50   75

100   200   300

Order each row of numbers, starting with the smallest.

213	312	123	230	32
32				

841	148	184	481	814

Order each row of numbers, starting with the largest.

627	276	672	267	726

150	100	105	500	510

Order this row, starting with the smallest amount.

$2.60	$6.20	$2.06	$6.02	$0.26

Order this row, starting with the largest amount.

$12.34	$21.43	$43.21	$43.12	$34.21

For each sum, put these numbers in order, starting with the largest. Then add.

50 + 200 + 8 = 200 + 50 + 8 = 258

7 + 60 + 400 = ___ + ___ + ___ = ___

12 + 750 = ___ + ___ = ___

24 + 370 = ___ + ___ = ___

Round each number to the nearest 10.

14 | 10   9 | 55 | 26 |

11 | 38 | 99 | 72 |

883 | 451 | 724 | 906 |

107 | 345 | 189 | 503 |

263 | 485 | 214 | 895 |

481 | 673 | 957 | 426 |

762 | 381 | 266 | 751 |

107 | 143 | 376 | 288 |

452 | 673 | 924 | 649 |

805 | 637 | 751 | 948 |

Circle the smaller number each time.

(3 x 4)   or   7 + 6   7 + 8   or   20 – 4   2 x 8   or   3 x 5

10 x 3   or   18 + 13   5 x 4   or   10 + 9   15 – 3   or   8 + 6

Circle the larger number each time.

10 x 4   or   19 + 13   8 + 9   or   3 x 6   12 + 12   or   7 x 3

5 x 3   or   8 + 6   10 + 12   or   5 x 5   7 + 13   or   30 – 9

Circle the smaller amount each time.

$2.00   or   80 ¢ + 70 ¢   65 ¢ – 25 ¢   or   56 ¢ – 30 ¢

$1.00   or   70 ¢ + 35 ¢   90 ¢ – 25 ¢   or   65 ¢ – 10 ¢

Circle the larger amount each time.

$5 + $2   or   250 ¢ + 250 ¢   47 ¢ – 8 ¢   or   35 ¢ + 3 ¢

$2.50   or $3.00 – 40 ¢   60 ¢ – 15 ¢   or   70 ¢ – 20 ¢

Circle the amount that is between $3.00 and $4.00.

$2.30 + 65 ¢ $5.00 – $1.50 $5.00 – 35 ¢

Circle the amount that is between 2 cm and 3 cm.

1.5 cm + 2.5 cm   6.5 cm – 2.5 cm   4 cm – 1.5 cm

Circle half ($\frac{1}{2}$) the vegetables in each group.

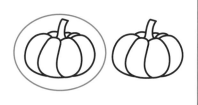  

Circle a quarter ($\frac{1}{4}$) of the fruit in each row.

What is half ($\frac{1}{2}$) of each number?

6 ☐   12 ☐   10 ☐   20 ☐   4 ☐

What is a quarter ($\frac{1}{4}$) of each number?

4 ☐   8 ☐   16 ☐   20 ☐   12 ☐

Half of a number is 3. What is the number?

Half of a number is 6. What is the number?

A quarter of a number is 1. What is the number?

A quarter of a number is 5. What is the number?

Fractions of shapes

Colour $\frac{1}{2}$ of each shape.

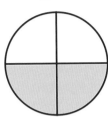  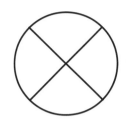

Now colour $\frac{1}{2}$ of the same shapes in a different way.

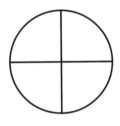 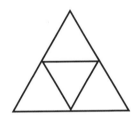 

Colour $\frac{2}{3}$ of each shape.

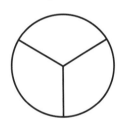 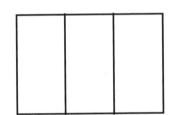 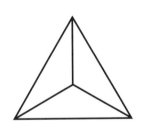

Colour $\frac{3}{5}$ of each shape.

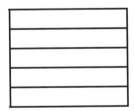  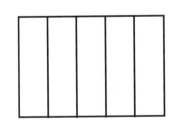

Colour $\frac{7}{10}$ of each shape.

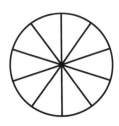 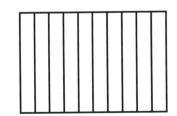 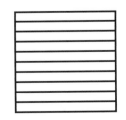

★ | Quarters

What is a quarter ($\frac{1}{4}$) of each number?

12 16 40 28

What is a quarter ($\frac{1}{4}$) of each amount?

4 ¢   20 ¢   12 ¢   16 ¢

How much is a quarter ($\frac{1}{4}$) of 40 ¢?

Fido eats 8 biscuits each day. Fido has a quarter ($\frac{1}{4}$) of the biscuits for breakfast. How many biscuits does Fido have for breakfast?

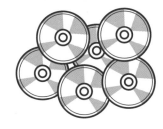

Daisy is given 20 CDs by her sister. Daisy gives a quarter ($\frac{1}{4}$) of the CDs to her brother. How many CDs does Daisy give to her brother?

Shen has to work for one hour but stops after a quarter of an hour. How long is a quarter of an hour in minutes?

Darius has to wait 24 minutes for a bus. He has waited a quarter ($\frac{1}{4}$) of that time. How long does Darius still have to wait?

166

Use a calculator to work out these problems.

7 x 12 = 84   9 x 9 =   10 x 12 =

7 x 6 =   14 x 10 =   12 x 50 =

16 x 3 =   200 x 6 =   120 x 7 =

12 x 8 =   20 x 20 =   150 x 6 =

26 + 49 + 58 =   74 + 59 + 82 =   29 + 69 + 84 =

546 + 512 =   785 + 897 =   209 + 109 + 56 =

432 + 777 =   812 + 564 =   231 + 321 + 412 =

576 – 299 =   600 – 345 =   708 – 544 =

1000 – 564 =   1645 – 789 =   1705 – 805 =

634 – 486 =   554 – 366 =   904 – 904 =

86 ÷ 2 =   100 ÷ 25 =   40 ÷ 8 =

160 ÷ 8 =   240 ÷ 12 =   300 ÷ 15 =

480 ÷ 20 =   500 ÷ 25 =   196 ÷ 14 =

Jake has to share $280 equally between himself and his four sisters.

How much will they each receive?

Which child has the most money?

Nada	Barbara	Ann	Harris
$230	$432	$402	$340

....

This thermometer shows the temperature during the day. Overnight, the temperature drops by 14°. What is the temperature at night?

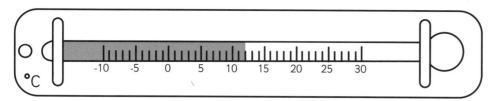

Write the children's names in order of height, starting with the shortest.

....

....

Harris	Doris	Dave	Taylor
1.10 m	1.42 m	1.02 m	1.25 m

....

Round each amount to the nearest dollar.

85 ¢ _____ $1.30 _____ $3.65 _____ $2.50 _____ $9.45 _____

James thinks of a number and then multiplies it by 3.
James then adds on 5 and gets the number 17.

What number did James begin with?

Maggie has $24 and spends one-quarter of it at a clothing store.

How much will Maggie have left?

Molly is going on vacation and can only pack half her T-shirts.
Cross out half of the T-shirts.

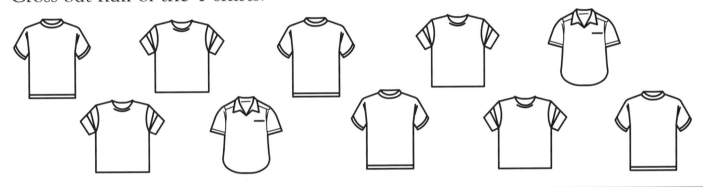

Peter has $5.00 and gives one-tenth ($\frac{1}{10}$) away to charity.

How much does he give to charity?

What fraction of $1.00 is 25 ¢?

Use a calculator to help you.

45 + 24 − 16 =

30 + 40 + 50 + 60 + 70 + 80 =

4231 − 1967 =

120 + 89 − 53 =

★ Adding three numbers

Write the answers.

$9 + 8 + 7 = \boxed{24}$ $10 + 8 + 7 = \boxed{}$ $20 + 17 + 14 = \boxed{}$

$11 + 5 + 3 = \boxed{}$ $15 + 10 + 5 = \boxed{}$ $30 + 20 + 10 = \boxed{}$

$50 + 30 + 10 = \boxed{}$ $12 + 11 + 10 = \boxed{}$ $21 + 11 + 1 = \boxed{}$

$7 + 14 + 21 = \boxed{}$ $9 + 18 + 30 = \boxed{}$ $50 + 30 + 20 = \boxed{}$

$40 + 18 + 20 = \boxed{}$ $30 + 19 + 10 = \boxed{}$ $10 + 23 + 40 = \boxed{}$

$70 + 9 + 10 = \boxed{}$ $50 + 17 + 20 = \boxed{}$ $40 + 20 + 40 = \boxed{}$

$17 + 18 + 19 = \boxed{}$ $23 + 24 + 25 = \boxed{}$ $36 + 37 + 38 = \boxed{}$

$51 + 52 + 53 = \boxed{}$ $35 + 45 + 55 = \boxed{}$ $20 + 80 + 60 = \boxed{}$

Write the answers.

23	45	19	56	38	73
34	16	15	42	13	12
+ 42	+ 18	+ 32	+ 17	+ 25	+ 15

Write the answers.

20 − 7 = 13   34 − 18 =   42 − 19 =   23 − 22 =

50 − 27 =   44 − 35 =   21 − 19 =   50 − 36 =

53 − 26 =   71 − 68 =   49 − 17 =   60 − 12 =

50 − 19 =   40 − 18 =   30 − 17 =   20 − 16 =

100 − 40 =   100 − 65 =   100 − 32 =   100 − 17 =

100 − 45 =   100 − 70 =   100 − 23 =   100 − 71 =

Write the answers.

43	67	80	120	105	102
− 21	− 14	− 54	− 30	− 45	− 56
22					

Matilda owns 145 pairs of shoes but gives 62 pairs away to a charity store.

How many pairs of shoes does Matilda have left?

Write the answers.

3 sets of 2 = 6

3 x 2 = 6

4 sets of 2 =

 x =

2 sets of 2 =

 x =

2 sets of 5 =

 x =

Write the answers.

1 x 2 = 　　　　2 x 2 = 　　　　3 x 2 = 　　　　4 x 2 =

5 x 2 = 　　　　6 x 2 = 　　　　9 x 2 = 　　　　10 x 2 =

2 x 3 = 　　　　2 x 4 = 　　　　2 x 6 = 　　　　2 x 8 =

2 x 1 = 　　　　2 x 3 = 　　　　2 x 5 = 　　　　2 x 7 =

Which number is missing?

　 x 3 = 6　　　　　 x 5 = 10　　　　　 x 8 = 16　　　　　 x 7 = 14

　 x 4 = 8　　　　　 x 10 = 20　　　　　 x 6 = 12　　　　　 x 9 = 18

What are 2 groups of each amount?

5 ¢ [10 ¢]   10 ¢ [   ]   20 ¢ [   ]   50 ¢ [   ] $2 [   ]

Multiply each amount by 2.

8 ¢ [   ]   12 ¢ [   ]   25 ¢ [   ]   30 ¢ [   ]   40 ¢ [   ]

Write the answers.

2 x 8 = [   ]   2 x 10 = [   ]   2 x 11 = [   ]   2 x 6 = [   ]

7 x 2 = [   ]   12 x 2 = [   ]   10 x 2 = [   ]   2 x 9 = [   ]

What is the missing number?

10 x [ ] = 20   8 x [ ] = 16   5 x [ ] = 10   6 x [ ] = 12

[ ] x 7= 14   2 x [ ] = 22   [ ] x 9 = 18   2 x [ ] = 100

20 x [ ] = 40   30 x [ ] = 60   40 x [ ] = 80   2 x [ ] = 50

100 x 2 = [   ]   200 x 2 = [   ]   300 x 2 = [   ]   400 x 2 = [   ]

Try this.

Start with 2, now double it, now double that number,
now double that number.

What number do you have?   [   ]

Match each dog to the right bone with a line.

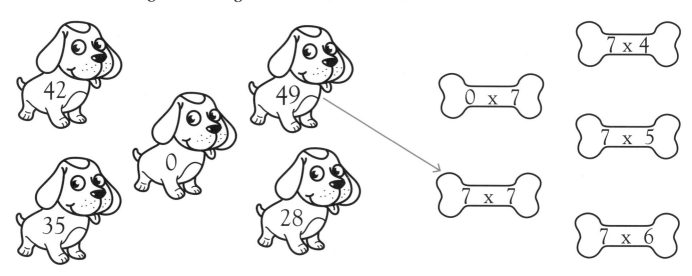

Write the answers.

1 x 7 = ☐   7 x 4 cm = ☐   4 x 7 = ☐   7 x 10 = ☐

2 x 7 = ☐   7 x 3 cm = ☐   6 x 7 = ☐   7 x 6 = ☐

7 x 1 = ☐   8 x 7 ¢ = ☐   7 x 7 = ☐   7 x 0 = ☐

7 x 4 = ☐   3 x 7 ¢ = ☐   7 x 2 = ☐   5 x 7 = ☐

☐ x 5 = 35   ☐ x 6 = 42   ☐ x 7 = 21   ☐ x 7 = 0

4 ¢ x ☐ = 28 ¢   7 ¢ x ☐ = 42 ¢   10¢ x ☐ = 70 ¢

How many sevens are the same as 21?   ☐

How many sevens are the same as 35?   ☐

How many sevens are the same as 49?   ☐

Match each mouse to the right cheese with a line.

Write the answers.

4 x 5 = ___   8 x 5 = ___   5 x 3 ¢ = ___   5 x 0 = ___

1 x 5 = ___   11 x 5 = ___   5 x 9 ¢ = ___   5 x 12 ¢ = ___

6 x 5 = ___   7 x 5 = ___   5 x 10 = ___   5 x ___ = 30

12 x 5 = ___   0 x 5 = ___   5 x 6 = ___   5 x ___ = 45

Circle the numbers that are **not** multiples of 5.

5   10   13   40   90   55   120   18   22   47   100

Write the answers.

5 + 5 = ___   2 groups of 5 = ___   5 groups of 2 are ___

5 x 2 = ___   3 groups of 5 = ___   3 groups of 5 are ___

Complete the grids.

X	2	6	8	11	9
2	4				
5	10				

X	0	1	8	6	4
2					
5					
10					

X	2	5	6	7	4	3	1
2							
5							
10							

X	3		5		
2		12		8	0
5		30		20	0
0		0		0	0

Write the answers.

9 x 3 = 27   10 x 6 =   8 x 4 =   6 x 7 =

7 x 5 =   9 x 4 =   6 x 5 =   10 x 10 =

6 x 2 =   6 x 4 =   6 x 10 =   12 x 0 =

4 x 7 =   5 x 9 =   3 x 8 =   7 x 10 =

1 x 1 =   3 x 3 =   5 x 5 =   6 x 6 =

7 x 7 =   2 x 2 =   4 x 4 =   0 x 0 =

Write the answers.

```
    8            7            9           10
  x 4          x 6          x 5          x 8
_____      _____      _____      _____



   12           13           14           15
  x 7          x 4          x 6          x 8
_____      _____      _____      _____
```

Don collects 6 new sports cards
every day for a week.

How many cards will Don have
at the end of the week?

★ | Multiples

Circle the numbers that are multiples of 3.

(12) 14 16 18 20 22 24 26 28 30

Circle the numbers that are multiples of 4.

2 4 6 8 10 12 14 16 18 20

Circle the numbers that are multiples of 5.

2 7 10 14 19 20 25 28 33 42

Circle the numbers that are multiples of 6.

4 6 8 10 12 14 16 18 20 24

Circle the numbers that are multiples of 10.

5 10 20 30 55 75 90 95 100 200

What is the smallest number that is a multiple of 3 and 4?

What is the smallest number that is a multiple of 2 and 5?

What is the smallest number that is a multiple of 3 and 5?

What is the smallest number that is a multiple of 2 and 4?

What is the smallest number that is a multiple of 3 and 10?

Write the answers.

$20 \div 4 =$ 5

$20 \div 10 =$

$12 \div 3 =$

$18 \div 6 =$

$30 \div 6 =$

$28 \div 7 =$

$32 \div 8 =$

$14 \div 2 =$

$10 \div 5 =$

$24 \div 3 =$

$21 \div 3 =$

$36 \div 4 =$

$50 \div 10 =$

$40 \div 10 =$

$4 \div 2 =$

$45 \div 5 =$

$20 \div 2 =$

$12 \div 2 =$

$12 \div 4 =$

$18 \div 9 =$

$24 \div 2 =$

$44 \div 4 =$

$24 \div 6 =$

$32 \div 4 =$

$14 \div 2 =$

$12 \div 2 =$

$27 \div 3 =$

$28 \div 4 =$

$70 \div 10 =$

$16 \div 2 =$

$14 \div 2 =$

$44 \div 4 =$

$20 \div 5 =$

$12 \div 6 =$

$18 \div 3 =$

$18 \div 2 =$

$40 \div 10 =$

$25 \div 5 =$

$12 \div 12 =$

$56 \div 7 =$

$20 \div 4 =$

$15 \div 5 =$

$16 \div 4 =$

$30 \div 5 =$

$60 \div 10 =$

$22 \div 2 =$

$24 \div 3 =$

$12 \div 6 =$

I add 16 to a number and then have 40.
What number did I begin with?

24

I subtract 25 from a number and have 14 left.
What number did I start with?

I multiplied a number by 6 and now have 54.
What number did I begin with?

Danny has a collection of 28 comics and
buys another 14. How many comics does
Danny have now?

I divided a number by 8 and now have 2. What
number did I begin with?

After adding 20 ¢ to some money, Gill has 75 ¢.
How much did Gill have to start with?

Margaret has to share 100 grapes with her three
sisters. How many grapes do they each receive?
Hint: Margaret wants some grapes too.

Peter adds three numbers together. Two of the numbers
are 8 and 7 and the total is 20. What number is missing?

Justin knows that six times a number is 48 but has
forgotten the number! Remind Justin what the number is.

Jonas has lost some money. He started
with $1.00 but now has only 58 ¢. How
much has Jonas lost?

Working with money

Fatima has this money but needs $2.00

How much more does Fatima need?

70 ¢

Angelo gives $3.50 to his sister and $1.50 to a friend.

How much money has Angelo given away?

Chantal receives $1.30 change after giving
the storekeeper $5.

How much did Chantal spend?

Otto buys a Chubby burger for $2.55 and pays with
three $1 coins.

How much change will Otto receive?

Sasha is given money by her
relatives on her birthday.

$10 $10 $5

How much does Sasha
receive in total?

From mom   From dad   From granny

Rudo wants to buy a toy that costs $8.60.
Rudo has $5.30.

How much more does Rudo need to buy the toy?

When Henry's dad empties his pockets he finds he has one loonie, two toonies, four 25 ¢ coins, and five 10 ¢ coins.

How much money has Henry's dad found?

Henry's mom finds this money behind some cushions – four loonies, five 25 ¢ coins, two 10 ¢ coins, and seven 1 ¢ coins.

How much money has Henry's mom found?

Henry's mom and dad put their money together.

How much do they have in total?

Jack and Jane together have $25. They spend their money on a takeout meal that costs $30.

How much more do they need?

What amount is missing?

$5   + $5   + $10   + $20   +   = $50

Write the answer.

How many 5 ¢ coins are the same as $1.00?

How many 10 ¢ coins are the same as $1.80?

How many 25 ¢ coins are the same as $2.00?

Write each amount in two ways.

Example: Thirty-five cents is either 35 ¢ or $0.35

Seven cents ☐ ☐   Ninety cents ☐ ☐

Twenty-nine cents ☐ ☐   Forty-two cents ☐ ☐

Thirty-one cents ☐ ☐   Fifteen cents ☐ ☐

Sixty-seven cents ☐ ☐   Fifty-five cents ☐ ☐

Ninety-three cents ☐ ☐   Seventy-eight cents ☐ ☐

Write the answers.

$1.20 + $0.80 = $2 $1.30 + $1.60 = ☐ $2.10 + $1.70 = ☐

$1.30 + $0.50 = ☐ $5.00 − $2.50 = ☐ $1.45 + $0.65 = ☐

$2.50 + $1.50 = ☐ $1.40 + $2.30 = ☐ $5.25 + $1.15 = ☐

$1.35 + $1.45 = ☐ $0.60 + $0.85 = ☐ $1.60 + $1.60 = ☐

$4.45 + $0.70 = ☐ $2.05 + $1.75 = ☐ $1.00 − $0.73 = ☐

$1.00 − $0.30 = ☐ $5.90 + $0.20 = ☐ $2.00 − $1.50 = ☐

$2.00 − $0.50 = ☐ $5.00 − $3.00 = ☐ $10.00 − $7.50 = ☐

Write the answers.

What is $1.60 plus 45 ¢? ☐   How much is $5.00 minus 8 ¢? ☐

What is $3.80 plus 70 ¢? ☐   How much is $2.00 minus 30 ¢?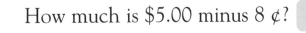

Complete this grid.

X	4		10	
5	20	45	50	
2		18		12

Write the answers.

$$\begin{array}{r} 24 \\ -17 \\ \hline \end{array}$$
$$\begin{array}{r} 38 \\ -12 \\ \hline \end{array}$$
$$\begin{array}{r} 40 \\ -23 \\ \hline \end{array}$$
$$\begin{array}{r} 51 \\ -36 \\ \hline \end{array}$$

Bart has to mark these products for Homer.
Help Bart to mark the products right (✓) or wrong (✗).

8 x 3 = 42

5 x 6 = 30

2 x 10 = 22

10 x 5 = 50

3 x 9 = 24

8 x 4 = 31

What is the smallest number that is a multiple of 4 and 5?

What is the largest number that is a multiple of 3 and 2 but less than 20?

Lucy has to share 3 pizzas equally between herself and three friends. Each pizza has 8 pieces.

How many pieces of pizza will each girl receive?

Share the 20 apples equally among the 4 children.

How many apples will each child get?

Write the answers.

12 shared by 2 = ⬚   12 shared by 3 = ⬚

12 shared by 4 = ⬚   12 shared by 12 = ⬚

Write the missing answers.

8 + ⬚ = 15   5 x ⬚ = 15

30 ÷ ⬚ =15   21 − ⬚ =15

Stefan is given 20 ¢ and now has 75 ¢.
How much did Stefan have before?

Anzelm has 45 model animals and buys another 18.
How many model animals does Anzelm have now?

Add each list.

$3.20	$1.80	$2.60
$1.40	$1.30	$1.20
+ $5.00	+ $1.60	+ $2.80

★ Measuring length

This is a centimetres ruler.

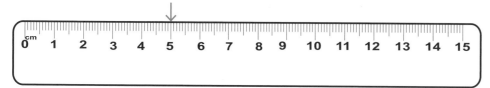

What length is shown on each ruler?

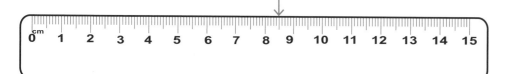

5 cm

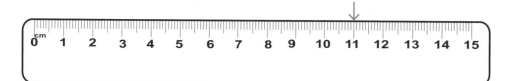

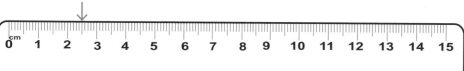

Mark the lengths on the ruler.

3.7 cm

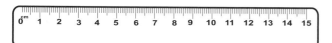

10.3 cm

3.5 cm

5.5 cm

This is a part of a measuring tape.

What length is shown on each measuring tape?

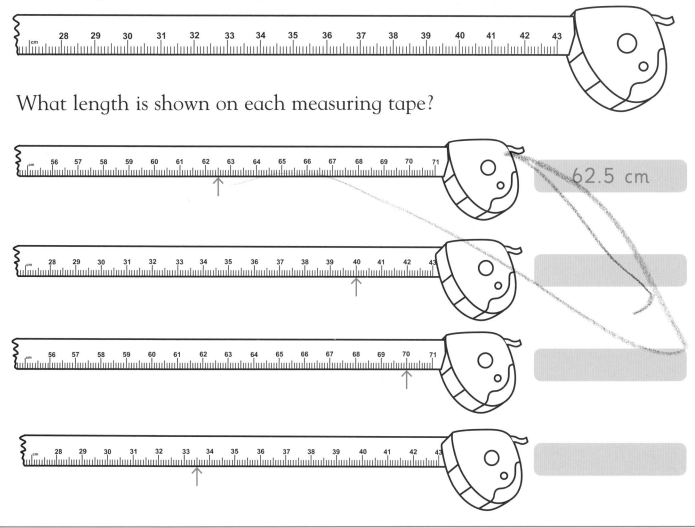

62.5 cm

Mark the lengths on the tape.

30 cm

63.5 cm

40 cm

Show the time on each clock.

2:10

5:40

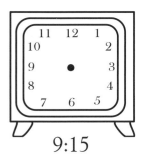

9:15

7:50

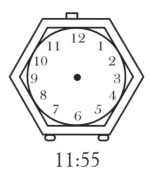

11:55

10:20

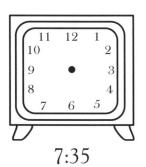

7:35

1:05

8:05

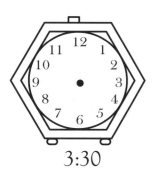

3:30

5:05

6:25

Write the answers.

What is the time 10 minutes after 8:30?

What is the time 20 minutes before 9:00?

What is the time 15 minutes after 6:45?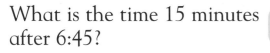

What is the time 20 minutes before 5:30?

What is the time on each clock face?

3:40

Write these times on the clock faces.

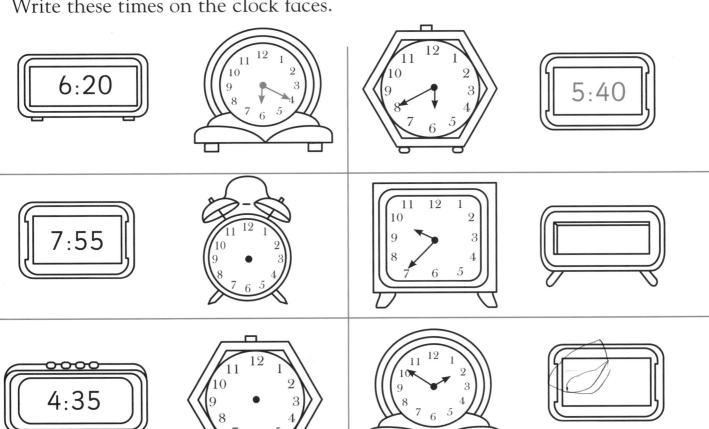

6:20

5:40

7:55

4:35

Yasir leaves for school at 8:35 and it is a 15-minute walk. At what time does Yasir arrive at school?

8:50

Matty starts her homework at 4:15 p.m. and it takes 30 minutes. What time will Matty finish?

Simone spends 90 minutes at a friend's house. She arrived at noon. What time does Simone leave her friend's house?

Ebba is waiting for a bus. The bus will arrive at 10:10 but the time is 9:50. How long does Ebba have to wait?

It is 9:15 when Emma starts to watch a movie. The movie lasts 90 minutes. What time will the movie end?

Konrad starts swimming at 8:45 and swims for half an hour. What time does Konrad finish swimming?

Mark cooks for two hours. He starts cooking at 11:00 in the morning. What time will Mark finish cooking?

Salama runs for 25 minutes before she gets tired. She starts running at 3:40 p.m. What time will Salama finish running?

Umi's watch is 20 minutes slow. The watch shows the time as 9:45. What time should the watch show?

Clara's bedside clock is 10 minutes fast. The clock shows 7:05. What is the correct time?

Days, weeks, months, years

How many days are in each number of weeks?

2 weeks [14]   3 weeks [   ]   4 weeks [   ]

5 weeks [   ]   10 weeks [   ]   8 weeks [   ]

How many whole weeks are in each number of months? **Hint**: Multiply by 4.

1 month [   ]   2 months [   ]   3 months [   ]

5 months [   ]   6 months [   ]   12 months [   ]

A leap year is every four years. When are the next five leap years after 2012?

[   ]   [   ]   [   ]   [   ]   [   ]

How many days are in two weeks?

[   ]

Which months begin with the letter J?

....

Which day comes
before Saturday?

....

Which days begin with the letter T?

....

Which month comes
before October?

....

Which month comes between
February and April?

....

How many days are in February
in a leap year?

[   ]

What will the year after 2019 be?

[   ]

Look at the drawing and answer the questions.

The girl makes a quarter turn to her right. What animal does she see?

Dog

The girl is facing the dog and makes a half-turn. What animal does she see?

The girl is facing the horse and makes a quarter turn to her left. What animal does she see?

The girl faces the cow and makes a clockwise three-quarter turn. What animal is she facing?

The girl faces the monkey and makes a full turn clockwise. What animal does she see?

Look at the spinner and answer the questions.

If the arrow spins a quarter turn clockwise, which number will it be on?

If the arrow spins a quarter turn counterclockwise, which number will it be on?

If the arrow spins around to number 6, how much has it turned?

Amy asked children in her school about favourite places to go on vacation. She recorded the information on a tally chart.

Favourite countries

Countries	Number of votes
France	ЦЩ ЦЩ ЦЩ ЦЩ ЦЩ |||
U.S.	ЦЩ ЦЩ ЦЩ ЦЩ ЦЩ ЦЩ ЦЩ ЦЩ	
England	ЦЩ ЦЩ ЦЩ ||
Spain	ЦЩ ЦЩ ||||
Canada	ЦЩ ЦЩ ЦЩ ЦЩ ||

Amy forgot to record 4 votes for the U.S. Add these to the chart.

Which was the most popular choice? ....

How many children liked this country?

Which was the least popular country? ....

How many children liked this country?

How many more children preferred France to England?

How many children did Amy ask in total?

Which country had 17 votes? ....

How many votes did Canada and Spain have in total?

Put the countries in order of votes with the least popular first.

....

Mike asks his class about their favourite countries visited during the summer vacations. He records his findings on a bar graph.

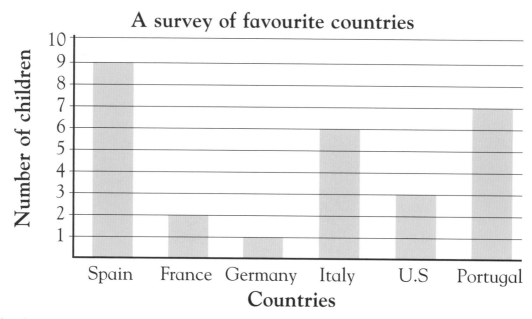

A survey of favourite countries

Number of children

Countries

Rank the countries in order of popularity, starting with the least favourite.

....

How many children preferred Spain?

Which two countries had a total of 13? ....

The pictograph shows how many children took part in various sports.

A survey of favourite sports

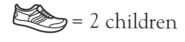 = 2 children

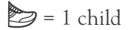 = 1 child

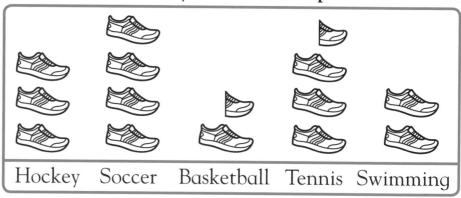

Hockey Soccer Basketball Tennis Swimming

Which is the most popular sport? ....

Which sport had 7 votes? ....

How many children liked basketball?

How many children took part in the survey?

Give the correct name for each shape.

Oval

....

....

....

....

....

....

....

....

....

Look at the shapes above. List the shapes that have curved sides.

....

Look at the shapes above. List the shapes that have right angles.

....

Draw a pentagon that is not regular.

Draw a right-angle triangle.

Is the dotted line a line of symmetry?

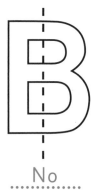

No
....

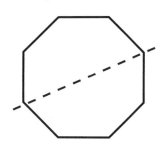

....

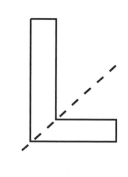

....

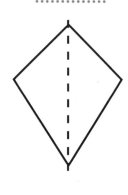

....

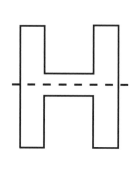

....

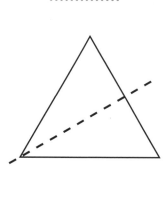

....

Complete each drawing.

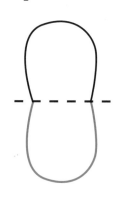

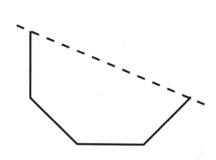

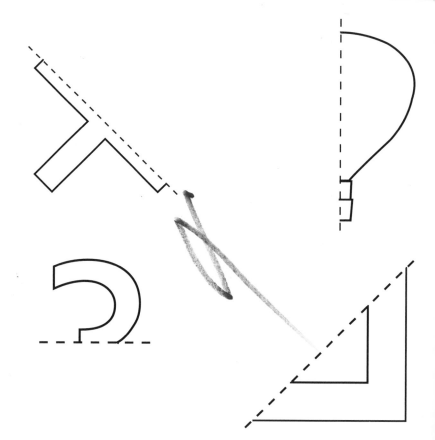

Look carefully for the right angles and mark them on the shapes.

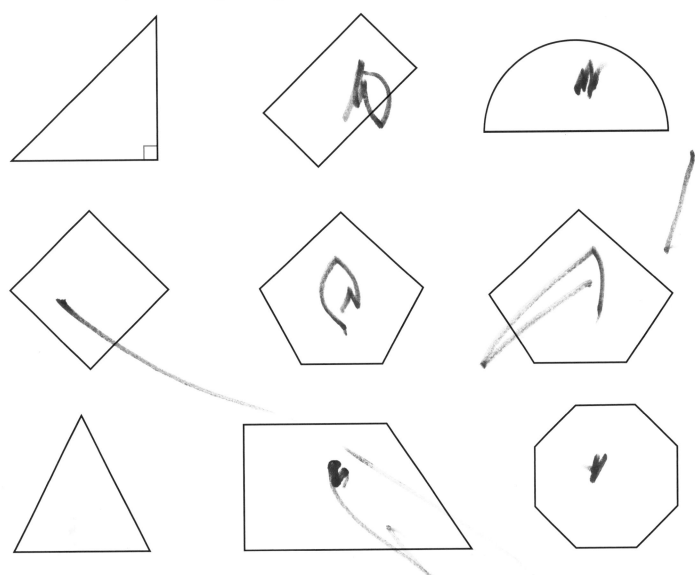

Draw a shape of your own that has only one right angle.

Draw a shape of your own that has no right angles.

★ | More angles

This angle is **less than** a right angle.

This angle is **more than** a right angle.

Look at each angle and write "more than," "less than," or "right angle."

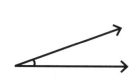

Less than

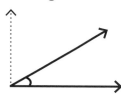

....

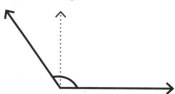

....

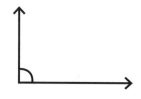

....

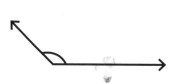

....

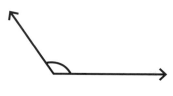

....

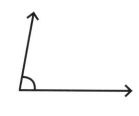

....

....

....

Look at the diagram.

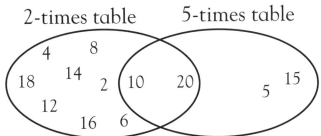

Which numbers are only in
the 2-times table?

Which numbers are only in
the 5-times table?

Which numbers are in both
the 2- and 5-times tables?

Look at the diagram.

	Odd numbers	Even numbers
In 5-times table	5 15	20 10
In 2-times table		4 8 6 18 16 12 10 2 20 14

How many numbers are odd?   How many numbers are even?

Which numbers are even and in the
5-times table?

Why are no numbers in the 2-times table and odd section?

....

Barry's watch shows this time in the evening.

Val's watch shows this time in the evening.

What is the difference between the two times? ....

Sean goes for a long walk and starts at 9:30. The walk takes two and a quarter hours. When does Sean arrive?

The dogs have walked these distances.

14 kilometres

17 kilometres

28 kilometres

How far have the dogs walked in total?

A teacher found out that 24 children had packed lunches, 7 bought school lunch, and 1 went home to lunch.

Show this information as a tally chart. Remember to write labels.

Draw a shape that has three sides.

Draw a shape that has two lines of symmetry. Mark the lines of symmetry on your shape.

What is the name of your shape? . . . .

Check (✓) the angle that is less than a right angle.

Sean divides a number by 3 and the answer is 9. What was the number?

Barbara multiplies a number by 6 and the answer is 66. What was the number?

Which number is 24 more than 24?

Which number is 36 less than 36?

A playground is a rectangle 90 m by 30 m.

Darius walks around the sides of the playground. How far does he walk?

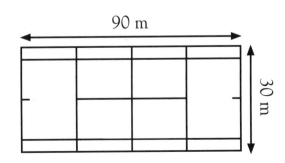

90 m

30 m

Certificate

Congratulations to

....

for successfully finishing this book.

Grade 3

WELL DONE!

You're a star.

Date

....

Answer Section with Parents' Notes

Grade 3
ages 8–9
Workbook

This section provides answers to all the activities in the book. These pages will enable you to mark your children's work, or they can be used by your children if they prefer to do their own marking.

The notes for each page help to explain common errors and problems and, where appropriate, indicate the kind of practice needed to ensure that your children understand where and how they have made errors.

Numbers

Write the number in words.
567 — Five hundred sixty-seven

Write the number in standard form.
Four hundred eighty-six. — 486

Write each number in words.

85	Eighty-five
26	Twenty-six
43	Forty-three
38	Thirty-eight

Write the numbers in standard form.

Forty-seven.	47	Fifty-eight.	58
Seventy-three.	73	Three hundred eighty-two.	382
Sixty-one.	61	Seven hundred twenty-four.	724

Write each number in words.

207	Two hundred seven
46	Forty-six
58	Fifty-eight
39	Thirty-nine

Write the numbers in standard form.

Three hundred twenty-one.	321	Two hundred seven.	207
Eighty-two.	82		

Children may use zeros incorrectly in numbers. In word form, zeros are omitted, but children should take care to include them when writing numbers in standard form.

3

Place value

645 is the same as:
6 hundreds, 4 tens, 5 ones
or
645 is the same as 600 + 40 + 5

Write the correct number in the space.

945 = 900 + 40 + 5   312 = 300 + 10 + 2
749 = 700 + 40 + 9   263 = 200 + 60 + 3
294 = 200 + 90 + 4   742 = 700 + 40 + 2
176 = 100 + 70 + 6   375 = 300 + 70 +5
264 = 200 + 60 + 4   286 = 200 + 80 + 6

Write the number that is the same as:

Two hundred eighty-four	284
One hundred sixty-nine	169
Eight hundred seventy-two	872
Two hundred sixty-six	266
Four hundred twenty-seven	427
Nine hundred forty-three	943
Two hundred ten	210
One hundred three	103
Three hundred eleven	311
Three hundred thirty-eight	338

Look at these numbers: 8 3 0 7

Arrange these digits to make the largest number you can.	8730
Arrange these digits to make the smallest number you can.	378

Again, make sure that children understand the use of zeros in numbers. For example, children should understand that they should not write 0378 or 3780 as the answer to the final question of the page.

Multiplying by 10

Multiply each number by 10.

7	70	12	120	3	30	13	130

Multiply each of these numbers by 10.

6	60	14	140	12	120	17	170	20	200
9	90	15	150	13	130	2	20	23	230
1	10	19	190	24	240	28	280	22	220
5	50	3	30	26	260	11	110	25	250

Multiply each of these numbers by 10.

20	200	17	170	12	120	14	140	6	60
23	230	2	20	13	130	15	150	9	90
22	220	28	280	24	240	19	190	1	10
25	250	11	110	26	260	3	30	5	50

Multiply each of these numbers by 10.

56	560	48	480	67	670	39	390	82	820
69	690	32	320	74	740	57	570	43	430
95	950	63	630	55	550	77	770	40	400

Multiply each of these numbers by 10.

38	380	67	670	48	480	56	560	74	740
32	320	69	690	82	820	63	630	95	950
43	430	57	570	99	990	40	400	77	770

Children should realize that multiplying by 10 means adding a zero to a number. The ones become tens and the tens become hundreds, leaving a blank space—the zero—in the ones column.

Ordering

Write these numbers in order, from smallest to largest.

675	830	390	617
390	617	675	830

Write these numbers in order, from smallest to largest.

574	683	847	563	563	574	683	847
473	670	371	421	371	421	473	670
389	726	995	843	389	726	843	995
562	264	923	674	264	562	674	923
853	567	684	557	557	567	684	853
241	785	538	647	241	538	647	785

Write these numbers in order, from smallest to largest.

705	390	903	704	390	704	705	903
67	809	330	35	35	67	330	809
207	380	105	127	105	127	207	380
45	28	36	106	28	36	45	106
104	140	410	800	104	140	410	800

Write these numbers in order, from smallest to largest.

780	365	968	89	89	365	780	968
890	78	678	999	78	678	890	999
950	230	845	102	102	230	845	950
804	800	840	980	800	804	840	980
679	375	753	573	375	573	679	753

Children who do not understand the place value of digits may make errors in thinking that a "tens" number is bigger than a "hundreds" number because the first digit is higher.

6

Rounding

What is 132 rounded to the nearest ten?

100 110 120 130 140 150 160 170 180

132 rounded to the nearest 10 is 130 .

Round each number to the nearest ten.

| 247 | 250 | 306 | 310 | 493 | 490 | 733 | 730 |
| 834 | 830 | 651 | 650 | 379 | 380 | 215 | 220 |

Round each number to the nearest ten.

Number line	Answer
120 130 140 150 160 170 180 190 200	160
320 330 340 350 360 370 380 390 400	350
220 230 240 250 260 270 280 290 300	270
480 490 500 510 520 530 540 550 560	550
700 710 720 730 740 750 760 770 780	720
60 70 80 90 100 110 120 130 140	110
450 460 470 480 490 500 510 520 530	500
170 180 190 200 210 220 230 240 250	250
640 650 660 670 680 690 700 710 720	700
500 510 520 530 540 550 560 570 580	530

Children should remember that numbers ending in 5 or greater are rounded up.

7

Polygons

Match the polygon with a solid figure.

Circle the octagon.

Circle the rectangle.

Match the polygon to the solid object in which it appears.

hexagon   octagon   rectangle   pentagon   triangle

Children can count the sides of the polygons to match them with other polygons or with the names that identify them.

Identifying patterns

Continue each pattern.

0	6	12	18	24	30
0	7	14	21	28	35
60	52	44	36	28	20

Continue each pattern.

3	9	15	21	27	33	39	45
2	9	16	23	30	37	44	51
1	9	17	25	33	41	49	57
7	15	23	31	39	47	55	63
7	13	19	25	31	37	43	49
7	12	17	22	27	32	37	42

Continue each pattern.

71	65	59	53	47	41	35	29
90	82	74	66	58	50	42	34
56	49	42	35	28	21	14	7
72	66	60	54	48	42	36	30
96	88	80	72	64	56	48	40
48	42	36	30	24	18	12	6

Continue each pattern.

36	43	50	57	64	71	78	85
61	55	49	43	37	31	25	19
0	7	14	21	28	35	42	49
7	14	21	28	35	42	49	56
4	12	20	28	36	44	52	60

It may help to point out that some patterns show an increase and some a decrease. Children should double-check that the operation that turns the first number into the second also turns the second number into the third. They can then continue the pattern.

Odds and evens

Multiply the odd number by the odd number.   7 x 5 = 35

Multiply the even number by the even number.   6 x 8 = 48

Multiply the odd number by the odd number.

5 x 7 = 35	3 x 9 = 27	1 x 5 = 5	3 x 5 = 15
7 x 3 = 21	3 x 7 = 21	7 x 1 = 7	7 x 7 = 49
3 x 3 = 9	3 x 1 = 3	5 x 9 = 45	1 x 1 = 1
5 x 3 = 15	9 x 3 = 27	5 x 5 = 25	7 x 5 = 35

What do you notice about the numbers in your answer boxes?
They are all odd numbers.

Multiply the even number by the even number.

2 x 8 = 16	6 x 4 = 24	6 x 10 = 60	2 x 6 = 12
4 x 4 = 16	8 x 2 = 16	6 x 8 = 48	6 x 6 = 36
4 x 6 = 24	10 x 4 = 40	4 x 8 = 32	2 x 4 = 8
2 x 2 = 4	8 x 6 = 48	6 x 2 = 12	10 x 10 = 100

What do you notice about the numbers in your answer boxes?
They are all even numbers.

Multiply the odd number by the even number.

3 x 6 = 18	10 x 5 = 50	7 x 4 = 28	2 x 9 = 18
4 x 7 = 28	3 x 10 = 30	4 x 9 = 36	10 x 7 = 70
5 x 8 = 40	6 x 9 = 54	8 x 5 = 40	6 x 7 = 42
9 x 6 = 54	6 x 3 = 18	9 x 4 = 36	10 x 3 = 30

What do you notice about the numbers in your answer boxes?
They are all even numbers.

If children fail to notice any similarity in the products, suggest that they check to see if all of the products are even or if all are odd.

Addion fact families

Circle the number sentence that is in the same fact family.

12 − 5 = 7
5 + 7 = 12   12 − 4 = 8   (7 + 5 = 12)   12 + 12 = 24

10 − 8 = 2
8 + 2 = 10   8 − 6 = 2   (2 + 8 = 10)   8 − 2 = 6

Circle the number sentence that is in the same fact family.

| 7 + 8 = 15
8 + 7 = 15	7 + 5 = 12	(15 − 8 = 7)	8 − 7 = 1
17 − 6 = 11
11 + 6 = 17	(17 − 11 = 6)	17 + 6 = 23	5 + 6 = 11
14 − 5 = 9
14 − 9 = 5	9 − 3 = 6	14 + 9 = 23	(5 + 9 = 14)
9 + 7 = 16
7 + 9 = 16	(16 − 9 = 7)	16 + 7 = 23	9 − 7 = 2
19 − 9 = 10
19 − 10 = 9	9 + 3 = 12	(9 + 10 = 19)	18 − 8 = 10
4 + 7 = 11
11 − 4 = 7	11 + 4 = 15	(7 + 4 = 11)	7 + 7 = 14

Write the fact family for each group of numbers.

5, 6, 11	6, 10, 4	5, 13, 8
5 + 6 = 11	6 + 4 = 10	5 + 8 = 13
6 + 5 = 11	4 + 6 = 10	8 + 5 = 13
11 − 6 = 5	10 − 6 = 4	13 − 8 = 5
11 − 5 = 6	10 − 4 = 6	13 − 5 = 8

Children should understand that subtraction "undoes" addition. You may want to use counters to show the addition fact families.

Fractions

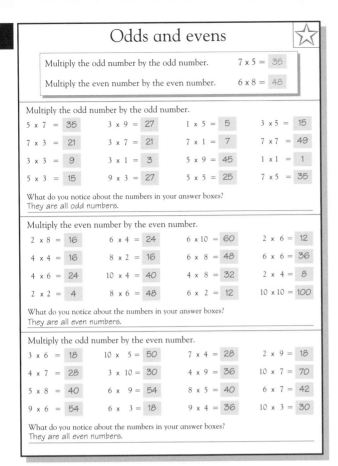

Write the fraction for the part that is shaded.

How many shaded circles?   3
How many circles?   8

So, the fraction of circles shaded = $\frac{3}{8}$ numerator / denominator

Circle the fraction that shows the part that is shaded.

$(\frac{2}{5})$ $\frac{2}{3}$ $\frac{3}{5}$ $\frac{3}{4}$ $\frac{4}{7}$ $(\frac{3}{7})$

Write the fraction for the part that is shaded.

$\frac{3}{4}$ $\frac{5}{8}$ $\frac{1}{3}$

$\frac{4}{9}$ $\frac{5}{6}$ $\frac{1}{8}$

$\frac{5}{7}$ $\frac{2}{7}$ $\frac{5}{12}$

If children have difficulty, point out that the denominator (the bottom number of the fraction) is the total number of parts, and the numerator (the top number of the fraction) is the number of shaded parts.

Fractions

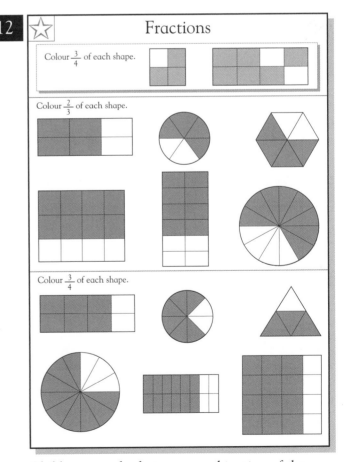

Colour $\frac{3}{4}$ of each shape.

Colour $\frac{2}{3}$ of each shape.

Colour $\frac{3}{4}$ of each shape.

Children may shade in any combination of the sections as long as the total shaded area represents the fraction.

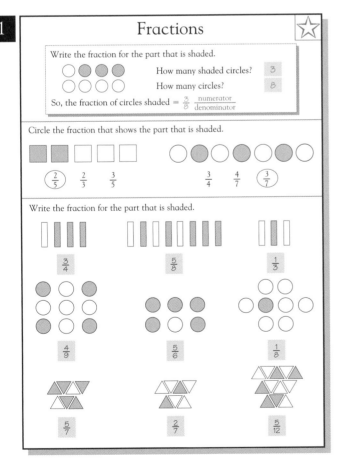

Ordering

Write these numbers in order, from smallest to largest.

606 303 707 505 90 | 90 | 303 | 505 | 606 | 707

Write these numbers in order, from smallest to largest.

320	230	421	124	35	35	124	230	320	421
160	762	85	146	641	85	146	160	641	762
76	189	99	340	430	76	99	189	340	430
460	64	237	173	426	64	173	237	426	460
701	189	89	382	328	89	189	328	382	701

Write these numbers in order, from smallest to largest.

99	119	201	911	319	99	119	201	319	911
746	47	647	747	74	47	74	647	746	747
673	701	77	637	360	77	360	637	673	701
700	160	155	70	17	17	70	155	160	700
89	390	93	244	98	89	93	98	244	390

Write these numbers in order, from smallest to largest.

692	291	270	39	401	39	270	291	401	692
125	81	18	89	99	18	81	89	99	125
75	750	260	140	350	75	140	260	350	750
280	340	460	180	230	180	230	280	340	460
530	480	290	190	350	190	290	350	480	530

Adding

Write the answer between the lines.

34	28	75
+ 42	+ 11	+ 14
76	39	89

Write the answer between the lines.

24	36	45	61
+ 14	+ 23	+ 13	+ 17
38	59	58	78

63	71	48	53
+ 14	+ 16	+ 10	+ 16
77	87	58	69

60	46	54	83
+ 36	+ 21	+ 33	+ 6
96	67	87	89

28	53	74	38
+ 31	+ 36	+ 25	+ 21
59	89	99	59

57	65	79	47
+ 22	+ 14	+ 10	+ 12
79	79	89	59

35	46	57	68
+ 13	+ 22	+ 31	+ 40
48	68	88	108

44	53	26	62
+ 25	+ 34	+ 33	+ 17
69	87	59	79

50	47	66	45
+ 37	+ 11	+ 22	+ 32
87	58	88	77

These are straightforward addition problems with no regrouping needed. This page prepares children for the next page, which involves regrouping.

Adding

Write the answer between the lines.

15	25	55
+ 20	+ 40	+ 5
35	65	60

Write the answer between the lines.

50	70	90	20
+ 25	+ 15	+ 5	+ 45
75	85	95	65

65	25	35	85
+ 30	+ 40	+ 50	+ 10
95	65	85	95

30	60	55	75
+ 25	+ 35	+ 30	+ 20
55	95	85	95

25	45	65	15
+ 15	+ 5	+ 25	+ 15
40	50	90	30

75	15	35	45
+ 10	+ 25	+ 25	+ 15
85	40	60	60

65	45	5	55
+ 35	+ 25	+ 65	+ 35
100	70	70	90

35	45	15	75
+ 45	+ 35	+ 30	+ 5
80	80	45	80

5	50	45	80
+ 95	+ 35	+ 45	+ 15
100	85	90	95

Children must remember that when they regroup, they must add 1 to the tens column.

Subtracting

Write the answer between the lines.

36	25	57
– 14	– 13	– 26
22	12	31

Write the answer between the lines.

27	35	47	63
– 14	– 12	– 32	– 20
13	23	15	43

54	38	47	56
– 23	– 16	– 12	– 21
31	22	35	35

44	57	65	78
– 32	– 24	– 32	– 35
12	33	33	43

66	75	84	93
– 26	– 35	– 64	– 33
40	40	20	60

87	76	67	49
– 34	– 45	– 33	– 28
53	31	34	21

56	73	47	54
– 35	– 40	– 25	– 32
21	33	22	22

79	45	76	75
– 38	– 21	– 43	– 12
41	24	33	63

43	55	67	53
– 30	– 12	– 33	– 12
13	43	34	41

Children will not need to regroup to subtract the numbers on this page. Discuss any mistakes with them to determine whether they are due to lapses of concentration or a basic misunderstanding of subtraction.

Subtracting

Write the answer between the lines.

$$\begin{array}{r}^{1\,13}\\ 2\!\!\!/3\!\!\!/\\ -\ 16\\ \hline 7\end{array}\qquad\begin{array}{r}^{2\,14}\\ 3\!\!\!/4\!\!\!/\\ -\ 17\\ \hline 17\end{array}\qquad\begin{array}{r}^{3\,13}\\ 4\!\!\!/3\!\!\!/\\ -\ 18\\ \hline 25\end{array}$$

Write the answer between the lines.

$\begin{array}{r}36\\-\ 28\\\hline 8\end{array}$	$\begin{array}{r}41\\-\ 35\\\hline 6\end{array}$	$\begin{array}{r}53\\-\ 46\\\hline 7\end{array}$	$\begin{array}{r}65\\-\ 47\\\hline 18\end{array}$
$\begin{array}{r}44\\-\ 27\\\hline 17\end{array}$	$\begin{array}{r}35\\-\ 18\\\hline 17\end{array}$	$\begin{array}{r}62\\-\ 24\\\hline 38\end{array}$	$\begin{array}{r}73\\-\ 44\\\hline 29\end{array}$
$\begin{array}{r}56\\-\ 46\\\hline 10\end{array}$	$\begin{array}{r}37\\-\ 18\\\hline 19\end{array}$	$\begin{array}{r}43\\-\ 26\\\hline 17\end{array}$	$\begin{array}{r}68\\-\ 49\\\hline 19\end{array}$
$\begin{array}{r}34\\-\ 12\\\hline 22\end{array}$	$\begin{array}{r}45\\-\ 18\\\hline 27\end{array}$	$\begin{array}{r}63\\-\ 46\\\hline 17\end{array}$	$\begin{array}{r}37\\-\ 15\\\hline 22\end{array}$
$\begin{array}{r}60\\-\ 43\\\hline 17\end{array}$	$\begin{array}{r}47\\-\ 24\\\hline 23\end{array}$	$\begin{array}{r}63\\-\ 40\\\hline 23\end{array}$	$\begin{array}{r}86\\-\ 29\\\hline 57\end{array}$
$\begin{array}{r}73\\-\ 34\\\hline 39\end{array}$	$\begin{array}{r}56\\-\ 47\\\hline 9\end{array}$	$\begin{array}{r}48\\-\ 36\\\hline 12\end{array}$	$\begin{array}{r}80\\-\ 45\\\hline 35\end{array}$
$\begin{array}{r}54\\-\ 38\\\hline 16\end{array}$	$\begin{array}{r}70\\-\ 45\\\hline 25\end{array}$	$\begin{array}{r}37\\-\ 18\\\hline 19\end{array}$	$\begin{array}{r}53\\-\ 26\\\hline 27\end{array}$
$\begin{array}{r}34\\-\ 18\\\hline 16\end{array}$	$\begin{array}{r}71\\-\ 44\\\hline 27\end{array}$	$\begin{array}{r}25\\-\ 17\\\hline 8\end{array}$	$\begin{array}{r}83\\-\ 29\\\hline 54\end{array}$

Most of the problems on this page require regrouping. Make sure that children do not neglect to regroup when it is necessary.

Choosing the operation

Write either + or – in the box to make each problem correct.

$$15\ \boxed{+}\ 25 = 40 \qquad 30\ \boxed{-}\ 8 = 22 \qquad 50\ \boxed{-}\ 25 = 25$$

Write either + or – in the box to make each problem correct.

$45\ \boxed{-}\ 12 = 33$	$48\ \boxed{-}\ 14 = 34$	$31\ \boxed{+}\ 15 = 46$
$17\ \boxed{+}\ 13 = 30$	$60\ \boxed{-}\ 35 = 25$	$70\ \boxed{-}\ 35 = 35$
$27\ \boxed{-}\ 15 = 12$	$26\ \boxed{+}\ 18 = 44$	$50\ \boxed{+}\ 12 = 62$
$65\ \boxed{-}\ 25 = 40$	$80\ \boxed{-}\ 35 = 45$	$63\ \boxed{-}\ 23 = 40$

Write either + or – in the box to make each problem correct.

$12\ m\ \boxed{+}\ 5\ m = 17\ m$	$34\ cm\ \boxed{-}\ 18\ cm = 16\ cm$
$29\ cm\ \boxed{-}\ 17\ cm = 12\ cm$	$42\ cm\ \boxed{+}\ 20\ cm = 62\ cm$
$28\ cm\ \boxed{+}\ 28\ cm = 56\ cm$	$60\ cm\ \boxed{-}\ 15\ cm = 45\ cm$
$40\ cm\ \boxed{-}\ 8\ cm = 32\ cm$	$90\ cm\ \boxed{-}\ 35\ cm = 55\ cm$
$28\ cm\ \boxed{+}\ 15\ cm = 43\ cm$	$70\ m\ \boxed{-}\ 29\ m = 41\ m$
$90\ cm\ \boxed{-}\ 12\ cm = 78\ cm$	$28\ m\ \boxed{+}\ 21\ m = 49\ m$

Write the answer in the box.

I start with 12 apples and end up with 18 apples. How many have I added or subtracted? **added 6**

A number is added to 14 and the result is 20. What number has been added? **6**

I start with 14 pens. I finish up with 9 pens. How many pens have I lost or gained? **lost 5**

I take a number away from 30 and have 12 left. What number did I take away? **18**

Children should realize that if the answer is greater than the first number, they should add, and if the answer is smaller than the first number, they should subtract. They should check some of their answers to make sure that they are correct.

Multiplying

Solve the problems.

$$\begin{array}{r}2\\\times\ 2\\\hline 4\end{array}\qquad\begin{array}{r}1\\\times\ 3\\\hline 3\end{array}\qquad\begin{array}{r}5\\\times\ 4\\\hline 20\end{array}\qquad\begin{array}{r}5\\\times\ 2\\\hline 10\end{array}$$

Solve the problems.

$\begin{array}{r}1\\\times\ 4\\\hline 4\end{array}$	$\begin{array}{r}3\\\times\ 3\\\hline 9\end{array}$	$\begin{array}{r}4\\\times\ 2\\\hline 8\end{array}$	$\begin{array}{r}2\\\times\ 4\\\hline 8\end{array}$
$\begin{array}{r}5\\\times\ 4\\\hline 20\end{array}$	$\begin{array}{r}4\\\times\ 3\\\hline 12\end{array}$	$\begin{array}{r}4\\\times\ 4\\\hline 16\end{array}$	$\begin{array}{r}3\\\times\ 2\\\hline 6\end{array}$
$\begin{array}{r}5\\\times\ 3\\\hline 15\end{array}$	$\begin{array}{r}7\\\times\ 2\\\hline 14\end{array}$	$\begin{array}{r}2\\\times\ 3\\\hline 6\end{array}$	$\begin{array}{r}6\\\times\ 2\\\hline 12\end{array}$

Solve the problems.

$\begin{array}{r}8\\\times\ 2\\\hline 16\end{array}$	$\begin{array}{r}8\\\times\ 3\\\hline 24\end{array}$	$\begin{array}{r}6\\\times\ 3\\\hline 18\end{array}$	$\begin{array}{r}9\\\times\ 2\\\hline 18\end{array}$
$\begin{array}{r}3\\\times\ 4\\\hline 12\end{array}$	$\begin{array}{r}5\\\times\ 7\\\hline 35\end{array}$	$\begin{array}{r}10\\\times\ 2\\\hline 20\end{array}$	$\begin{array}{r}10\\\times\ 7\\\hline 70\end{array}$
$\begin{array}{r}5\\\times\ 5\\\hline 25\end{array}$	$\begin{array}{r}3\\\times\ 5\\\hline 15\end{array}$	$\begin{array}{r}2\\\times\ 5\\\hline 10\end{array}$	$\begin{array}{r}4\\\times\ 5\\\hline 20\end{array}$
$\begin{array}{r}1\\\times\ 5\\\hline 5\end{array}$	$\begin{array}{r}7\\\times\ 5\\\hline 35\end{array}$	$\begin{array}{r}9\\\times\ 5\\\hline 45\end{array}$	$\begin{array}{r}8\\\times\ 5\\\hline 40\end{array}$
$\begin{array}{r}10\\\times\ 5\\\hline 50\end{array}$	$\begin{array}{r}10\\\times\ 6\\\hline 60\end{array}$	$\begin{array}{r}10\\\times\ 3\\\hline 30\end{array}$	$\begin{array}{r}20\\\times\ 2\\\hline 40\end{array}$

Make sure that children multiply the ones first, and then the tens. None of the problems on this page require regrouping.

Multiplying

Solve each problem.

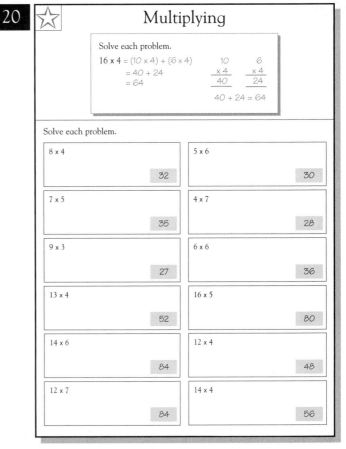

$$16 \times 4 = (10 \times 4) + (6 \times 4)$$
$$= 40 + 24$$
$$= 64$$

$$\begin{array}{r}10\\\times\ 4\\\hline 40\end{array}\qquad\begin{array}{r}6\\\times\ 4\\\hline 24\end{array}$$

$$40 + 24 = 64$$

Solve each problem.

8×4 **32**	5×6 **30**
7×5 **35**	4×7 **28**
9×3 **27**	6×6 **36**
13×4 **52**	16×5 **80**
14×6 **84**	12×4 **48**
12×7 **84**	14×4 **56**

Some children may use the distributive property, as shown in the example, to multiply. Others may set up the problems in vertical format, and multiply with regrouping. Both methods are acceptable.

21

Dividing

Write the answer to each division problem.

$27 \div 3 = \boxed{9}$ $40 \div 10 = \boxed{4}$ $5)\overline{35} \quad ^{\boxed{7}}$
$\underline{-35}$
$\ 0$

Write the answer to each division problem.

$30 \div 10 = \boxed{3}$	$28 \div 4 = \boxed{7}$	$18 \div 2 = \boxed{9}$	$40 \div 5 = \boxed{8}$
$20 \div 10 = \boxed{2}$	$40 \div 4 = \boxed{10}$	$20 \div 2 = \boxed{10}$	$35 \div 5 = \boxed{7}$
$60 \div 10 = \boxed{6}$	$24 \div 4 = \boxed{6}$	$16 \div 2 = \boxed{8}$	$45 \div 5 = \boxed{9}$
$90 \div 10 = \boxed{9}$	$32 \div 4 = \boxed{8}$	$14 \div 2 = \boxed{7}$	$30 \div 5 = \boxed{6}$

Write the answer in the box.

$5)\overline{25}\ ^{\boxed{5}}$ $3)\overline{15}\ ^{\boxed{5}}$ $4)\overline{24}\ ^{\boxed{6}}$ $2)\overline{12}\ ^{\boxed{6}}$ $3)\overline{21}\ ^{\boxed{7}}$

$2)\overline{8}\ ^{\boxed{4}}$ $10)\overline{70}\ ^{\boxed{7}}$ $5)\overline{20}\ ^{\boxed{4}}$ $3)\overline{30}\ ^{\boxed{10}}$ $2)\overline{10}\ ^{\boxed{5}}$

Write the answer in the box.

What is the remainder when 15 is divided by 2? $\boxed{1}$

How many groups of 5 are there in 45? $\boxed{9}$

How many groups of 3 are there in 21 and what is the remainder? $\boxed{7,\ none}$

What is the remainder when 63 is divided by 10? $\boxed{3}$

Divide 27 by 3. $\boxed{9}$

How many groups of 4 are there in 26? $\boxed{6}$

Solving division problems tests children's knowledge of times tables. If they have difficulty with long division, "walk" them through a few examples.

22

Dividing

Write the answer to each division problem.

$14 \div 3 = \boxed{4\ r\ 2}$ $18 \div 5 = \boxed{3\ r\ 3}$ $2)\overline{9}\ ^{\boxed{4\ r\ 1}}$
$\underline{-8}$
$\ 1$

Write the answer in the box.

$15 \div 3 = \boxed{5}$	$25 \div 5 = \boxed{5}$	$10 \div 10 = \boxed{1}$	$24 \div 4 = \boxed{6}$
$12 \div 3 = \boxed{4}$	$20 \div 5 = \boxed{4}$	$60 \div 10 = \boxed{6}$	$36 \div 4 = \boxed{9}$
$24 \div 3 = \boxed{8}$	$35 \div 5 = \boxed{7}$	$40 \div 10 = \boxed{4}$	$16 \div 4 = \boxed{4}$
$30 \div 3 = \boxed{10}$	$30 \div 5 = \boxed{6}$	$80 \div 10 = \boxed{8}$	$24 \div 4 = \boxed{6}$

Write the answer in the box.

$3)\overline{15}\ ^{\boxed{5}}$ $5)\overline{15}\ ^{\boxed{3}}$ $10)\overline{40}\ ^{\boxed{4}}$ $4)\overline{12}\ ^{\boxed{3}}$ $3)\overline{25}\ ^{\boxed{8\ r\ 1}}$

$3)\overline{9}\ ^{\boxed{3}}$ $5)\overline{14}\ ^{\boxed{2\ r\ 4}}$ $10)\overline{41}\ ^{\boxed{4\ r\ 1}}$ $4)\overline{20}\ ^{\boxed{5}}$ $10)\overline{69}\ ^{\boxed{6\ r\ 9}}$

Write the answer in the box.

What is the remainder when 36 is divided by 10? $\boxed{6}$

How many whole sets of 3 are there in 16? $\boxed{5}$

How many sets of 4 are there in 30 and what is the remainder? $\boxed{7\ r\ 2}$

What is the remainder when 44 is divided by 40? $\boxed{4}$

Divide 26 by 3. $\boxed{8\ r\ 2}$

Divide 40 by 6. $\boxed{6\ r\ 4}$

Most of the questions involve remainders. Make sure children do not feel they have to include a remainder if there is none. In the final section, the question that asks how many whole sets there are does not require a remainder.

23

Choosing the operation

Write either x or ÷ in the box to make the product correct.

$12 \boxed{\div} 2 = 6$ $12 \boxed{\times} 2 = 24$ $10 \boxed{\div} 2 = 5$

Write either x or ÷ in the box to make the product correct.

$18 \boxed{\div} 3 = 6$	$20 \boxed{\div} 10 = 2$	$6 \boxed{\times} 3 = 18$
$2 \boxed{\times} 9 = 18$	$20 \boxed{\div} 2 = 10$	$12 \boxed{\div} 4 = 3$
$7 \boxed{\times} 10 = 70$	$24 \boxed{\div} 3 = 8$	$30 \boxed{\div} 10 = 3$
$27 \boxed{\div} 3 = 9$	$18 \boxed{\div} 3 = 6$	$14 \boxed{\times} 2 = 28$
$16 \boxed{\div} 4 = 4$	$24 \boxed{\div} 4 = 6$	$30 \boxed{\div} 3 = 10$
$3 \boxed{\times} 8 = 24$	$5 \boxed{\times} 10 = 50$	$6 \boxed{\div} 2 = 3$

Write either x or ÷ in the box to make the product correct.

$27\,cm \boxed{\div} 3 = 9\,cm$	$40\,cm \boxed{\div} 10 = 4\,cm$	$15\,cm \boxed{\div} 3 = 5\,cm$
$18\,cm \boxed{\div} 2 = 9\,cm$	$4\,m \boxed{\times} 5 = 20\,m$	$10\,cm \boxed{\times} 4 = 40\,cm$
$30\,cm \boxed{\div} 10 = 3\,cm$	$50\,cm \boxed{\div} 5 = 10\,cm$	$60\,cm \boxed{\div} 2 = 30\,cm$
$5\,m \boxed{\times} 8 = 40\,m$	$4\,cm \boxed{\div} 2 = 2\,cm$	$4\,m \boxed{\times} 2 = 8\,m$
$20\,cm \boxed{\div} 5 = 4\,cm$	$20\,cm \boxed{\div} 4 = 5\,cm$	$20\,cm \boxed{\times} 2 = 40\,cm$
$12\,m \boxed{\div} 2 = 6\,m$	$1\,cm \boxed{\times} 10 = 10\,cm$	$4\,m \boxed{\times} 3 = 12\,m$

Write the answer in the box.

Which number multiplied by 3 equals 24? $\boxed{8}$

Which number divided by 10 equals 7? $\boxed{70}$

Which number divided by 8 equals 5? $\boxed{40}$

Which number multiplied by 6 equals 6? $\boxed{1}$

Which number multiplied by 9 equals 36? $\boxed{4}$

Which number multiplied by 5 equals 30? $\boxed{6}$

Children will probably realize that if the answer is greater than the first number, they should multiply, and if the answer is smaller than the first number, they should divide. They should check some of the answers to make sure they are correct.

Word problems

Write the answer in the box.
I multiply a number by 6 and the answer is 24.
What number did I begin with? $\boxed{4}$

Write the answer in the box.

A number multiplied by 7 equals 35. What is the number? $\boxed{5}$

I divide a number by 10 and the answer is 3. What number did I divide? $\boxed{30}$

I multiply a number by 4 and the answer is 20. What is the number I multiplied? $\boxed{5}$

After dividing a piece of wood into four equal sections, each section is 4 cm long. How long was the piece of wood I started with? $\boxed{16\ cm}$

A number multiplied by 6 gives the answer 24. What is the number? $\boxed{4}$

Some money is divided into five equal amounts. Each amount is 10 cents. How much money was there before it was divided? $\boxed{50¢}$

I multiply a number by 4 and the result is 24. What number was multiplied? $\boxed{6}$

A number divided by 6 is 3. What number was divided? $\boxed{18}$

Three children share 18 peanuts equally among themselves. How many peanuts does each child receive? $\boxed{6}$

A number divided by 4 is 4. What is the number? $\boxed{16}$

I multiply a number by 6 and the answer is 30. What is the number? $\boxed{5}$

Four sets of a number equal 16. What is the number? $\boxed{4}$

A number divided by 5 is 5. What is the number? $\boxed{25}$

A child divides a number by 4 and gets 2. What number was divided? $\boxed{8}$

Three groups of a number equal 9. What is the number? $\boxed{3}$

I multiply a number by 10 and the result is 100. What is the number? $\boxed{10}$

Some children find these sorts of problems difficult even if they are good with times tables and division. Many of the problems require children to perform the inverse operation to the one named. Ask them to check their answers to make sure they are correct.

Word problems

Write the answer in the box.

A child is given four dimes. How much money does she have altogether? 40¢

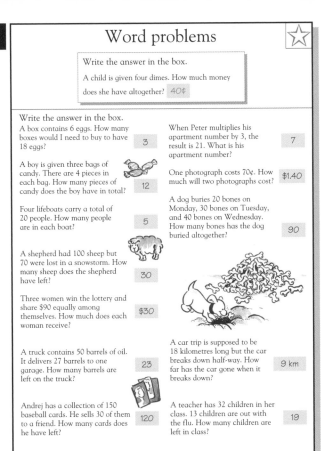

Write the answer in the box.

A box contains 6 eggs. How many boxes would I need to buy to have 18 eggs? 3

A boy is given three bags of candy. There are 4 pieces in each bag. How many pieces of candy does the boy have in total? 12

Four lifeboats carry a total of 20 people. How many people are in each boat? 5

A shepherd had 100 sheep but 70 were lost in a snowstorm. How many sheep does the shepherd have left? 30

Three women win the lottery and share $90 equally among themselves. How much does each woman receive? $30

A truck contains 50 barrels of oil. It delivers 27 barrels to one garage. How many barrels are left on the truck? 23

Andrej has a collection of 150 baseball cards. He sells 30 of them to a friend. How many cards does he have left? 120

When Peter multiplies his apartment number by 3, the result is 21. What is his apartment number? 7

One photograph costs 70¢. How much will two photographs cost? $1.40

A dog buries 20 bones on Monday, 30 bones on Tuesday, and 40 bones on Wednesday. How many bones has the dog buried altogether? 90

A car trip is supposed to be 18 kilometres long but the car breaks down half-way. How far has the car gone when it breaks down? 9 km

A teacher has 32 children in her class. 13 children are out with the flu. How many children are left in class? 19

Children will need to think carefully about how they will solve each question. If they have difficulty, talk each problem through with them.

26

Problems with measures

Which would be the best unit to use for the length of a worm? centimetre

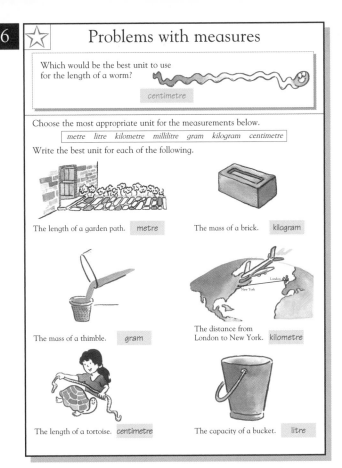

Choose the most appropriate unit for the measurements below.

metre litre kilometre millilitre gram kilogram centimetre

Write the best unit for each of the following.

The length of a garden path. metre

The mass of a brick. kilogram

The mass of a thimble. gram

The distance from London to New York. kilometre

The length of a tortoise. centimetre

The capacity of a bucket. litre

Most children are familiar with the units of measurement given. If necessary, give other examples of items that would be measured using these units.

27

Telling time

What time is shown by these clocks?

28 minutes to 7

3:14

14 minutes past 3

What time is shown by these clocks?

13 minutes to 8

10 past 4

5:52

8 minutes to 6

twenty-six minutes past 6

12 minutes to 10

10:54

6 minutes to 11

24 minutes to 2

12:08

8 minutes past 12

Because of the popularity of digital watches, children could write 7:47 for the first answer and be correct, although the convention is to say the minutes to an hour or past an hour. Children should know both ways of saying the time.

Telling time

Draw the time on each clock face.
Twenty-six minutes past four.

4:26

Draw the time on each clock face.

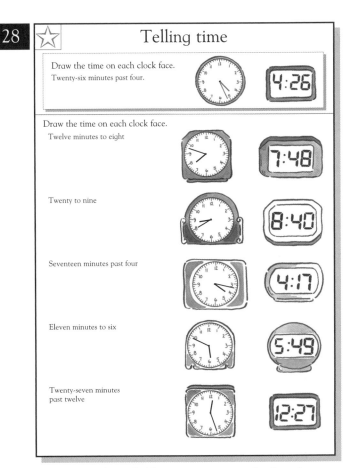

Twelve minutes to eight

7:48

Twenty to nine

8:40

Seventeen minutes past four

4:17

Eleven minutes to six

5:49

Twenty-seven minutes past twelve

12:27

Make sure that children can position the hands or numbers on the clocks. Show them that the space between numbers on an analog clock is divided into five minutes. The hour hand can be drawn in an approximate position between the correct numbers.

Tables and graphs

Look at this bar graph.

Rashir's marbles

green
blue

2 4 6 8 10
Number of marbles

How many green marbles does Rashir have?

10

Look at this bar graph.

Ines' marbles

green
blue
red
clear

2 4 6 8 10
Number of marbles

How many green marbles does Ines have?

5

Ines has 7 marbles of which colour?

red

How many clear marbles does Ines have?

6

Of which colour does Ines have the most marbles?

blue

How many marbles does Ines have altogether?

26

Complete the table.

Favourite pets

Pets		tally marks	total
	hamsters	⊬⊬ ⅠⅠ	7
	mice	ⅠⅠⅠⅠ	4
	gerbils	ⅠⅠⅠ	3
	rats	⊬⊬	5

Number of children

How many more children have hamsters than have rats?

2

Which animal is owned by 4 children?

mice

The first section requires children to notice that the divisions on the scale are in twos rather than ones. To answer some of the questions about the bar graph, children will have to add and compare data.

30

Necessary information

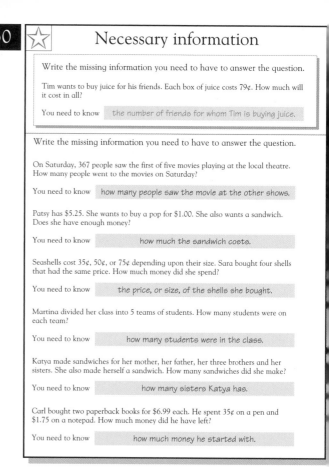

Write the missing information you need to have to answer the question.

Tim wants to buy juice for his friends. Each box of juice costs 79¢. How much will it cost in all?

You need to know   the number of friends for whom Tim is buying juice.

Write the missing information you need to have to answer the question.

On Saturday, 367 people saw the first of five movies playing at the local theatre. How many people went to the movies on Saturday?

You need to know   how many people saw the movie at the other shows.

Patsy has $5.25. She wants to buy a pop for $1.00. She also wants a sandwich. Does she have enough money?

You need to know   how much the sandwich costs.

Seashells cost 35¢, 50¢, or 75¢ depending upon their size. Sara bought four shells that had the same price. How much money did she spend?

You need to know   the price, or size, of the shells she bought.

Martina divided her class into 5 teams of students. How many students were on each team?

You need to know   how many students were in the class.

Katya made sandwiches for her mother, her father, her three brothers and her sisters. She also made herself a sandwich. How many sandwiches did she make?

You need to know   how many sisters Katya has.

Carl bought two paperback books for $6.99 each. He spent 35¢ on a pen and $1.75 on a notepad. How much money did he have left?

You need to know   how much money he started with.

Some children may read a problem and not know how to proceed. Suggest several pieces of information, one of which needs to be found to solve the problem. Help them understand how to identify the missing information.

31

Number pairs

Write the number pairs of the letter A.

A = (2,1)

Look at this grid and write the number pairs of each letter.

A = (4,6)	G = (0,6)
B = (3,1)	H = (4,2)
C = (2,5)	I = (3,3)
D = (0,3)	J = (2,3)
E = (1,4)	K = (5,1)
F = (5,4)	L = (1,6)

Use the grid to write the number pairs.

Write the number pairs of each corner of the square.

(1,3)   (1,7)   (5,7)   (5,3)

Write the number pairs of each corner of the triangle.

(4,0)   (8,0)   (8,4)

Make sure that children understand that the order of the number pairs is important. The first number is from the horizontal or *x*-axis, and the second number is from the vertical or *y*-axis.

32

2 times table

Count in 2s, colour, and find a pattern.

1	2	3	4	5
6	7	8	9	10
11	12	13	14	15
16	17	18	19	20
21	22	23	24	25

Write the answers.

$1 \times 2 = 2$ $2 \times 2 = 4$ $3 \times 2 = 6$ $4 \times 2 = 8$

$5 \times 2 = 10$ $6 \times 2 = 12$ $7 \times 2 = 14$ $8 \times 2 = 16$

$9 \times 2 = 18$ $10 \times 2 = 20$

How many ears?

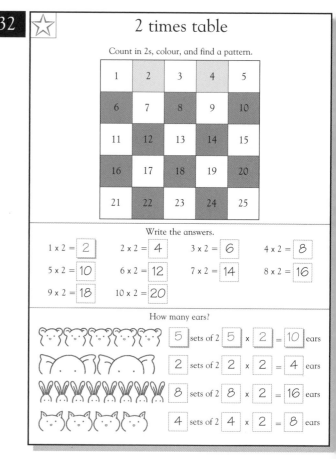

5 sets of 2 $5 \times 2 = 10$ ears

2 sets of 2 $2 \times 2 = 4$ ears

8 sets of 2 $8 \times 2 = 16$ ears

4 sets of 2 $4 \times 2 = 8$ ears

3

Multiplying by 2

Write the problems.

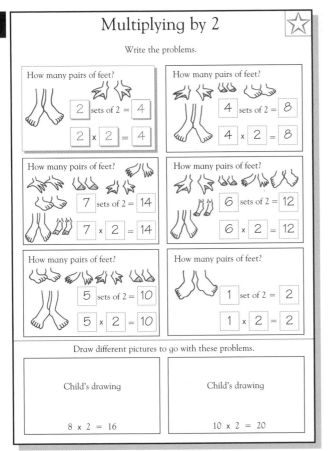

How many pairs of feet?

2 sets of 2 = 4

2 x 2 = 4

How many pairs of feet?

4 sets of 2 = 8

4 x 2 = 8

How many pairs of feet?

7 sets of 2 = 14

7 x 2 = 14

How many pairs of feet?

6 sets of 2 = 12

6 x 2 = 12

How many pairs of feet?

5 sets of 2 = 10

5 x 2 = 10

How many pairs of feet?

1 set of 2 = 2

1 x 2 = 2

Draw different pictures to go with these problems.

Child's drawing

8 x 2 = 16

Child's drawing

10 x 2 = 20

Dividing by 2

Share the eggs equally between the nests.

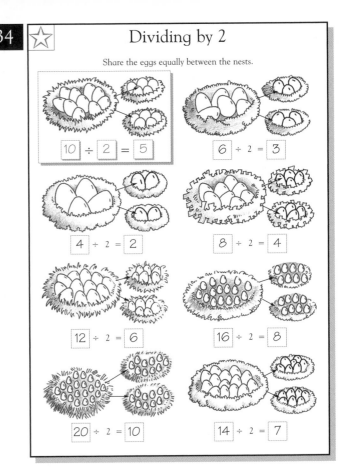

10 ÷ 2 = 5

6 ÷ 2 = 3

4 ÷ 2 = 2

8 ÷ 2 = 4

12 ÷ 2 = 6

16 ÷ 2 = 8

20 ÷ 2 = 10

14 ÷ 2 = 7

Using the 2 times table

Write the problems to match the stamps.

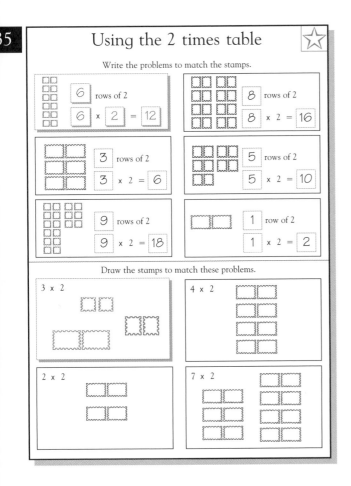

6 rows of 2

6 x 2 = 12

8 rows of 2

8 x 2 = 16

3 rows of 2

3 x 2 = 6

5 rows of 2

5 x 2 = 10

9 rows of 2

9 x 2 = 18

1 row of 2

1 x 2 = 2

Draw the stamps to match these problems.

3 x 2

4 x 2

2 x 2

7 x 2

Using the 2 times table

Each face stands for 2. Join each set of faces to the correct number.

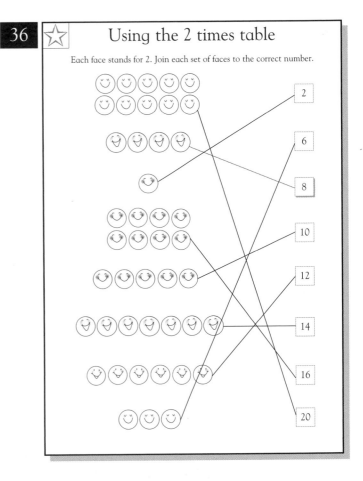

2

6

8

10

12

14

16

20

37

Using the 2 times table

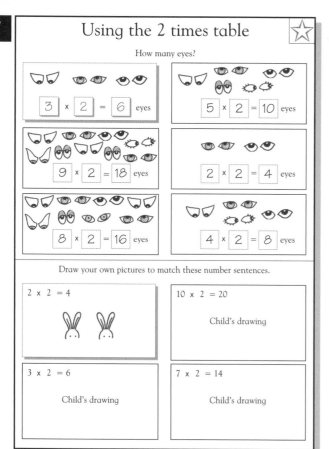

How many eyes?

3 x 2 = 6 eyes

5 x 2 = 10 eyes

9 x 2 = 18 eyes

2 x 2 = 4 eyes

8 x 2 = 16 eyes

4 x 2 = 8 eyes

Draw your own pictures to match these number sentences.

2 x 2 = 4

10 x 2 = 20

Child's drawing

3 x 2 = 6

7 x 2 = 14

Child's drawing

Child's drawing

38

5 times table

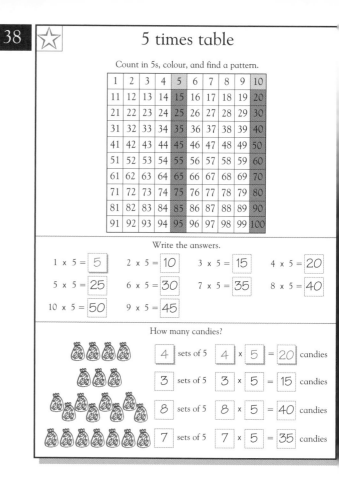

Count in 5s, colour, and find a pattern.

1	2	3	4	5	6	7	8	9	10
11	12	13	14	15	16	17	18	19	20
21	22	23	24	25	26	27	28	29	30
31	32	33	34	35	36	37	38	39	40
41	42	43	44	45	46	47	48	49	50
51	52	53	54	55	56	57	58	59	60
61	62	63	64	65	66	67	68	69	70
71	72	73	74	75	76	77	78	79	80
81	82	83	84	85	86	87	88	89	90
91	92	93	94	95	96	97	98	99	100

Write the answers.

1 x 5 = 5 2 x 5 = 10 3 x 5 = 15 4 x 5 = 20

5 x 5 = 25 6 x 5 = 30 7 x 5 = 35 8 x 5 = 40

10 x 5 = 50 9 x 5 = 45

How many candies?

4 sets of 5 4 x 5 = 20 candies

3 sets of 5 3 x 5 = 15 candies

8 sets of 5 8 x 5 = 40 candies

7 sets of 5 7 x 5 = 35 candies

39

Multiplying by 5

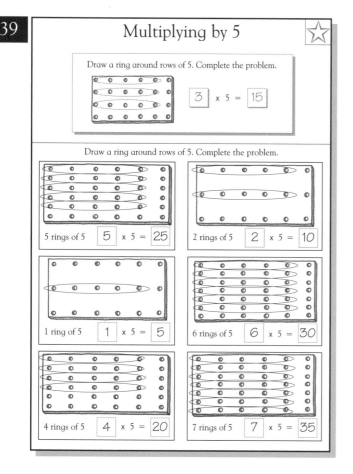

Draw a ring around rows of 5. Complete the problem.

3 x 5 = 15

Draw a ring around rows of 5. Complete the problem.

5 rings of 5 5 x 5 = 25

2 rings of 5 2 x 5 = 10

1 ring of 5 1 x 5 = 5

6 rings of 5 6 x 5 = 30

4 rings of 5 4 x 5 = 20

7 rings of 5 7 x 5 = 35

40

Dividing by 5

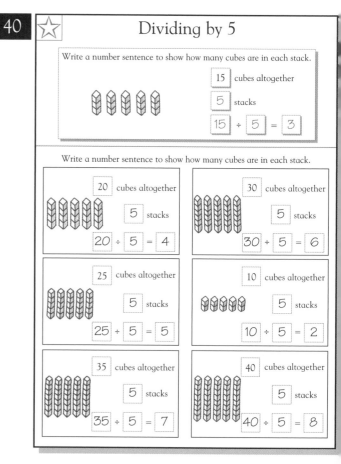

Write a number sentence to show how many cubes are in each stack.

15 cubes altogether

5 stacks

15 ÷ 5 = 3

Write a number sentence to show how many cubes are in each stack.

20 cubes altogether   5 stacks 20 ÷ 5 = 4

30 cubes altogether   5 stacks 30 ÷ 5 = 6

25 cubes altogether   5 stacks 25 ÷ 5 = 5

10 cubes altogether   5 stacks 10 ÷ 5 = 2

35 cubes altogether   5 stacks 35 ÷ 5 = 7

40 cubes altogether   5 stacks 40 ÷ 5 = 8

Using the 5 times table

Write the number that is hiding under the star.

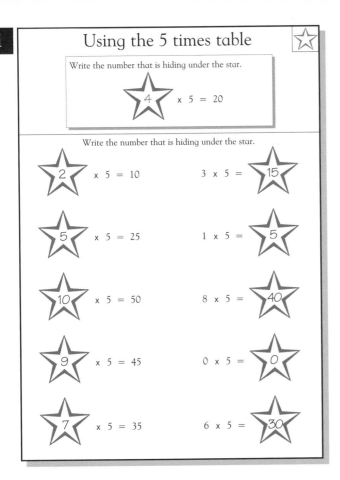

$\star$ 4 $\star$ x 5 = 20

Write the number that is hiding under the star.

2 x 5 = 10   3 x 5 = 15

5 x 5 = 25   1 x 5 = 5

10 x 5 = 50   8 x 5 = 40

9 x 5 = 45   0 x 5 = 0

7 x 5 = 35   6 x 5 = 30

Using the 5 times table

Each frog stands for 5. Join each set of frogs to the correct number.

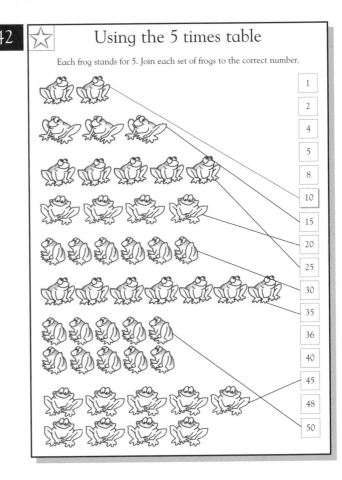

| 1 |
| 2 |
| 4 |
| 5 |
| 8 |
| 10 |
| 15 |
| 20 |
| 25 |
| 30 |
| 35 |
| 36 |
| 40 |
| 45 |
| 48 |
| 50 |

Using the 5 times table

How many altogether?

Georgia had 7 cats. Each cat had 5 kittens. How many kittens were there altogether?   7 x 5 = 35 kittens

How many altogether?

Charlie had 6 boxes. He had 5 trains in each box. How many trains did he have altogether?   6 x 5 = 30 trains

Zoe had 3 jackets. Each jacket had 5 buttons. How many buttons were there altogether?   3 x 5 = 15 buttons

Yan had 8 fish tanks. Each tank had 5 fish in it. How many fish were there altogether?   8 x 5 = 40 fish

How many in each?

Joe had 45 pencils and 5 pencil cases. How many pencils were in each case?   45 ÷ 5 = 9 pencils

How many in each?

Heather had 10 mice and 5 cages. How many mice were in each cage?   10 ÷ 5 = 2 mice

Shannon had 35 candies in 5 bags. How many candies were in each bag?   35 ÷ 5 = 7 candies

Mark put 25 seeds into 5 pots. How many seeds were in each pot?   25 ÷ 5 = 5 seeds

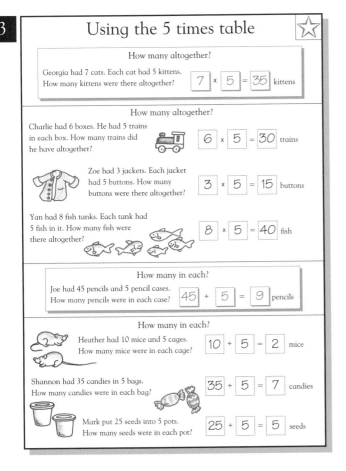

---

10 times table

Count in 10s, colour, and find a pattern.

1	2	3	4	5	6	7	8	9	10
11	12	13	14	15	16	17	18	19	20
21	22	23	24	25	26	27	28	29	30
31	32	33	34	35	36	37	38	39	40
41	42	43	44	45	46	47	48	49	50
51	52	53	54	55	56	57	58	59	60
61	62	63	64	65	66	67	68	69	70
71	72	73	74	75	76	77	78	79	80
81	82	83	84	85	86	87	88	89	90
91	92	93	94	95	96	97	98	99	100

Write the answers.

1 x 10 = 10   2 x 10 = 20   3 x 10 = 30   4 x 10 = 40

5 x 10 = 50   6 x 10 = 60   7 x 10 = 70   8 x 10 = 80

10 x 10 = 100   9 x 10 = 90

Each box contains 10 crayons. How many crayons are there altogether?

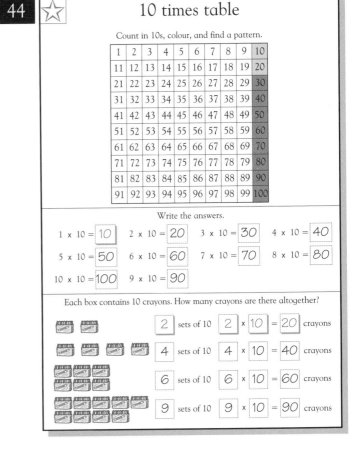

2 sets of 10   2 x 10 = 20 crayons

4 sets of 10   4 x 10 = 40 crayons

6 sets of 10   6 x 10 = 60 crayons

9 sets of 10   9 x 10 = 90 crayons

Multiplying and dividing

Each pod contains 10 peas. How many peas are there altogether?

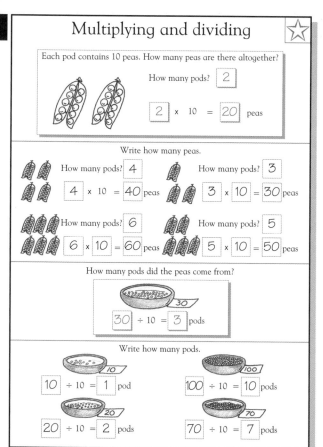

How many pods? $\boxed{2}$

$\boxed{2}$ x 10 = $\boxed{20}$ peas

Write how many peas.

How many pods? $\boxed{4}$

$\boxed{4}$ x 10 = $\boxed{40}$ peas

How many pods? $\boxed{3}$

$\boxed{3}$ x $\boxed{10}$ = $\boxed{30}$ peas

How many pods? $\boxed{6}$

$\boxed{6}$ x $\boxed{10}$ = $\boxed{60}$ peas

How many pods? $\boxed{5}$

$\boxed{5}$ x $\boxed{10}$ = $\boxed{50}$ peas

How many pods did the peas come from?

$\boxed{30}$ ÷ 10 = $\boxed{3}$ pods

Write how many pods.

$\boxed{10}$ ÷ 10 = $\boxed{1}$ pod

$\boxed{100}$ ÷ 10 = $\boxed{10}$ pods

$\boxed{20}$ ÷ 10 = $\boxed{2}$ pods

$\boxed{70}$ ÷ 10 = $\boxed{7}$ pods

46

Dividing by 10

One dollar is worth the same as ten dimes.

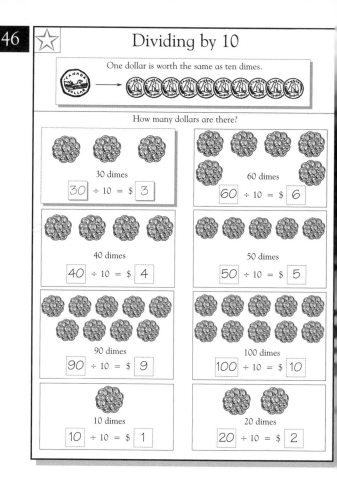

How many dollars are there?

30 dimes
$\boxed{30}$ ÷ 10 = \$ $\boxed{3}$

60 dimes
$\boxed{60}$ ÷ 10 = \$ $\boxed{6}$

40 dimes
$\boxed{40}$ ÷ 10 = \$ $\boxed{4}$

50 dimes
$\boxed{50}$ ÷ 10 = \$ $\boxed{5}$

90 dimes
$\boxed{90}$ ÷ 10 = \$ $\boxed{9}$

100 dimes
$\boxed{100}$ ÷ 10 = \$ $\boxed{10}$

10 dimes
$\boxed{10}$ ÷ 10 = \$ $\boxed{1}$

20 dimes
$\boxed{20}$ ÷ 10 = \$ $\boxed{2}$

47

Using the 10 times table

How many altogether?

The squirrels had 4 food dens. Each den had 10 acorns. How many acorns were there altogether?

$\boxed{4}$ x $\boxed{10}$ = $\boxed{40}$ acorns

How many altogether?

The monkeys had 6 trees. There were 10 bananas in each tree. How many bananas did they have altogether?

$\boxed{6}$ x $\boxed{10}$ = $\boxed{60}$ bananas

The frogs had 2 ponds. Each pond had 10 lily pads. How many lily pads were there altogether?

$\boxed{2}$ x $\boxed{10}$ = $\boxed{20}$ lily pads

The snakes had 5 nests. Each nest had 10 eggs in it. How many eggs were there altogether?

$\boxed{5}$ x $\boxed{10}$ = $\boxed{50}$ eggs

The lions had 7 cubs. Each cub already had 10 teeth. How many teeth did the cubs have altogether?

$\boxed{7}$ x $\boxed{10}$ = $\boxed{70}$ teeth

How many in each?

The crows had 40 eggs and 10 nests. How many eggs were in each nest?

$\boxed{40}$ ÷ $\boxed{10}$ = $\boxed{4}$ eggs

How many in each?

There were 90 mice living in 10 nests. How many mice were in each nest?

$\boxed{90}$ ÷ $\boxed{10}$ = $\boxed{9}$ mice

There were 60 foxes hiding in 10 dens. How many foxes were in each den?

$\boxed{60}$ ÷ $\boxed{10}$ = $\boxed{6}$ foxes

48

Using the 10 times table

Match each dog to the right bone.

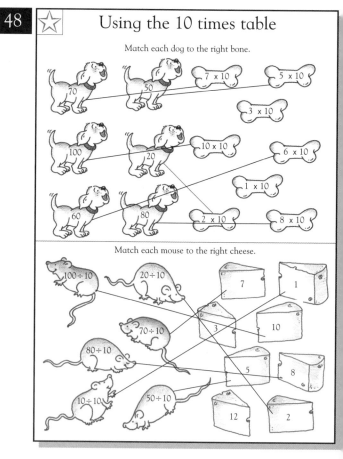

Match each mouse to the right cheese.

Using the 10 times table

Write in the missing numbers.

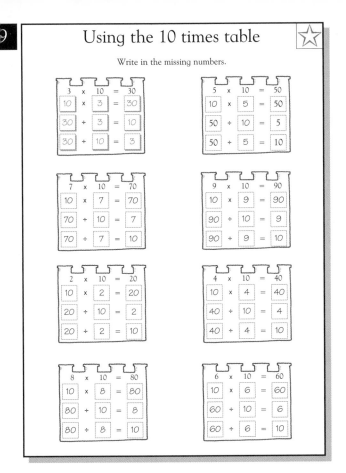

| 3 x 10 = 30 |
| 10 x 3 = 30 |
| 30 ÷ 3 = 10 |
| 30 ÷ 10 = 3 |

| 5 x 10 = 50 |
| 10 x 5 = 50 |
| 50 ÷ 10 = 5 |
| 50 ÷ 5 = 10 |

| 7 x 10 = 70 |
| 10 x 7 = 70 |
| 70 ÷ 10 = 7 |
| 70 ÷ 7 = 10 |

| 9 x 10 = 90 |
| 10 x 9 = 90 |
| 90 ÷ 10 = 9 |
| 90 ÷ 9 = 10 |

| 2 x 10 = 20 |
| 10 x 2 = 20 |
| 20 ÷ 10 = 2 |
| 20 ÷ 2 = 10 |

| 4 x 10 = 40 |
| 10 x 4 = 40 |
| 40 ÷ 10 = 4 |
| 40 ÷ 4 = 10 |

| 8 x 10 = 80 |
| 10 x 8 = 80 |
| 80 ÷ 10 = 8 |
| 80 ÷ 8 = 10 |

| 6 x 10 = 60 |
| 10 x 6 = 60 |
| 60 ÷ 10 = 6 |
| 60 ÷ 6 = 10 |

3 times table

Count in 3s, colour, and find a pattern.

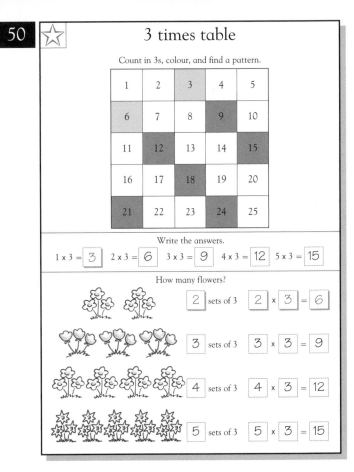

1	2	3	4	5
6	7	8	9	10
11	12	13	14	15
16	17	18	19	20
21	22	23	24	25

Write the answers.

1 x 3 = 3   2 x 3 = 6   3 x 3 = 9   4 x 3 = 12   5 x 3 = 15

How many flowers?

2 sets of 3   2 x 3 = 6

3 sets of 3   3 x 3 = 9

4 sets of 3   4 x 3 = 12

5 sets of 3   5 x 3 = 15

51

Multiplying by 3

Write the number sentences to match the pictures.

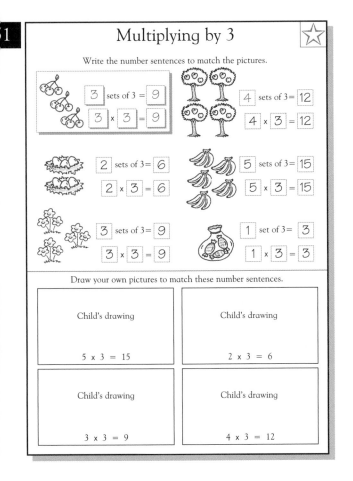

3 sets of 3 = 9
3 x 3 = 9

4 sets of 3 = 12
4 x 3 = 12

2 sets of 3 = 6
2 x 3 = 6

5 sets of 3 = 15
5 x 3 = 15

3 sets of 3 = 9
3 x 3 = 9

1 set of 3 = 3
1 x 3 = 3

Draw your own pictures to match these number sentences.

Child's drawing	Child's drawing
5 x 3 = 15	2 x 3 = 6
Child's drawing	Child's drawing
3 x 3 = 9	4 x 3 = 12

52

Dividing by 3

Divide the money equally among the purses.
Write a problem to show what you have done.
You might find it easier to change all the money into 1¢ coins.

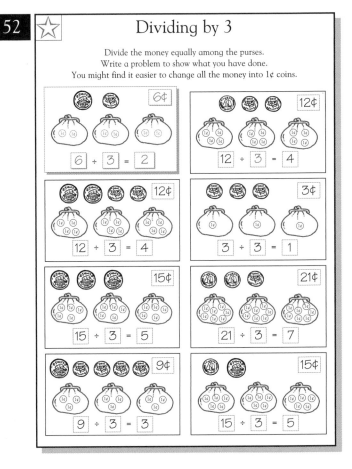

6¢   6 ÷ 3 = 2

12¢   12 ÷ 3 = 4

12¢   12 ÷ 3 = 4

3¢   3 ÷ 3 = 1

15¢   15 ÷ 3 = 5

21¢   21 ÷ 3 = 7

9¢   9 ÷ 3 = 3

15¢   15 ÷ 3 = 5

4 times table

Count in 4s, colour, and find a pattern.

1	2	3	4	5
6	7	8	9	10
11	12	13	14	15
16	17	18	19	20
21	22	23	24	25

Write the answers.

1 x 4 = 4   2 x 4 = 8   3 x 4 = 12   4 x 4 = 16   5 x 4 = 20

How many flowers?

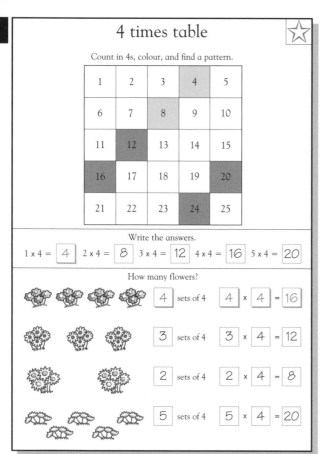

4 sets of 4   4 x 4 = 16

3 sets of 4   3 x 4 = 12

2 sets of 4   2 x 4 = 8

5 sets of 4   5 x 4 = 20

54

Multiplying by 4

Write number sentences to match the pictures.

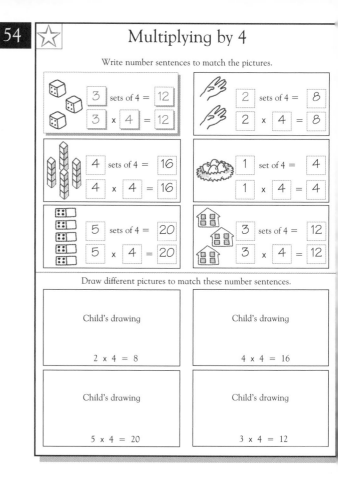

3 sets of 4 = 12
3 x 4 = 12

2 sets of 4 = 8
2 x 4 = 8

4 sets of 4 = 16
4 x 4 = 16

1 set of 4 = 4
1 x 4 = 4

5 sets of 4 = 20
5 x 4 = 20

3 sets of 4 = 12
3 x 4 = 12

Draw different pictures to match these number sentences.

Child's drawing	Child's drawing
2 x 4 = 8	4 x 4 = 16
Child's drawing	Child's drawing
5 x 4 = 20	3 x 4 = 12

55

Dividing by 4

How many on each plate?

There are 4 children. How many things will each child have?
Draw the objects in the circles.

8 sandwiches

8 ÷ 4 = 2 each

12 cookies

12 ÷ 4 = 3 each

4 drinks

4 ÷ 4 = 1 each

20 cherries

20 ÷ 4 = 5 each

16 cupcakes

16 ÷ 4 = 4 each

8 cheese triangles

8 ÷ 4 = 2 each

Mixed tables

How many pegs are there in each pegboard?

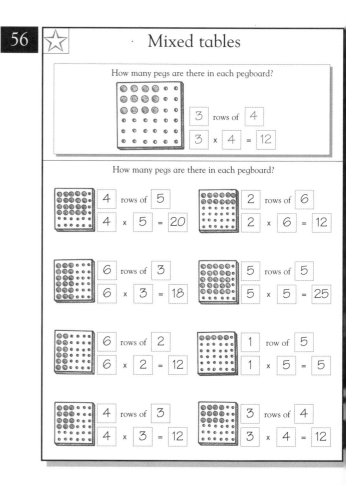

3 rows of 4
3 x 4 = 12

How many pegs are there in each pegboard?

4 rows of 5
4 x 5 = 20

2 rows of 6
2 x 6 = 12

6 rows of 3
6 x 3 = 18

5 rows of 5
5 x 5 = 25

6 rows of 2
6 x 2 = 12

1 row of 5
1 x 5 = 5

4 rows of 3
4 x 3 = 12

3 rows of 4
3 x 4 = 12

Mixed tables

Divide the 12 pennies equally. Draw the coins
and write the problem to show how many each person gets.

$12 \div 3 = 4$

4 ¢ each

$12 \div 2 = 6$

6 ¢ each

$12 \div 6 = 2$

2 ¢ each

$12 \div 1 = 12$

12 ¢ each

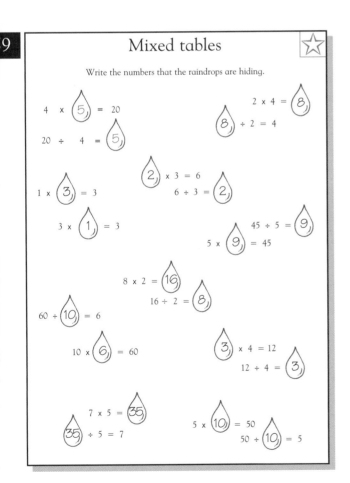

$12 \div 12 = 1$

1 ¢ each

Mixed tables

How much will they get paid?

Price List for Jobs	
Dust bedroom	3¢
Feed rabbit	2¢
Put toys away	6¢
Fetch newspaper	5¢
Walk dog	10¢

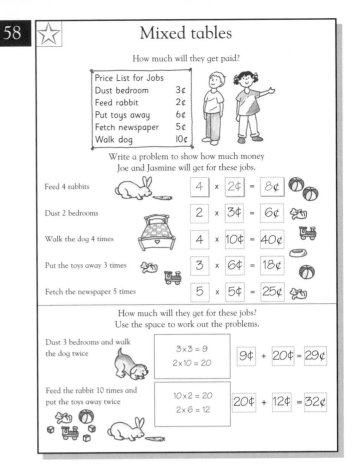

Write a problem to show how much money
Joe and Jasmine will get for these jobs.

Feed 4 rabbits $4 \times 2¢ = 8¢$

Dust 2 bedrooms $2 \times 3¢ = 6¢$

Walk the dog 4 times $4 \times 10¢ = 40¢$

Put the toys away 3 times $3 \times 6¢ = 18¢$

Fetch the newspaper 5 times $5 \times 5¢ = 25¢$

How much will they get for these jobs?
Use the space to work out the problems.

Dust 3 bedrooms and walk
the dog twice

$3 \times 3 = 9$
$2 \times 10 = 20$

$9¢ + 20¢ = 29¢$

Feed the rabbit 10 times and
put the toys away twice

$10 \times 2 = 20$
$2 \times 6 = 12$

$20¢ + 12¢ = 32¢$

Mixed tables

Write the numbers that the raindrops are hiding.

$4 \times 5 = 20$

$20 \div 4 = 5$

$2 \times 4 = 8$

$8 \div 2 = 4$

$1 \times 3 = 3$

$2 \times 3 = 6$

$6 \div 3 = 2$

$3 \times 1 = 3$

$45 \div 5 = 9$

$5 \times 9 = 45$

$8 \times 2 = 16$

$16 \div 2 = 8$

$60 \div 10 = 6$

$10 \times 6 = 60$

$3 \times 4 = 12$

$12 \div 4 = 3$

$7 \times 5 = 35$

$35 \div 5 = 7$

$5 \times 10 = 50$

$50 \div 10 = 5$

Mixed tables

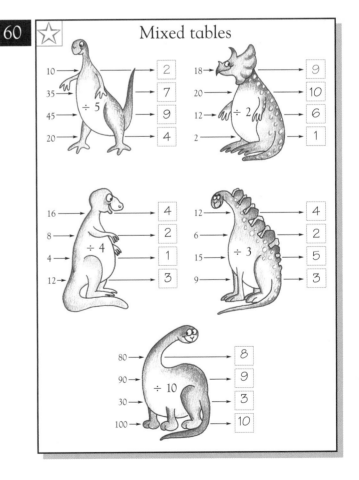

$10 \to \div 5 \to 2$
$35 \to 7$
$45 \to 9$
$20 \to 4$

$18 \to \div 2 \to 9$
$20 \to 10$
$12 \to 6$
$2 \to 1$

$16 \to \div 4 \to 4$
$8 \to 2$
$4 \to 1$
$12 \to 3$

$12 \to \div 3 \to 4$
$6 \to 2$
$15 \to 5$
$9 \to 3$

$80 \to \div 10 \to 8$
$90 \to 9$
$30 \to 3$
$100 \to 10$

61 — Mixed tables

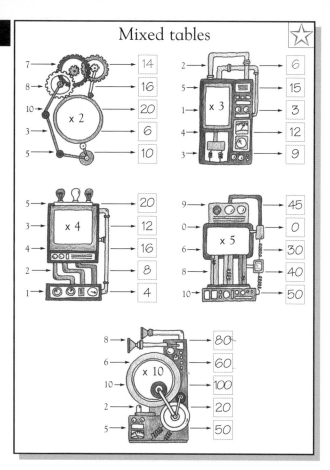

x 2
- 7 → 14
- 8 → 16
- 10 → 20
- 3 → 6
- 5 → 10

x 3
- 2 → 6
- 5 → 15
- 1 → 3
- 4 → 12
- 3 → 9

x 4
- 5 → 20
- 3 → 12
- 4 → 16
- 2 → 8
- 1 → 4

x 5
- 9 → 45
- 0 → 0
- 6 → 30
- 8 → 40
- 10 → 50

x 10
- 8 → 80
- 6 → 60
- 10 → 100
- 2 → 20
- 5 → 50

62 — Mixed tables

Work out how many.

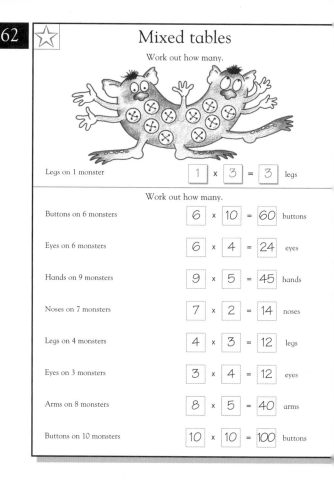

Legs on 1 monster $1 \times 3 = 3$ legs

Work out how many.

Buttons on 6 monsters $6 \times 10 = 60$ buttons

Eyes on 6 monsters $6 \times 4 = 24$ eyes

Hands on 9 monsters $9 \times 5 = 45$ hands

Noses on 7 monsters $7 \times 2 = 14$ noses

Legs on 4 monsters $4 \times 3 = 12$ legs

Eyes on 3 monsters $3 \times 4 = 12$ eyes

Arms on 8 monsters $8 \times 5 = 40$ arms

Buttons on 10 monsters $10 \times 10 = 100$ buttons

63 — Number pairs

Put an X at (3,2).

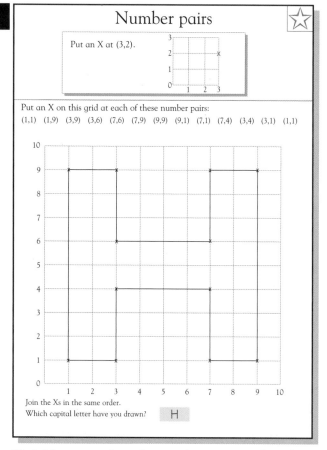

Put an X on this grid at each of these number pairs:
(1,1) (1,9) (3,9) (3,6) (7,6) (7,9) (9,9) (9,1) (7,1) (7,4) (3,4) (3,1) (1,1)

Join the Xs in the same order.
Which capital letter have you drawn?   H

If children complete the number pairs so that they form a capital letter H, they understand the concept. If not, find any errors that they have made and help them see what they did incorrectly.

64 — Logic problems

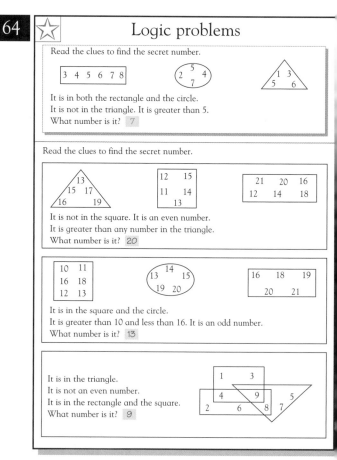

Read the clues to find the secret number.

3 4 5 6 7 8   2 5 4 7   1 3 5 6

It is in both the rectangle and the circle.
It is not in the triangle. It is greater than 5.
What number is it?   7

Read the clues to find the secret number.

13 15 17 16 19   12 15 11 14 13   21 20 16 12 14 18

It is not in the square. It is an even number.
It is greater than any number in the triangle.
What number is it?   20

10 11 16 18 12 13   13 14 15 19 20   16 18 19 20 21

It is in the square and the circle.
It is greater than 10 and less than 16. It is an odd number.
What number is it?   13

It is in the triangle.
It is not an even number.
It is in the rectangle and the square.
What number is it?   9

1 3 4 9 2 6 8 7 5

Children can solve these problems by guess-and-check, or they can use a systematic approach by eliminating numbers that do not meet the conditions given.

Dividing

Write the answer in the box.

$60 \div 10 =$ 6

$10)\overline{80}$ 8

$20 \div 10 =$ 2

Write the answer in the box.

$50 \div 10 =$ 5	$80 \div 10 =$ 8	$10 \div 10 =$ 1
$120 \div 10 =$ 12	$60 \div 10 =$ 6	$190 \div 10 =$ 19
$230 \div 10 =$ 23	$40 \div 10 =$ 4	$160 \div 10 =$ 16
$30 \div 10 =$ 3	$300 \div 10 =$ 30	$330 \div 10 =$ 33
$70 \div 10 =$ 7	$390 \div 10 =$ 39	$560 \div 10 =$ 56
$90 \div 10 =$ 9	$420 \div 10 =$ 42	$850 \div 10 =$ 85

Write the answer in the box.

6 $10)\overline{60}$	9 $10)\overline{90}$	12 $10)\overline{120}$	7 $10)\overline{70}$
1 $10)\overline{10}$	20 $10)\overline{200}$	4 $10)\overline{40}$	26 $10)\overline{260}$
37 $10)\overline{370}$	41 $10)\overline{410}$	56 $10)\overline{560}$	63 $10)\overline{630}$
69 $10)\overline{690}$	80 $10)\overline{800}$	85 $10)\overline{850}$	90 $10)\overline{900}$

Write the answer in the box.

$630 \div 10 =$ 63	$480 \div 10 =$ 48	$170 \div 10 =$ 17
$100 \div 10 =$ 10	$130 \div 10 =$ 13	$200 \div 10 =$ 20
$500 \div 10 =$ 50	$140 \div 10 =$ 14	$400 \div 10 =$ 40
$320 \div 10 =$ 32	$150 \div 10 =$ 15	$800 \div 10 =$ 80

Children should understand quickly that dividing multiples of 10 by 10 results in the removal of the final zero.

Rounding

Round each amount to the nearest tens.

17	28	89	42
20	30	90	40

Round each amount to the nearest tens.

46	50	36	40	72	70	28	30
41	40	48	50	83	80	67	70
57	60	82	80	64	60	32	30
28	30	63	60	13	10	56	60
61	60	87	90	77	80	54	50

Round each amount to the nearest hundreds.

145	100	260	300	115	100	565	600
335	300	770	800	835	800	225	200
470	500	290	300	605	600	245	200
730	700	405	400	655	700	380	400
295	300	160	200	925	900	645	600
350	400	450	500	280	300	860	900
659	700	510	500	150	200	333	300
250	300	750	800	740	700	650	700

Children should recognize that amounts of 50 and above are rounded up, and amounts below 50 are rounded down.

Congruency

Figures that are the same size and shape are congruent.
Are these figures congruent?

yes   no   no   yes

Circle the congruent figures.

Point out to children that figures do not have to be oriented in the same way to be congruent; it is the size and shape that is important. Make sure they know that there may be more than two congruent figures to identify.

Identifying patterns

Complete each pattern.

48	42	36	30	24	18	12	6
44	41	38	35	32	29	26	23

Complete each pattern.

21	19	17	15	13	11	9	7
38	34	30	26	22	18	14	10
36	31	26	21	16	11	6	1
55	50	45	40	35	30	25	20
42	37	32	27	22	17	12	7
52	48	44	40	36	32	28	24
62	57	52	47	42	37	32	27
35	31	27	23	19	15	11	7
41	39	37	35	33	31	29	27
38	33	28	23	18	13	8	3
42	36	30	24	18	12	6	0
50	44	38	32	26	20	14	8
63	57	51	45	39	33	27	21
37	34	31	28	25	22	19	16
58	53	48	43	38	33	28	23
78	70	62	54	46	38	30	22
67	60	53	46	39	32	25	18

Point out that some of the patterns show an increase and some a decrease. Children should check that the operation that turns the first number into the second also turns the second number into the third. They can then continue the pattern.

Odds and evens ☆

Write the answer in the box.

$3 + 3 =$ `6` $4 + 6 =$ `10` $7 + 3 =$ `10` $2 + 6 =$ `8`

Add the even numbers to the even numbers.

$4 + 8 =$ `12`	$12 + 6 =$ `18`	$10 + 6 =$ `16`	$8 + 14 =$ `22`
$20 + 14 =$ `34`	$14 + 12 =$ `26`	$16 + 10 =$ `26`	$30 + 20 =$ `50`
$14 + 16 =$ `30`	$18 + 6 =$ `24`	$22 + 8 =$ `30`	$20 + 40 =$ `60`

What do you notice about each answer?   All the answers are even numbers.

Add the odd numbers to the odd numbers.

$7 + 9 =$ `16`	$5 + 7 =$ `12`	$11 + 5 =$ `16`	$9 + 5 =$ `14`
$7 + 7 =$ `14`	$9 + 3 =$ `12`	$15 + 5 =$ `20`	$13 + 7 =$ `20`
$11 + 3 =$ `14`	$17 + 9 =$ `26`	$15 + 9 =$ `24`	$13 + 15 =$ `28`

What do you notice about each answer?   All the answers are even numbers.

Add the odd numbers to the even numbers.

$3 + 8 =$ `11`	$9 + 12 =$ `21`	$5 + 18 =$ `23`	$7 + 14 =$ `21`
$11 + 4 =$ `15`	$13 + 10 =$ `23`	$15 + 6 =$ `21`	$21 + 4 =$ `25`
$7 + 20 =$ `27`	$13 + 30 =$ `43`	$11 + 12 =$ `23`	$17 + 6 =$ `23`

What do you notice about each answer?   All the answers are odd numbers.

Add the even numbers to the odd numbers.

$6 + 7 =$ `13`	$8 + 5 =$ `13`	$10 + 9 =$ `19`	$2 + 17 =$ `19`
$10 + 29 =$ `39`	$14 + 3 =$ `17`	$8 + 13 =$ `21`	$12 + 5 =$ `17`
$14 + 7 =$ `21`	$8 + 51 =$ `59`	$16 + 9 =$ `25`	$30 + 17 =$ `47`

What do you notice about each answer?   All the answers are odd numbers.

Children should note that adding two even numbers results in an even number, adding two odd numbers results in an odd number, and adding an odd and an even number results in an odd number. The order in which numbers are added does not matter.

70

☆ Probability

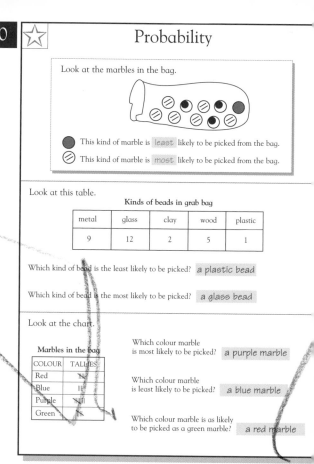

Look at the marbles in the bag.

● This kind of marble is `least` likely to be picked from the bag.

⊘ This kind of marble is `most` likely to be picked from the bag.

Look at this table.

Kinds of beads in grab bag

metal	glass	clay	wood	plastic
9	12	2	5	1

Which kind of bead is the least likely to be picked?   `a plastic bead`

Which kind of bead is the most likely to be picked?   `a glass bead`

Look at the chart.

Marbles in the bag

COLOUR	TALLIES
Red	ⅢⅢ
Blue	Ⅲ
Purple	ⅢⅡ
Green	Ⅲ

Which colour marble is most likely to be picked?   `a purple marble`

Which colour marble is least likely to be picked?   `a blue marble`

Which colour marble is as likely to be picked as a green marble?   `a red marble`

Children should realize that the more of a particular item there is in a set, the more likely it is to be picked.

71

Place value ☆

What is the value of each of the numbers in 573?

The value of 5 in 573 is `500` or `five hundred`

The value of 7 in 573 is `70` or `seventy`

The value of 3 in 573 is `3` or `three`

What is the value of 4 in these numbers? Write using number and words.

34	142	406	412
`4`	`40`	`400`	`400`
`four`	`forty`	`four hundred`	`four hundred`

942	462	34	140
`40`	`400`	`4`	`40`
`forty`	`four hundred`	`four`	`forty`

Circle each number with a 5 having the value of fifty.

685   (954)   (354)   (555)

Circle each number with a 4 having the value of four hundred.

(482)   954   (434)   984

Write increases or decreases and by how much.

Change the 2 in 24 to 3. The value of the number `increases` by `10`

Change the 6 in 86 to 3. The value of the number `decreases` by `3`

Change the 1 in 17 to 9. The value of the number `increases` by `80`

Change the 9 in 921 to 8. The value of the number `decreases` by `100`

Change the 7 in 276 to 9. The value of the number `increases` by `20`

Change the 5 in 547 to 1. The value of the number `decreases` by `400`

If children have difficulty, suggest that they read the numbers aloud, so that they can more easily identify the place value of each digit.

72

☆ Coins and bills

Draw the coins and bills to equal $14.25.

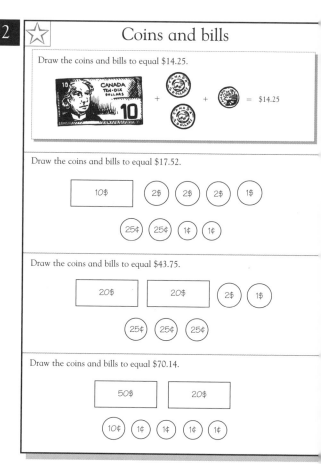

10 + + = $14.25

Draw the coins and bills to equal $17.52.

10$ 2$ 2$ 2$ 1$
25¢ 25¢ 1¢ 1¢

Draw the coins and bills to equal $43.75.

20$ 20$ 2$ 1$
25¢ 25¢ 25¢

Draw the coins and bills to equal $70.14.

50$ 20$
10¢ 1¢ 1¢ 1¢ 1¢

Chidren's drawings will vary. Use real coins and bills or manipulatives to help them understand.

Part of a whole

Write the fraction that shows the shaded part.

How many parts are shaded? **3 parts**
How many parts in all? **4 parts**
The shaded part is **3/4**

Circle the fraction that shows the shaded part.

(1/2) 1/3 1/4   2/5 3/4 (3/5)   (7/8) 1/6 4/5

Write the fraction that shows the shaded part.

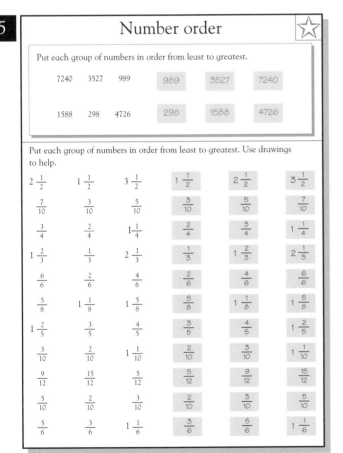

1/6   3/8   3/5

5/6   4/12   4/8

3/10   4/9   5/6

2/6   5/16   5/8

If children have difficulty, point out that the denominator (the bottom number of the fraction) is the total number of parts. The numerator (the top number of the fraction) is the number of shaded parts.

Creating patterns

What are the next two shapes?

☐ ☐ ○ ☐ ☐ ○ ☐ ☐

What are the next two numbers or letters?

0	1	1	0	1	1	0	1	1	0
0	1	2	3	0	1	2	3	0	1
0	4	0	4	0	4	0	4	0	4
a	b	b	a	a	b	b	a	a	b
a	b	c	a	b	c	a	b	c	a
2	4	6	8	2	4	6	8	2	4
1	3	5	7	1	3	5	7	1	3
0	1	2	0	1	2	0	1	2	0

Create your own patterns.

Children's own patterns will vary. Encourage them to discuss each rule.

Number order

Put each group of numbers in order from least to greatest.

7240 3527 989   **989** **3527** **7240**

1588 298 4726   **298** **1588** **4726**

Put each group of numbers in order from least to greatest. Use drawings to help.

2 1/2   1 1/2   3 1/2   **1 1/2**   **2 1/2**   **3 1/2**

7/10   3/10   5/10   **3/10**   **5/10**   **7/10**

3/4   2/4   1 1/4   **2/4**   **3/4**   **1 1/4**

1 2/3   1/3   2 1/3   **1/3**   **1 2/3**   **2 1/3**

6/6   2/6   4/6   **2/6**   **4/6**   **6/6**

5/8   1 1/8   1 5/8   **5/8**   **1 1/8**   **1 5/8**

1 2/5   3/5   4/5   **3/5**   **4/5**   **1 2/5**

3/10   2/10   1 1/10   **2/10**   **3/10**   **1 1/10**

9/12   15/12   5/12   **5/12**   **9/12**   **15/12**

5/10   2/10   3/10   **2/10**   **3/10**   **5/10**

5/6   3/6   1 1/6   **3/6**   **5/6**   **1 1/6**

If children have difficulty, you may want to use drawings to help them understand.

Adding

Write the answer between the lines.

46 + 25 = **71**   57 + 24 = **81**   48 + 24 = **72**

Write the answer between the lines.

26 + 15 = **41**   37 + 16 = **53**   48 + 14 = **62**   59 + 12 = **71**   25 + 15 = **40**

38 + 15 = **53**   25 + 16 = **41**   36 + 17 = **53**   43 + 19 = **62**   27 + 15 = **42**

56 + 17 = **73**   18 + 14 = **32**   28 + 14 = **42**   47 + 26 = **73**   58 + 15 = **73**

27 + 14 = **41**   19 + 14 = **33**   23 + 16 = **39**   57 + 15 = **72**   68 + 13 = **81**

26 + 35 = **61**   34 + 48 = **82**   13 + 27 = **40**   18 + 32 = **50**   25 + 45 = **70**

17 + 44 = **61**   33 + 58 = **91**   29 + 53 = **82**   32 + 53 = **85**   23 + 48 = **71**

Children must regroup to answer these addition problems. If they get confused when the lower number is larger than the upper, point out that the order of addition does not change the sum.

Adding

Write the answer between the lines.

45 + 15 **60**	66 + 23 **89**	43 + 18 **61**

Write the answer between the lines.

17 + 13 **30**	23 + 17 **40**	45 + 25 **70**	62 + 18 **80**	38 + 12 **50**
25 + 25 **50**	37 + 23 **60**	42 + 28 **70**	50 + 37 **87**	30 + 48 **78**
46 + 34 **80**	74 + 16 **90**	42 + 38 **80**	67 + 23 **90**	37 + 43 **80**
54 + 46 **100**	38 + 32 **70**	47 + 43 **90**	83 + 17 **100**	31 + 39 **70**
76 + 24 **100**	68 + 32 **100**	73 + 27 **100**	55 + 45 **100**	74 + 26 **100**
73 + 16 **89**	48 + 33 **81**	49 + 42 **91**	28 + 26 **54**	65 + 45 **110**

Many of these questions result in sums with a zero in the ones place. Make sure that children do not neglect to add the additional 10 when they regroup.

Subtracting

Write the answer between the lines.

38 – 23 **15**	42 – 20 **22**	64 – 34 **30**

Write the answer between the lines.

45 – 23 **22**	27 – 14 **13**	53 – 20 **33**	85 – 41 **44**	47 – 25 **22**
29 – 16 **13**	53 – 12 **41**	82 – 40 **42**	37 – 26 **11**	44 – 31 **13**
63 – 21 **42**	74 – 32 **42**	47 – 36 **11**	63 – 42 **21**	76 – 35 **41**
85 – 42 **43**	83 – 41 **42**	95 – 35 **60**	67 – 53 **14**	86 – 45 **41**
65 – 35 **30**	74 – 54 **20**	86 – 66 **20**	96 – 86 **10**	67 – 17 **50**
59 – 39 **20**	48 – 27 **21**	46 – 32 **14**	78 – 47 **31**	67 – 56 **11**

Children do not need to regroup to answer any of the questions on this page. Check any errors and make sure children understand what they did incorrectly.

Subtracting

Write the answer between the lines.

43 – 27 **16**	54 – 28 **26**	61 – 43 **18**

Write the answer between the lines.

45 – 28 **17**	36 – 18 **18**	42 – 17 **25**	50 – 45 **5**	62 – 17 **45**
43 – 29 **14**	74 – 47 **27**	90 – 37 **53**	65 – 48 **17**	63 – 49 **14**
57 – 39 **18**	64 – 48 **16**	62 – 34 **28**	78 – 69 **9**	36 – 27 **9**
54 – 26 **28**	68 – 39 **29**	50 – 27 **23**	38 – 28 **10**	44 – 36 **8**
31 – 16 **15**	43 – 28 **15**	70 – 36 **34**	53 – 37 **16**	46 – 28 **18**
90 – 46 **44**	50 – 26 **24**	54 – 35 **19**	66 – 48 **18**	90 – 44 **46**

Children must regroup to answer these subtraction questions.

Real-life problems

Write the answer in the box.

Sarah has eight wrenches and is given six more. How many wrenches does she have now?

8 + 6 = 14

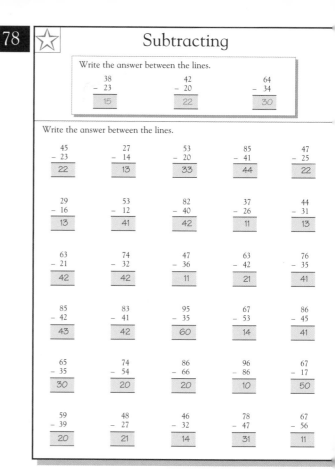

Write the answer in the box.

Karl has 20 marbles but loses 12 in a game of marbles contest. How many marbles does he have left?

20 – 12 = 8

After buying some candy for 30¢, Naomi still has 65¢ left. How much did she have to begin with?

30¢ + 65¢ = 95¢

Billy takes 20 balls out of a barrel and leaves 15 in the barrel. How many balls are there altogether?

20 + 15 = 35

June collected 150 stamps and her father gave her 60 more. How many stamps does June have now?

150 + 60 = 210

Angela puts 40 toys in a box that already has 35 toys in it. How many toys are in the box now?

40 + 35 = 75

Patrick leaves 45¢ at home and takes 50¢ with him. How much money does Patrick have altogether?

45 + 50 = 95¢

Don gives some of his allowance to his sister. He gives his sister 80¢ and has 60¢ left. How much allowance did Don have in the first place?

**80¢ + 60¢ = 140¢
= $1.40**

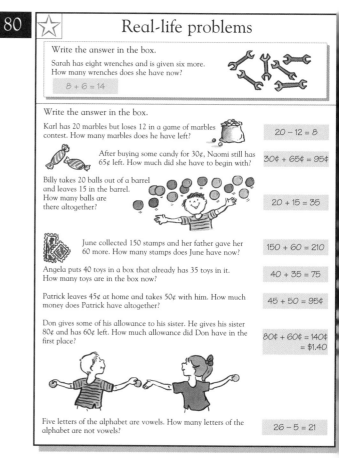

Five letters of the alphabet are vowels. How many letters of the alphabet are not vowels?

26 – 5 = 21

These problems test whether children know when to add and when to subtract. Some words such as 'altogether' may need to be explained.

Multiplying ☆

Write the answer between the lines.

4 ×3 **12**	1 ×6 **6**	6 ×3 **18**

Write the answer between the lines.

6 ×2 **12**	8 ×2 **16**	2 ×2 **4**	5 ×2 **10**	5 ×6 **30**
3 ×3 **9**	5 ×3 **15**	4 ×3 **12**	9 ×3 **27**	6 ×3 **18**
7 ×4 **28**	8 ×4 **32**	4 ×4 **16**	5 ×4 **20**	2 ×4 **8**
5 ×5 **25**	2 ×5 **10**	4 ×5 **20**	8 ×5 **40**	10 ×5 **50**
6 ×6 **36**	3 ×6 **18**	2 ×6 **12**	8 ×6 **48**	4 ×6 **24**
5 ×7 **35**	8 ×7 **56**	3 ×7 **21**	7 ×7 **49**	7 ×5 **35**

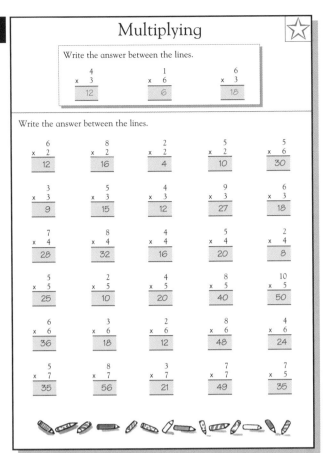

Go through any incorrect answers with children to find out whether the problem results from poor knowledge of times tables.

Multiplying

Write the answer between the lines.

5 ×7 **35**	7 ×4 **28**	2 ×6 **12**

Write the answer between the lines.

8 ×2 **16**	4 ×8 **32**	5 ×8 **40**	8 ×3 **24**	3 ×8 **24**
9 ×3 **27**	4 ×9 **36**	2 ×9 **18**	3 ×9 **27**	6 ×9 **54**
3 ×4 **12**	4 ×5 **20**	4 ×4 **16**	3 ×5 **15**	9 ×4 **36**
9 ×5 **45**	8 ×5 **40**	10 ×5 **50**	7 ×5 **35**	10 ×6 **60**
9 ×4 **36**	10 ×7 **70**	9 ×6 **54**	7 ×7 **49**	7 ×8 **56**
6 ×4 **24**	6 ×5 **30**	6 ×6 **36**	6 ×7 **42**	6 ×8 **48**

See the comments for the previous page.

83

Dividing ☆

Write the answer in the box.

56 ÷ 8 = **7**   34 ÷ 7 = **4 r 6**   37 ÷ 9 = **4 r 1**

Write the answer in the box.

26 ÷ 6 = **4 r 2**	34 ÷ 6 = **5 r 4**	36 ÷ 6 = **6**
42 ÷ 6 = **7**	38 ÷ 6 = **6 r 2**	54 ÷ 6 = **9**
19 ÷ 6 = **3 r 1**	25 ÷ 6 = **4 r 1**	30 ÷ 6 = **5**
21 ÷ 6 = **3 r 3**	33 ÷ 6 = **5 r 3**	42 ÷ 6 = **7**

36 ÷ 7 = **5 r 1**	46 ÷ 7 = **6 r 4**	52 ÷ 7 = **7 r 3**
38 ÷ 7 = **5 r 3**	28 ÷ 7 = **4**	50 ÷ 7 = **7 r 1**
39 ÷ 7 = **5 r 4**	35 ÷ 7 = **5**	24 ÷ 7 = **3 r 3**
49 ÷ 7 = **7**	30 ÷ 7 = **4 r 2**	53 ÷ 7 = **7 r 4**

40 ÷ 8 = **5**	53 ÷ 8 = **6 r 5**	48 ÷ 8 = **6**
40 ÷ 5 = **8**	55 ÷ 8 = **6 r 7**	46 ÷ 8 = **5 r 6**
56 ÷ 7 = **8**	32 ÷ 8 = **4**	51 ÷ 8 = **6 r 3**
56 ÷ 8 = **7**	37 ÷ 8 = **4 r 5**	44 ÷ 8 = **5 r 4**

63 ÷ 7 = **9**	70 ÷ 7 = **10**	36 ÷ 9 = **4**
63 ÷ 9 = **7**	37 ÷ 9 = **4 r 1**	36 ÷ 4 = **9**
45 ÷ 9 = **5**	22 ÷ 9 = **2 r 4**	24 ÷ 6 = **4**
45 ÷ 5 = **9**	23 ÷ 9 = **2 r 5**	50 ÷ 5 = **10**

These division problems test children's knowledge of times tables. Children should be able to calculate the remainders easily.

Dividing

Write the answer above the line.

5 r 2	**4 r 1**	**6 r 2**
6) 32	7) 29	9) 56
30	28	54
2	1	2

Write the answer in the box above the line.

7 r 3	**6 r 1**	**4 r 3**	**6 r 5**	**6 r 2**
6) 45	6) 37	6) 27	6) 41	6) 38
42	36	24	36	36
3	1	3	5	2

4 r 6	**6**	**10 r 4**	**5 r 1**	**5 r 6**
7) 34	7) 42	7) 74	7) 36	7) 41
28	42	70	35	35
6	0	4	1	6

4 r 5	**3 r 5**	**5 r 4**	**9 r 1**	**4 r 7**
8) 37	8) 29	8) 44	8) 73	8) 39
32	24	40	72	32
5	5	4	1	7

2 r 2	**3 r 7**	**4 r 8**	**8 r 2**	**4 r 2**
9) 20	9) 34	9) 44	9) 74	9) 38
18	27	36	72	36
2	7	8	2	2

These problems are similar to those on the previous page, but are presented using a division housing or box. Look for errors that highlight particular times tables that children need to work on.

Choosing the operation

Write either x or ÷ in the box.

4 ☒ 9 = 36   24 ☐÷ 4 = 6   80 ☐÷ 8 = 10

Write either x or ÷ in the box.

9 ☒ 7 = 63	8 ☒ 6 = 48	54 ÷ 9 = 6
5 ☒ 8 = 40	30 ÷ 6 = 5	49 ÷ 7 = 7
36 ÷ 4 = 9	45 ÷ 9 = 5	7 ☒ 8 = 56
48 ÷ 6 = 8	7 ☒ 9 = 63	27 ÷ 3 = 9
4 ☒ 6 = 24	24 ÷ 8 = 3	81 ÷ 9 = 9
8 ☒ 8 = 64	28 ÷ 7 = 4	48 ÷ 8 = 6
63 ÷ 7 = 9	30 ÷ 5 = 6	3 ☒ 8 = 24
6 ☒ 8 = 48	40 ÷ 8 = 5	56 ÷ 7 = 8
54 ÷ 6 = 9	18 ÷ 3 = 6	64 ÷ 8 = 8
16 ÷ 8 = 2	21 ÷ 7 = 3	28 ÷ 4 = 7
27 ÷ 9 = 3	50 ÷ 10 = 5	70 ÷ 7 = 10
8 ☒ 7 = 56	4 ☒ 9 = 36	5 ☒ 9 = 45
2 ☒ 6 = 12	70 ÷ 7 = 10	8 ÷ 8 = 1
10 ÷ 5 = 2	40 ÷ 8 = 5	14 ÷ 7 = 2
42 ÷ 6 = 7	60 ÷ 10 = 6	9 ÷ 9 = 1
5 ☒ 5 = 25	100 ÷ 10 = 10	6 ÷ 6 = 1

Children will probably realize that if the answer is larger than the first number, they should multiply, and if the answer is smaller than the first number they should divide. They can check some of their answers to make sure that they are correct.

86

Real-life problems

Write the answer in the box.
A number multiplied by 8 is 56.
What is the number?   7

I divide a number by 9 and the result is 6.
What is the number?   54

Write the answer in the box.

A number multiplied by 6 is 42.
What is the number?   7

I divide a number by 4 and the result is 7. What is the number?   28

I divide a number by 8 and the result is 6. What number did I begin with?   48

A number multiplied by itself gives the answer 25. What is the number?   5

I divide a number by 7 and the result is 7. What number did I begin with?   49

A number multiplied by itself gives the answer 49. What is the number?   7

I multiply a number by 7 and I end up with 56. What number did I begin with?   8

Seven times a number is 63. What is the number?   9

What do I have to multiply 8 by to get the result 32?   4

Six times a number is 36. What is the number?   6

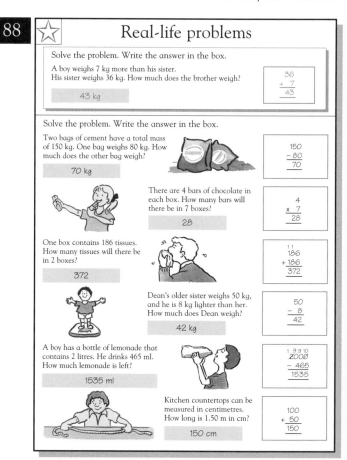

When 6 is multiplied by a number the result is 42. What number was 6 multiplied by?   7

A number divided by 5 gives the answer 10. What was the starting number?   50

I multiply a number by 9 and end up with 45. What number did I multiply?   5

I multiply a number by 7 and the result is 49. What number did I begin with?   7

Some children find these problems difficult even if they are good with times tables and division. Many of the problems require children to perform the operation inverse to the one named. Have children check their answers to make sure they are correct.

87

Real-life problems

Solve the problem. Write the answer in the box.
A jump rope is supposed to be 130 cm long but 35 cm has been cut off. How much of the skipping rope is left?

95 cm

$$\begin{array}{r} 1\overset{2}{\cancel{3}}\overset{10}{\cancel{0}} \\ -\ 35 \\ \hline 95 \end{array}$$

Solve the problem. Write the answer in the box.

Mario is given three cans of juice. Each can contains 425 ml. How much does Mario have altogether?

1275 ml

$$\begin{array}{r} 1 \\ 425 \\ 425 \\ +\ 425 \\ \hline 1275 \end{array}$$

Trang sees these toys on sale in a store window. She buys two of the toys and pays $10.10. Which toys does Trang buy?

$4.30 $6.40 $7.50 $3.70

Kite and ball

$$\begin{array}{r} 1 \\ \$6.40 \\ +\ \$3.70 \\ \hline \$10.10 \end{array}$$

A school playground is 145 m long. 68 m are used by the 3rd grade children and the rest by the 4th grade children. How much space is used by the 4th grade children?

77 m

$$\begin{array}{r} \overset{3}{\cancel{1}}\overset{15}{4}\cancel{5} \\ -\ 68 \\ \hline 77 \end{array}$$

Mary buys a box of chocolates that costs $7.85. She pays for the chocolates with a ten dollar bill. How much change should she receive?

$2.15

$$\begin{array}{r} \overset{9}{\cancel{1}}\overset{9}{0}.\overset{10}{\cancel{0}}\cancel{0} \\ -\ \$7.85 \\ \hline \$2.15 \end{array}$$

A box of tea contains 350 grams. Half of the tea has been used. How much of the tea is left?

175 g

$$\begin{array}{r} 175 \\ 2\overline{)350} \\ 2 \\ \hline 15 \\ 14 \\ \hline 10 \\ 10 \\ \hline 0 \end{array}$$

These problems involve fairly large or awkward numbers and may be a challenge.

Real-life problems

Solve the problem. Write the answer in the box.
A boy weighs 7 kg more than his sister. His sister weighs 36 kg. How much does the brother weigh?

43 kg

$$\begin{array}{r} 36 \\ +\ 7 \\ \hline 43 \end{array}$$

Solve the problem. Write the answer in the box.

Two bags of cement have a total mass of 150 kg. One bag weighs 80 kg. How much does the other bag weigh?

70 kg

$$\begin{array}{r} 150 \\ -\ 80 \\ \hline 70 \end{array}$$

There are 4 bars of chocolate in each box. How many bars will there be in 7 boxes?

28

$$\begin{array}{r} 4 \\ \times\ 7 \\ \hline 28 \end{array}$$

One box contains 186 tissues. How many tissues will there be in 2 boxes?

372

$$\begin{array}{r} 11 \\ 186 \\ +\ 186 \\ \hline 372 \end{array}$$

Dean's older sister weighs 50 kg, and he is 8 kg lighter than her. How much does Dean weigh?

42 kg

$$\begin{array}{r} 50 \\ -\ 8 \\ \hline 42 \end{array}$$

A boy has a bottle of lemonade that contains 2 litres. He drinks 465 ml. How much lemonade is left?

1535 ml

$$\begin{array}{r} \overset{1}{\cancel{2}}\overset{9}{0}\overset{9}{0}\overset{10}{0} \\ -\ 465 \\ \hline 1535 \end{array}$$

Kitchen countertops can be measured in centimetres. How long is 1.50 m in cm?

150 cm

$$\begin{array}{r} 100 \\ +\ 50 \\ \hline 150 \end{array}$$

The two final problems require children to convert between units. Make sure that children understand how to convert metrical units.

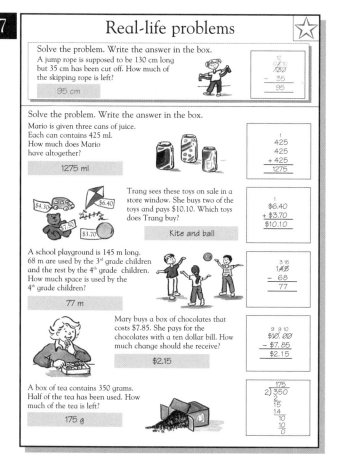

Problems using time

Write the answer in the box.

5:35

What time will it be in 15 minutes?
5:50

Write the answer in the box.

7:45

What time will it be in 45 minutes?
8:30

What time was it 2 hours ago?
5:45

What time was it ten minutes ago?
7:35

Write the answer in the box.

12:15

What time will it be in half an hour?
12:45

What time will it be in 45 minutes?
1:00

What time was it half an hour ago?
11:45

Write the answer in the box.

9:30

What time was it half an hour ago?
9:00

How many hours until 12:30?
3 hours

What time was it 45 minutes ago?
8:45

When regrouping in addition problems involving time, children should avoid using decimal regrouping and must understand that 60 minutes (not 100 minutes) is added as 1 hour.

90

Charts

	Period 1	Period 2	Period 3	Period 4
Monday	Math	Reading	Social Studies	Design and Technology
Tuesday	Math	Reading	Writing	Gym
Wednesday	Math	Reading	Science	Science
Thursday	Math	Reading	Art	Art
Friday	Reading	Gym	Science	Music

A.M.   P.M.

Write the answer in the box.

What subject does the class have last period on Tuesday?
Gym

How many periods of Math does the class have?
4

When does the class have an afternoon of Art?
Thursday

How many periods of Reading does the class have?
5

What subject comes before Music?
Science

Which day is the Writing lesson?
Tuesday

Which subject is taught third period on Monday?
Social Studies

What is the last lesson on Friday morning?
Gym

When is Science?
Wednesday and Friday

What subject is taught second period on Thursday?
Reading

If children have difficulty reading the information in the chart, help them to answer one question, reading across the appropriate row and down the appropriate column, to show them the intersection of the two.

91

Symmetry

The dotted line is a mirror line. Complete each shape.

Complete each shape.

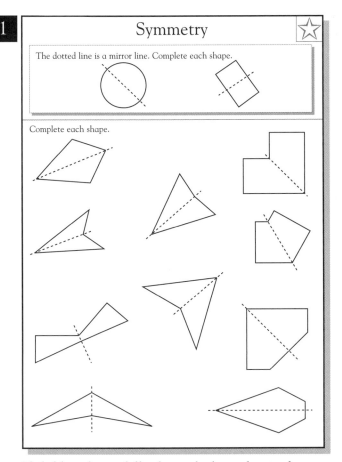

If children have difficulty with these shapes, let them use a mirror. Even if they are confident, let them check the shapes with a mirror when they finish.

3-dimensional shapes

Draw a small circle around each vertex in this shape.

Draw a small circle around each vertex in these shapes.

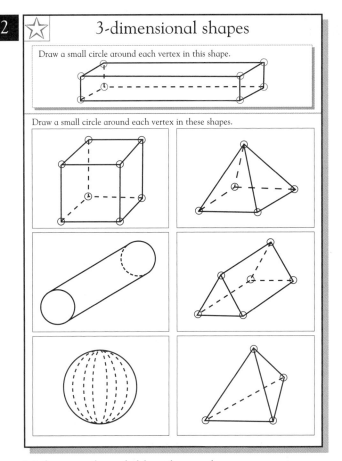

Make sure that children know that a vertex is a single point and that a cylinder and a sphere have no vertices.

Number pairs

Look at this grid.

Write the number pairs of the X by each letter.

A = 2, 3   D = 5, 4   G = 7, 5   J = 8, 4

B = 4, 1   E = 7, 2   H = 7, 3   K = 4, 3

C = 3, 7   F = 4, 5   I = 6, 7   L = 5, 6

Make sure that children understand that the order of the number pairs is important. The first number is from the horizontal or *x*-axis, and the second number is from the vertical or *y*-axis.

94

Adding and subtracting

Add 100 to 356.   **456**   Add 100 to 376.   **476**

Subtract 100 from 324.   **224**   Subtract 100 from 296.   **196**

Add 100 to each number.

376	476	795	895	646	746	585	685
286	386	57	157	312	412	634	734
12	112	789	889	724	824	803	903

Add 100 to each number.

485	585	607	707	37	137	843	943
587	687	56	156	45	145	707	807
897	997	564	664	499	599	1	101

Subtract 100 from each number.

364	264	729	629	477	377	765	665
103	3	146	46	203	103	599	499
100	0	745	645	178	78	107	7

Subtract 100 from each number.

734	634	610	510	307	207	362	262
675	575	907	807	445	345	401	301
400	300	638	538	832	732	256	156

There is no regrouping on this page, so children should realize that they need only change the digit in the hundreds place for each number.

95

Dividing by 10

Divide 90 by 10.   **9**   Divide 400 by 10.   **40**

Divide each number by 10.

60	6	80	8	10	1	50	5
100	10	150	15	230	23	800	80
210	21	170	17	20	2	260	26
40	4	360	36	590	59	730	73
420	42	380	38	820	82	540	54

Multiply each number by 10.

30	300	70	700	90	900	10	100
60	600	80	800	11	110	14	140
17	170	19	190	23	230	28	280
38	380	41	410	84	840	94	940
60	600	100	1000	75	750	56	560

Divide each number by 10.

700	70	310	31	100	10	650	65
480	48	280	28	540	54	130	13
30	3	670	67	320	32	400	40
300	30	900	90	120	12	660	66
220	22	180	18	600	60	890	89

Children should understand quickly that dividing multiples of 10 by 10 results in the removal of the final zero.

96

Length

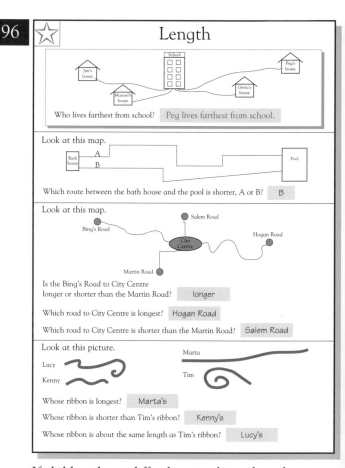

Who lives farthest from school?   Peg lives farthest from school.

Look at this map.

Which route between the bath house and the pool is shorter, A or B?   B

Look at this map.

Is the Bing's Road to City Centre longer or shorter than the Martin Road?   longer

Which road to City Centre is longest?   Hogan Road

Which road to City Centre is shorter than the Martin Road?   Salem Road

Look at this picture.

Whose ribbon is longest?   Marta's

Whose ribbon is shorter than Tim's ribbon?   Kenny's

Whose ribbon is about the same length as Tim's ribbon?   Lucy's

If children have difficulty visualizing lengths, have them use a ruler or a piece of string for making comparisons.

Identifying patterns

Continue each pattern.

11	22	33	44	55	66	77	88
12	24	36	48	60	72	84	96

Continue each pattern.

12	23	34	45	56	67	78	89
9	21	33	45	57	69	81	93
32	43	54	65	76	87	98	109
2	14	26	38	50	62	74	86
2	13	24	35	46	57	68	79
6	18	30	42	54	66	78	90
3	8	13	18	23	28	33	38
12	24	36	48	60	72	84	96

Continue each pattern.

78	67	56	45	34	23	12	1
94	82	70	58	46	34	22	10
88	77	66	55	44	33	22	11
96	84	72	60	48	36	24	12
7	18	29	40	51	62	73	84
14	26	38	50	62	74	86	98
8	19	30	41	52	63	74	85
10	22	34	46	58	70	82	94

Point out that some of the patterns show an increase and some a decrease. Children should check that the operation that turns the first number into the second also turns the second into the third. They can then continue the pattern.

98

Properties of polygons

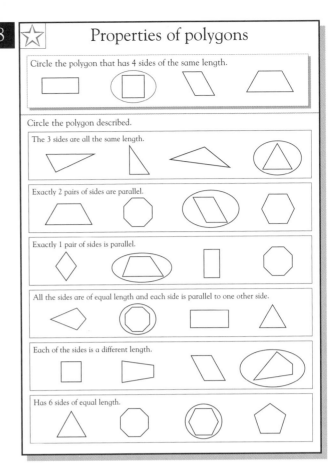

Circle the polygon that has 4 sides of the same length.

Circle the polygon described.

The 3 sides are all the same length.

Exactly 2 pairs of sides are parallel.

Exactly 1 pair of sides is parallel.

All the sides are of equal length and each side is parallel to one other side.

Each of the sides is a different length.

Has 6 sides of equal length.

Make sure children understand the term *parallel*.

99

Square numbers

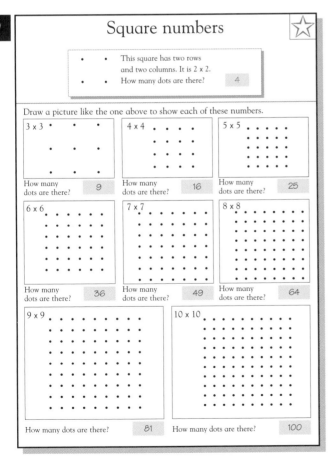

This square has two rows and two columns. It is 2 x 2. How many dots are there? 4

Draw a picture like the one above to show each of these numbers.

3 x 3 — How many dots are there? 9

4 x 4 — How many dots are there? 16

5 x 5 — How many dots are there? 25

6 x 6 — How many dots are there? 36

7 x 7 — How many dots are there? 49

8 x 8 — How many dots are there? 64

9 x 9 — How many dots are there? 81

10 x 10 — How many dots are there? 100

This page introduces the concept of square numbers, and is a precursor to understanding area.

100

Mixed numbers

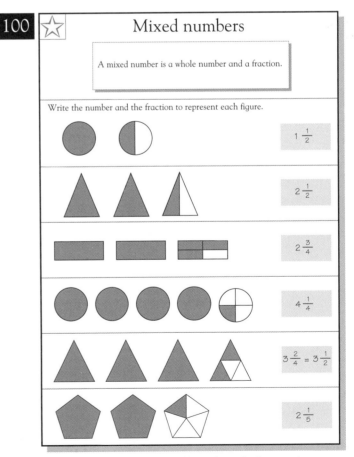

A mixed number is a whole number and a fraction.

Write the number and the fraction to represent each figure.

$1\frac{1}{2}$

$2\frac{1}{2}$

$2\frac{3}{4}$

$4\frac{1}{4}$

$3\frac{2}{4} = 3\frac{1}{2}$

$2\frac{1}{5}$

Children should realize that the whole number is represented by a completely shaded figure and the fraction is the partially shaded figure.

101

Fractions of shapes

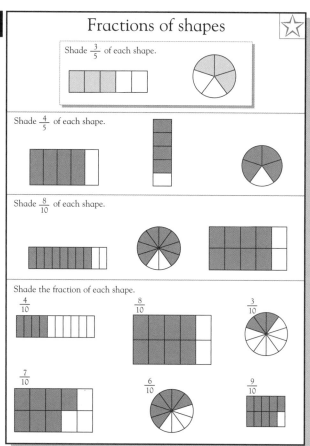

Shade $\frac{3}{5}$ of each shape.

Shade $\frac{4}{5}$ of each shape.

Shade $\frac{8}{10}$ of each shape.

Shade the fraction of each shape.

$\frac{4}{10}$ $\frac{8}{10}$ $\frac{3}{10}$

$\frac{7}{10}$ $\frac{6}{10}$ $\frac{9}{10}$

Children may shade in any combination of the sections as long as the shaded area represents the fraction.

102

Comparing fractions

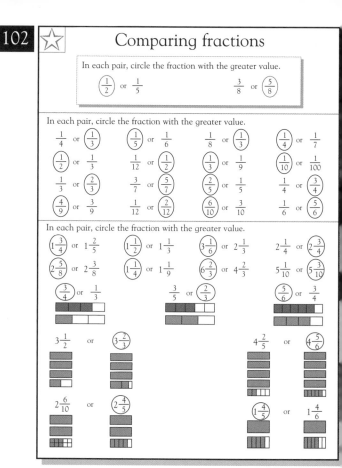

In each pair, circle the fraction with the greater value.

$\left(\frac{1}{2}\right)$ or $\frac{1}{5}$ $\frac{3}{8}$ or $\left(\frac{5}{8}\right)$

In each pair, circle the fraction with the greater value.

$\frac{1}{4}$ or $\left(\frac{1}{3}\right)$ $\left(\frac{1}{5}\right)$ or $\frac{1}{6}$ $\frac{1}{8}$ or $\left(\frac{1}{3}\right)$ $\left(\frac{1}{4}\right)$ or $\frac{1}{7}$

$\left(\frac{1}{2}\right)$ or $\frac{1}{3}$ $\frac{1}{12}$ or $\left(\frac{1}{2}\right)$ $\left(\frac{1}{3}\right)$ or $\frac{1}{9}$ $\left(\frac{1}{10}\right)$ or $\frac{1}{100}$

$\frac{1}{3}$ or $\left(\frac{2}{3}\right)$ $\frac{3}{7}$ or $\left(\frac{5}{7}\right)$ $\left(\frac{2}{5}\right)$ or $\frac{1}{5}$ $\frac{1}{4}$ or $\left(\frac{3}{4}\right)$

$\left(\frac{4}{9}\right)$ or $\frac{3}{9}$ $\frac{1}{12}$ or $\left(\frac{2}{12}\right)$ $\left(\frac{6}{10}\right)$ or $\frac{3}{10}$ $\frac{1}{6}$ or $\left(\frac{5}{6}\right)$

In each pair, circle the fraction with the greater value.

$\left(1\frac{3}{4}\right)$ or $1\frac{2}{5}$ $\left(1\frac{1}{2}\right)$ or $1\frac{1}{3}$ $\left(3\frac{1}{6}\right)$ or $2\frac{1}{3}$ $2\frac{1}{4}$ or $\left(2\frac{3}{4}\right)$

$\left(2\frac{5}{8}\right)$ or $2\frac{3}{8}$ $\left(1\frac{1}{4}\right)$ or $1\frac{1}{9}$ $\left(4\frac{2}{3}\right)$ or $4\frac{2}{3}$ $5\frac{1}{10}$ or $\left(5\frac{3}{10}\right)$

$\left(\frac{3}{4}\right)$ or $\frac{1}{3}$ $\frac{3}{5}$ or $\left(\frac{2}{3}\right)$ $\left(\frac{5}{6}\right)$ or $\frac{3}{4}$

$3\frac{1}{2}$ or $\left(3\frac{2}{3}\right)$ $4\frac{2}{5}$ or $\left(4\frac{5}{6}\right)$

$2\frac{6}{10}$ or $\left(2\frac{4}{5}\right)$ $\left(1\frac{4}{5}\right)$ or $1\frac{4}{6}$

If children have difficulty comparing fractions, you may want to model the fractions with a cut-up paper plate or sheet of paper.

103

Rounding

Write each amount to the nearest dollar.

$1.67 → $2.00 $2.83 → $3.00 $1.23 → $1.00 $3.28 → $3.00

Write each amount to the nearest dollar.

$2.67 $3.00 $3.18 $3.00 $6.75 $7.00 $7.43 $7.00
$8.28 $8.00 $8.67 $9.00 $4.97 $5.00 $2.43 $2.00
$4.66 $5.00 $8.12 $8.00 $6.08 $6.00 $5.40 $5.00
$7.02 $7.00 $6.74 $7.00 $7.83 $8.00 $2.78 $3.00
$1.64 $2.00 $8.64 $9.00 $5.67 $6.00 $1.37 $1.00

Write each number to the nearest ten.

75 80   32 30   67 70   35 40
74 70   81 80   73 70   63 60
54 50   28 30   59 60   19 20
58 60   66 70   71 70   46 50
64 60   19 20   51 50   77 80

Write each number to the nearest hundred.

346 300   540 500   729 700
125 100   177 200   290 300
350 400   501 500   88 100
467 500   750 800   345 300
838 800   550 600   545 500

Children should recognize that amounts of 50 and above are rounded up, and amounts below 50 are rounded down. Make sure that children increase the whole number by 1 when they round up.

104

Adding

Write the answer between the lines.

67 + 32 = 99   39 + 43 = 82   45 + 26 = 71

Write the answer between the lines.

43 + 25 = 68   72 + 16 = 88   56 + 14 = 70   28 + 15 = 43   47 + 13 = 60

36 + 15 = 51   54 + 17 = 71   84 + 13 = 97   47 + 16 = 63   54 + 19 = 73

45 + 15 = 60   48 + 14 = 62   64 + 19 = 83   70 + 14 = 84   45 + 17 = 62

18 + 33 = 51   17 + 44 = 61   14 + 56 = 70   18 + 44 = 62   14 + 54 = 68

26 + 36 = 62   45 + 34 = 79   74 + 18 = 92   36 + 17 = 53   81 + 8 = 89

45 + 35 = 80   43 + 28 = 71   57 + 44 = 101   49 + 37 = 86   37 + 46 = 83

Most of the sums require regrouping. Make sure that children do not neglect to add 10 to the tens column when they regroup.

Adding

Write the answer between the lines.

35 cm	74 cm	46 cm
+25 cm	+18 cm	+36 cm
60 cm	92 cm	82 cm

Write the answer between the lines.

37 cm	56 cm	68 cm	49 cm	28 cm
+ 46 cm	+ 36 cm	+ 45 cm	+ 27 cm	+ 36 cm
83 cm	92 cm	113 cm	76 cm	64 cm

47 km	29 km	56 km	55 km	38 km
+ 44 km	+ 34 km	+ 35 km	+ 37 km	+ 44 km
91 km	63 km	91 km	92 km	82 km

65 kg	43 kg	52 kg	47 kg	36 kg
+ 27 kg	+ 18 kg	+ 17 kg	+ 27 kg	+ 17 kg
92 kg	61 kg	69 kg	74 kg	53 kg

57 ml	48 ml	44 ml	66 ml	43 ml
+ 42 ml	+ 24 ml	+ 18 ml	+ 27 ml	+ 29 ml
99 ml	72 ml	62 ml	93 ml	72 ml

Write the answer between the lines.

$23.00	$36.00	$75.00	$27.00
+ $18.00	+ $43.00	+ $16.00	+ $38.00
$41.00	$79.00	$91.00	$65.00

This page is similar to the previous page, but includes units of measure. Make sure that children include the units in their answers.

Adding

Write the answer between the lines.

35	18	24
17	14	16
+ 16	+ 17	+ 19
68	49	59

Write the answer between the lines.

12	17	15	12	18
13	10	13	14	10
+ 13	+ 11	+ 11	+ 12	+ 11
38	38	39	38	39

17	19	16	12	19
26	13	21	25	32
+ 12	+ 14	+ 31	+ 33	+ 12
55	46	68	70	63

20	30	40	50	60
32	26	42	21	14
+ 16	+ 25	+ 25	+ 21	+ 8
68	81	107	92	82

25	35	45	55	65
15	25	15	35	15
+ 5	+ 5	+ 5	+ 5	+ 5
45	65	65	95	85

23	34	45	56	67
45	32	16	16	12
+ 32	+ 13	+ 9	+ 7	+ 8
100	79	70	79	87

Children should add the ones column first, regrouping when necessary. In some of the questions, children must add 20 to the tens column, rather than 10.

Subtracting

Write the answer between the lines.

57	42	36
− 15	− 16	− 29
42	26	7

Write the answer between the lines.

40	60	70	50	90
− 18	− 23	− 37	− 18	− 27
22	37	33	32	63

41	62	85	64	71
− 14	− 15	− 37	− 45	− 36
27	47	48	19	35

45	65	75	95	85
− 18	− 34	− 69	− 49	− 38
27	31	6	46	47

73	82	74	81	64
− 27	− 38	− 47	− 39	− 47
46	44	27	42	17

61	52	61	53	73
− 14	− 17	− 19	− 23	− 44
47	35	42	30	29

70	63	83	53	47
− 26	− 7	− 56	− 36	− 43
44	56	27	17	4

Most of the subtraction problems on this page require regrouping.

Subtracting

Write the answer between the lines.

56 cm	37 km	58 kg
− 18 cm	− 19 km	− 19 kg
38 cm	18 km	39 kg

Write the answer between the lines.

45 cm	63 cm	74 cm	82 cm	40 cm
− 23 cm	− 44 cm	− 38 cm	− 29 cm	− 17 cm
22 cm	19 cm	36 cm	53 cm	23 cm

61 cm	81 cm	62 cm	83 cm	43 cm
− 27 cm	− 36 cm	− 27 cm	− 36 cm	− 17 cm
34 cm	45 cm	35 cm	47 cm	26 cm

45 cm	60 cm	73 cm	74 cm	85 cm
− 26 cm	− 47 cm	− 48 cm	− 39 cm	− 47 cm
19 cm	13 cm	25 cm	35 cm	38 cm

Write the answer between the lines.

50 km	37 km	75 km	84 km	90 km
− 28 km	− 18 km	− 39 km	− 29 km	− 37 km
22 km	19 km	36 km	55 km	53 km

Write the answer between the lines.

68 kg	47 kg	64 kg	79 kg	56 kg
− 39 kg	− 38 kg	− 27 kg	− 27 kg	− 45 kg
29 kg	9 kg	37 kg	52 kg	11 kg

This page is similar to the previous page, but includes units of measure. Make sure that children include the units in their answers.

Real-life problems

Solve the problem and then write the answer.

Tuhil is reading a book that
has 72 pages. He has read 38 pages.
How many more pages does
Tuhil have to read?

34 pages

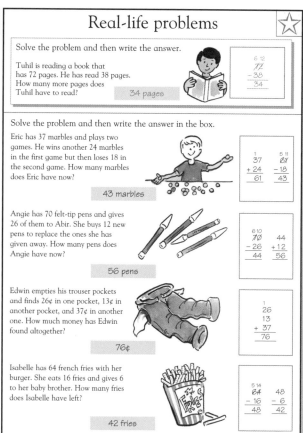

```
  6 12
   7̸2̸
 − 3 8
   3 4
```

Solve the problem and then write the answer in the box.

Eric has 37 marbles and plays two
games. He wins another 24 marbles
in the first game but then loses 18 in
the second game. How many marbles
does Eric have now?

43 marbles

```
   1            5 11
  37           6̸1̸
+ 24         − 1 8
  61           4 3
```

Angie has 70 felt-tip pens and gives
26 of them to Abir. She buys 12 new
pens to replace the ones she has
given away. How many pens does
Angie have now?

56 pens

```
  6 10
  7̸0̸          44
− 2 6        + 1 2
  4 4          5 6
```

Edwin empties his trouser pockets
and finds 26¢ in one pocket, 13¢ in
another pocket, and 37¢ in another
one. How much money has Edwin
found altogether?

76¢

```
   1
  26
  13
+ 37
  76
```

Isabelle has 64 french fries with her
burger. She eats 16 fries and gives 6
to her baby brother. How many fries
does Isabelle have left?

42 fries

```
  5 14
  6̸4̸          48
− 1 6        − 6
  4 8          4 2
```

These problems require children to do multiple
operations. If they have difficulty, discuss the
problems and "walk" them through the steps.

Multiplying

Write the answer between the lines.

```
   7        3        6        9
 x 5      x 4      x 3      x 4
  35       12       18       36
```

Write the answer between the lines.

```
   6       10        7        8        4
 x 4      x 4      x 4      x 4      x 4
  24       40       28       32       16

   9        1        8        2        4
 x 3      x 3      x 3      x 3      x 3
  27        3       24        6       12

   3        9       10        8       10
 x 5      x 5      x 5      x 5      x 3
  15       45       50       40       30

   4        5        4        7        8
 x 2      x 2      x 2      x 2      x 2
   8       10        8       14       16

   5        3        4       10        2
 x 6      x 6      x 6      x 6      x 6
  30       18       24       60       12

   7        5        1        4       10
 x 8      x 8      x 8      x 8      x 8
  56       40        8       32       80
```

Go through any incorrect answers with children
to find out whether the problem results from poor
knowledge of times tables.

Multiplying

Write the answer between the lines.

```
   4        5        8        7
 x 4      x 6      x 4      x 5
  16       30       32       35
```

Write the answer between the lines.

```
   3        0        7        9        6
 x 7      x 7      x 7      x 7      x 7
  21        0       49       63       42

   7        8        6        4        1
 x 9      x 9      x 9      x 9      x 9
  63       72       54       36        9

   3        7        9        8        4
x 10     x 10     x 10     x 10     x 10
  30       70       90       80       40

   7       11        7       11        7
 x 4      x 5      x 6      x 6      x 8
  28       55       42       66       56

   8        8        8       11       11
 x 6      x 7      x 8      x 9      x 8
  48       56       64       99       88

   9        9       11        9        9
 x 5      x 6      x 7      x 8      x 9
  45       54       77       72       81
```

See the comments for the previous page.

112

Dividing

Write the answer in the box.

```
24 ÷ 7 =  3 r 3            4 r 1         43 ÷ 8 =  5 r 3
                       5 ) 2 1                  8 ) 4 3
                          − 2 0                    − 4 0
                             1                        3
```

Write the answer in the box.

```
27 ÷ 3 =   9      14 ÷ 3 =  4 r 2    23 ÷ 3 =  7 r 2
 7 ÷ 3 =  2 r 1   31 ÷ 4 =  7 r 3    14 ÷ 4 =  3 r 2
38 ÷ 4 =  9 r 2    4 ÷ 4 =    1      42 ÷ 5 =  8 r 2
23 ÷ 5 =  4 r 3   15 ÷ 5 =    3      27 ÷ 5 =  5 r 2
47 ÷ 6 =  7 r 5   35 ÷ 5 =    7      46 ÷ 5 =  9 r 1
```

Write the answer in the box.

```
    4 r 2        5 r 6        2 r 5         7            3
  8 ) 3 4      8 ) 4 6      8 ) 2 1      8 ) 5 6      9 ) 2 7
    − 3 2        − 4 0        − 1 6        − 5 6        − 2 7
        2            6            5            0            0

    1 r 1          8          5 r 2        7 r 2         10
  2 ) 3        2 ) 1 6      3 ) 1 7      3 ) 2 3      3 ) 3 0
    − 2          − 1 6        − 1 5        − 2 1        − 3 0
      1              0            2            2            0
```

Write the answer in the box.

```
45 ÷ 8 =   5 r 5   73 ÷ 8 =  9 r 1    56 ÷ 8 =    7
73 ÷ 9 =   8 r 1   41 ÷ 9 =  4 r 5    50 ÷ 9 =  5 r 5
54 ÷ 10 =  5 r 4   89 ÷ 10 = 8 r 9    42 ÷ 10 = 4 r 2
```

These division problems test children's knowledge
of times tables. Children should be able to
calculate the remainders easily.

Dividing ☆

Write the answer in the box.

31 ÷ 4 = 7 r 3   2 r 5   31 ÷ 9 = 3 r 4
                   6)17   9)31
                    −12   −27
                      5   4

Write the answer in the box.

46 ÷ 9 = 5 r 1	28 ÷ 7 = 4	45 ÷ 9 = 5
74 ÷ 8 = 9 r 2	32 ÷ 3 = 10 r 2	45 ÷ 7 = 6 r 3
61 ÷ 7 = 8 r 5	65 ÷ 9 = 7 r 2	12 ÷ 9 = 1 r 3
17 ÷ 4 = 4 r 1	24 ÷ 6 = 4	36 ÷ 6 = 6
37 ÷ 8 = 4 r 5	37 ÷ 9 = 4 r 1	37 ÷ 10 = 3 r 7

Write the answer in the box.

6 r 3   7   4 r 7   3 r 3   3 r 8
7)45   8)56   9)43   9)30   9)35
 −42   −56   −36   −27   −27
   3   0   7   3   8

5 r 8   8 r 4   6   4 r 7   3
9)53   9)76   9)54   9)43   9)27
 −45   −72   −54   −36   −27
   8   4   0   7   0

Write the answer in the box.

8 ÷ 6 = 1 r 2	12 ÷ 10 = 1 r 2	11 ÷ 9 = 1 r 2
13 ÷ 10 = 1 r 3	17 ÷ 7 = 2 r 3	23 ÷ 8 = 2 r 7
70 ÷ 10 = 7	70 ÷ 7 = 10	54 ÷ 6 = 9

See the comments for the previous page.

Choosing the operation

Write either x or ÷ in the box to make the number sentence true.

6 x 7 = 42   24 ÷ 6 = 4   10 ÷ 2 = 5

Write either x or ÷ in the box to make the number sentence true.

35 ÷ 7 = 5	35 ÷ 5 = 7	7 x 5 = 35
5 x 7 = 35	6 x 9 = 54	54 ÷ 6 = 9
9 x 6 = 54	54 ÷ 9 = 6	32 ÷ 4 = 8
4 x 8 = 32	8 x 4 = 32	32 ÷ 8 = 4
4 x 9 = 36	36 ÷ 4 = 9	9 x 4 = 36
36 ÷ 9 = 4	80 ÷ 8 = 10	8 x 10 = 80
7 x 9 = 63	63 ÷ 7 = 9	63 ÷ 9 = 7
9 x 7 = 63	9 x 9 = 81	81 ÷ 9 = 9
64 ÷ 8 = 8	8 x 8 = 64	25 ÷ 5 = 5
5 x 5 = 25	16 ÷ 4 = 4	4 x 4 = 16
7 x 7 = 49	49 ÷ 7 = 7	3 x 3 = 9
9 ÷ 3 = 3	100 ÷ 10 = 10	10 x 10 = 100
50 ÷ 10 = 5	5 x 8 = 40	40 ÷ 4 = 10
20 ÷ 5 = 4	4 x 10 = 40	36 ÷ 6 = 6
3 x 7 = 21	21 ÷ 3 = 7	7 x 4 = 28
14 x 10 = 140	140 ÷ 2 = 70	70 ÷ 10 = 7
42 ÷ 6 = 7	7 x 10 = 70	72 ÷ 8 = 9
50 ÷ 5 = 10	20 ÷ 4 = 5	3 x 8 = 24

Children will probably realize that if the answer is larger than the first number, they should multiply, and if the answer is smaller than the first number they should divide. They can check some of their answers to make sure that they are correct.

Real-life problems ☆

Write the answer in the box.

There are 8 ink cartridges in each pack. How many cartridges will there be in 6 packs?

8 x 6 = 48

48 cartridges

Write the answer in the box.

Ian shares 50 oranges equally among 6 elephants and gives the remainder to the giraffes. How many oranges do the giraffes receive?

        8 r 2
      6)50
        48
         2

2 oranges

There are 9 children at a birthday party and each child has 4 chocolate cupcakes. How many cupcakes do the children have altogether?

9 x 4 = 36

36 cupcakes

Ben has 60 building blocks and puts them in stacks of 7. How many stacks of 7 can Ben make?

        8 r 4
      7)60
        56
         4

8 stacks

Katie has seven dimes, four nickels, and four pennies. How much does she have altogether?

10 x 7 = 70
4 x 5 = 20
4 x 1 = 4 +
        94

94¢

The dog wants to bury four bones in each hole. The dog has 36 bones. How many holes must the dog dig?

        9
      4)36
        36
         0

9 holes

Make sure that children understand which operation to perform for each problem.

Perimeter

Write the perimeter of this shape in the answer box.

2 cm

8 cm

      8 cm
      2 cm
      8 cm
    + 2 cm
    20 cm

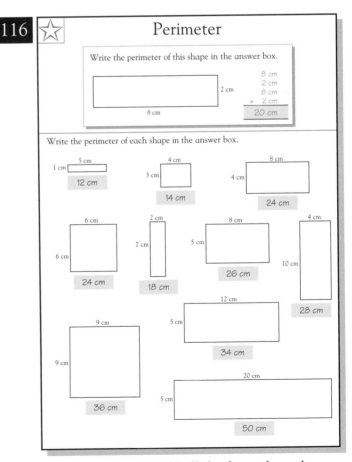

Write the perimeter of each shape in the answer box.

5 cm, 1 cm → 12 cm

4 cm, 3 cm → 14 cm

8 cm, 4 cm → 24 cm

6 cm, 6 cm → 24 cm

2 cm, 7 cm → 18 cm

8 cm, 5 cm → 26 cm

4 cm, 10 cm → 28 cm

9 cm, 9 cm → 36 cm

12 cm, 5 cm → 34 cm

20 cm, 5 cm → 50 cm

Some children may add all the four sides; others may double each different length and add the results; yet others may add the two different lengths and then double the sum. Each of these methods is acceptable.

Area

Write the area of the shape in the answer box.

1 cm
7 cm
$1 \times 7 = 7$
7 cm²

Write the area of each shape in the answer box.

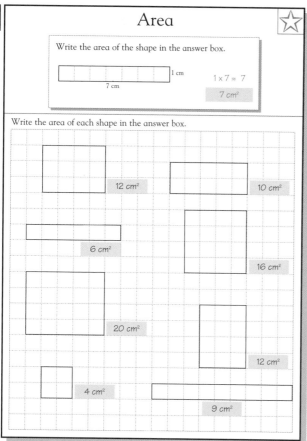

12 cm²

10 cm²

6 cm²

16 cm²

20 cm²

12 cm²

4 cm²

9 cm²

Since the area of a shape is the amount of space inside it, the number of squares inside each shape gives the area. Children may realize that multiplying one side of a rectangle by the other will give the same result more quickly.

118

Area

Write the area of this shape in the answer box.

3 cm
8 cm
$3 \times 8 = 24$
24 cm²

Write the area of each shape in the answer box.

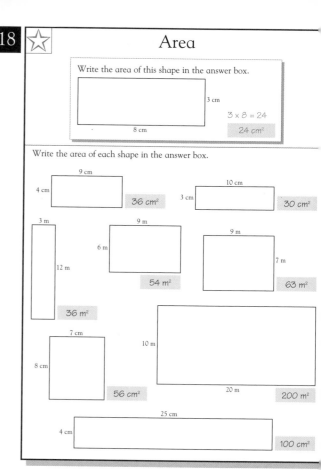

9 cm
4 cm
36 cm²

10 cm
3 cm
30 cm²

3 m
12 m
36 m²

9 m
6 m
54 m²

9 m
7 m
63 m²

7 cm
8 cm
56 cm²

10 m
20 m
200 m²

25 cm
4 cm
100 cm²

Following from the last page, this page requires children to find the areas by multiplying the sides together. If they are unsure of the method, sketch in squares on the shapes to help.

119

Problems using time

Write the answer in the box.

How many minutes until 12 o'clock?

90 minutes

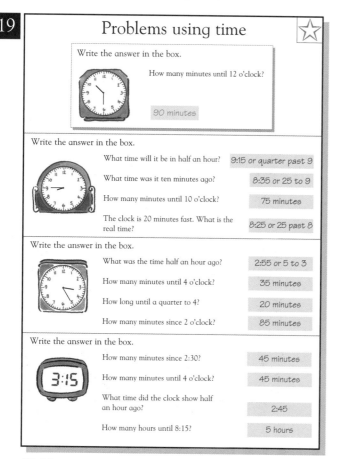

Write the answer in the box.

What time will it be in half an hour?	9:15 or quarter past 9
What time was it ten minutes ago?	8:35 or 25 to 9
How many minutes until 10 o'clock?	75 minutes
The clock is 20 minutes fast. What is the real time?	8:25 or 25 past 8

Write the answer in the box.

What was the time half an hour ago?	2:55 or 5 to 3
How many minutes until 4 o'clock?	35 minutes
How long until a quarter to 4?	20 minutes
How many minutes since 2 o'clock?	85 minutes

Write the answer in the box.

How many minutes since 2:30?	45 minutes
How many minutes until 4 o'clock?	45 minutes
What time did the clock show half an hour ago?	2:45
How many hours until 8:15?	5 hours

Children may use any method that gives the correct answers.

120

Reading timetables

	Frostburg	Elmhurst	Badger Farm	Winchester
Redline bus	8:00	8:05	8:15	8:25
Blueline bus	8:05	No stop	8:12	8:20
City taxi	8:30	8:35	8:45	8:55
Greenline bus	8:07	No stop	No stop	8:15

The timetable shows the times it takes to travel using different transport companies between Frostburg and Winchester.

Write the answer in the box.

How long does the Redline bus take between Frostburg and Winchester?

25 minutes

When does the Blueline bus arrive at Badger Farm?

8:12

Where does the Greenline bus not stop?

Elmhurst

Where is City taxi at 8:35?

Elmhurst

Does the Blueline bus stop at Elmhurst?

No

How long does the Redline bus take to travel between Badger Farm and Winchester?

10 minutes

Which is the fastest trip between Frostburg and Winchester?

Greenline bus

Which service arrives at five minutes to nine?

City taxi

How long does City taxi take between Frostburg and Badger Farm?

15 minutes

Where is the Blueline bus at twelve minutes past eight?

Badger Farm

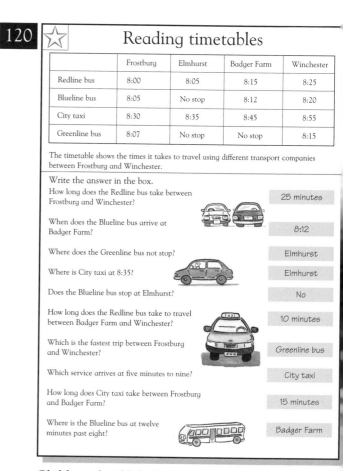

Children should find this exercise fairly straightforward. If they have difficulty, help them read across the rows and down the columns to find the information they need.

Averages

Write the average of this row in the box.

4	2	2	2	6	3	2

The average is **3**.

Write the average of each row in the box.

2	3	7	4	2	7	2	5	**4**
7	4	5	4	8	5	3	4	**5**
5	3	5	3	5	2	4	5	**4**
7	5	9	7	2	4	8	6	**6**
4	3	4	3	4	3	4	7	**4**
1	4	2	7	3	8	2	5	**4**
3	2	1	2	2	3	2	1	**2**
8	3	6	3	8	2	8	2	**5**

Write the average of each row in the box.

4	8	6	3	9	6	6	**6**
5	9	2	6	9	1	3	**5**
6	3	8	6	1	5	6	**5**
3	8	6	7	5	9	4	**6**
1	8	3	4	2	6	4	**4**
9	5	8	7	4	7	9	**7**
1	3	2	3	1	2	2	**2**
6	3	7	4	5	4	6	**5**

If necessary, remind children that the average of a set of quantities is the sum of the quantities divided by the number of quantities.

Estimating

Estimate to find the answer.

One crate of apples sells for between $8 and $12. If Sam sold 10 crates of apples, about how much did he earn?

Sam earned about **$100**.

Estimate to find the answer.

The river ferry makes 5 trips a day. There are between 40 and 60 people on each trip. About how many people ride the ferry every day?

About **250 people**

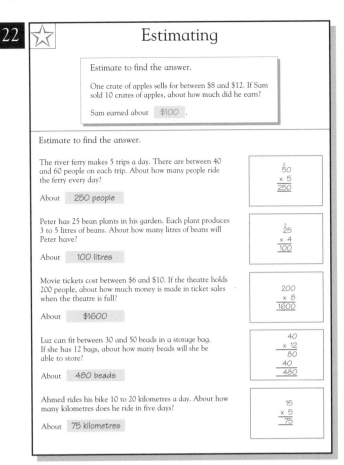

Peter has 25 bean plants in his garden. Each plant produces 3 to 5 litres of beans. About how many litres of beans will Peter have?

About **100 litres**

Movie tickets cost between $6 and $10. If the theatre holds 200 people, about how much money is made in ticket sales when the theatre is full?

About **$1600**

Luz can fit between 30 and 50 beads in a storage bag. If she has 12 bags, about how many beads will she be able to store?

About **480 beads**

Ahmed rides his bike 10 to 20 kilometres a day. About how many kilometres does he ride in five days?

About **75 kilometres**

Children should use a compatible number—one that is easy to manipulate in the problem—while they estimate.

Calculating change

Circle the correct change.

Carlo bought a ball. He paid

How much change did he get?

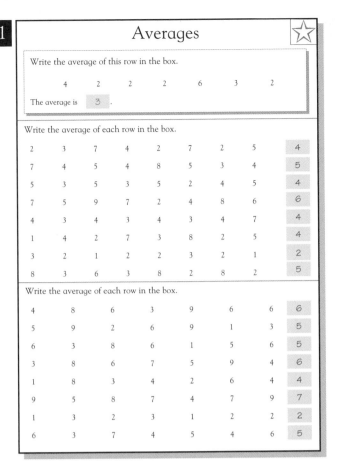

Circle the correct change.

Snack Menu

Banana	25¢
Pear	75¢
Apple	60¢

Kate bought an apple. She paid

How much change did she get?

Ali bought a banana. He paid

How much change did he get?

Dan bought a pear. He paid

How much change did he get?

Allow children to set up subtraction problems if they cannot complete the calculations mentally.

Counting money

Count the coins. Write the total amount.

25¢ + 25¢ + 25¢ + 5¢ + 5¢ + 10¢ = **95¢**

Count the coins. Write the total amount.

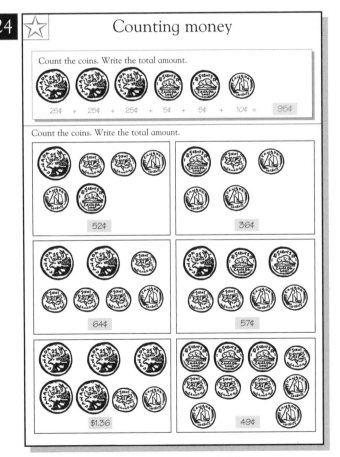

52¢

36¢

64¢

57¢

$1.36

49¢

As on the previous page, allow children to set up addition problems if they need to.

Number pairs

Look at the grid and then answer the questions below.

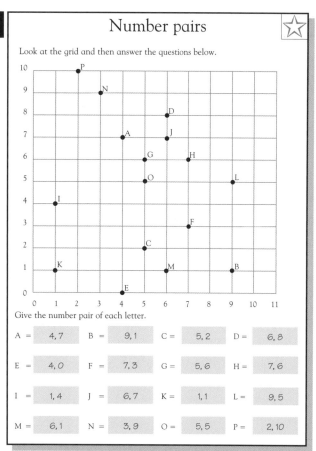

Give the number pair of each letter.

A =	4, 7	B =	9, 1	C =	5, 2	D =	6, 8
E =	4, 0	F =	7, 3	G =	5, 6	H =	7, 6
I =	1, 4	J =	6, 7	K =	1, 1	L =	9, 5
M =	6, 1	N =	3, 9	O =	5, 5	P =	2, 10

Make sure that children understand that the order of the number pairs is important. The first number is from the horizontal or *x*-axis, and the second number is from the vertical or *y*-axis.

126

Multiply or divide?

Write + or − in the box.

6 $\times$ 5 = 30   18 $\div$ 2 = 9   5 $\times$ 10 = 50

Write x or ÷ in the box.

7 $\times$ 5 = 35		10 $\div$ 2 = 5		12 $\div$ 2 = 6	
30 $\div$ 5 = 6		30 $\div$ 10 = 3		9 $\times$ 2 = 18	
14 $\div$ 2 = 7		35 $\div$ 5 = 7		6 $\times$ 10 = 60	
40 $\div$ 10 = 4		20 $\div$ 4 = 5		5 $\times$ 3 = 15	
5 $\times$ 6 = 30		3 $\times$ 10 = 30		90 $\div$ 10 = 9	
50 $\div$ 5 = 10		18 $\div$ 2 = 9		15 $\div$ 3 = 5	

Write the answers in the boxes.

A number divided by 4 is 10. What is the number?	40
I multiply a number by 6 and the answer is 30. What is the number?	5
A number multiplied by 10 gives the answer 10. What is the number?	1
I divide a number by 8 and the answer is 5. What is the number?	40
A number divided by 7 is 5. What is the number?	35
I multiply a number by 2 and the answer is 18. What is the number?	9
A number multiplied by 5 is 45. What is the number?	9
I divide a number by 2 and the answer is 1. What is the number?	2

Write x or ÷ in the box.

7 $\times$ 10 = 70		5 $\times$ 5 = 25		10 $\div$ 10 = 1	
5 $\div$ 5 = 1		9 $\times$ 2 = 18		2 $\times$ 2 = 4	
15 $\div$ 5 = 3		10 $\times$ 10 = 100		50 $\div$ 5 = 10	
100 $\div$ 10 = 10		2 $\div$ 2 = 1		20 $\div$ 5 = 4	

The second section requires children to perform the inverse operation to reach the answer. For the other sections, children should realize that if the answer is larger than the first number, they must multiply, and if it is smaller, they must divide.

127

Lines of symmetry

Draw the line of symmetry on each shape.

Draw the line of symmetry on each shape.

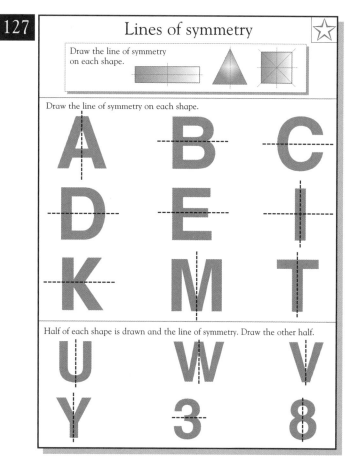

Half of each shape is drawn and the line of symmetry. Draw the other half.

If children pick an incorrect line of symmetry, you can use a small mirror to show them their mistake.

128

Counting by 2s, 5s, and 10s

Find the pattern. Continue each row.

Count by 2s.	9	11	13	15	17	19	21
Count by 5s.	8	13	18	23	28	33	38
Count by 10s.	65	55	45	35	25	15	5

Find the pattern. Continue each row.

0	2	4	6	8	10	12	14
8	10	12	14	16	18	20	22
38	43	48	53	58	63	68	73
40	45	50	55	60	65	70	75
63	73	83	93	103	113	123	133
85	90	95	100	105	110	115	120
6	8	10	12	14	16	18	20
21	19	17	15	13	11	9	7
68	66	64	62	60	58	56	54
85	80	75	70	65	60	55	50
43	41	39	37	35	33	31	29
49	44	39	34	29	24	19	14
71	69	67	65	63	61	59	57
83	78	73	68	63	58	53	48
39	34	29	24	19	14	9	4

Some of the patterns show an increase, while others show a decrease. Children should be able to complete these questions using mental math.

Multiples

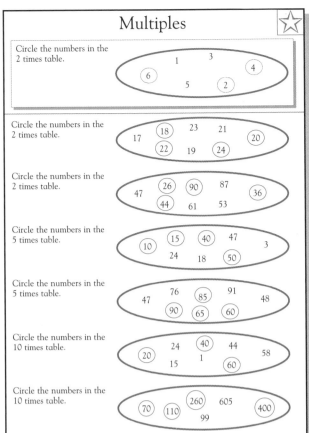

Circle the numbers in the 2 times table.
1 3 4 6 5 2

Circle the numbers in the 2 times table.
17 18 23 21 20 22 19 24

Circle the numbers in the 2 times table.
47 26 90 87 44 61 53 36

Circle the numbers in the 5 times table.
10 15 40 47 24 18 50 3

Circle the numbers in the 5 times table.
47 76 85 91 90 65 60 48

Circle the numbers in the 10 times table.
24 40 44 20 15 1 60 58

Circle the numbers in the 10 times table.
70 110 260 605 99 400

These questions test children's familiarity with the 2, 5, and 10 times tables.

Comparing and ordering

Write these numbers in order, starting with the smallest.
431 678 273 586   273 431 586 678

Write these numbers in order, starting with the smallest.

267	931	374	740	267	374	740	931
734	218	625	389	218	389	625	734
836	590	374	669	374	590	669	836
572	197	469	533	197	469	533	572
948	385	846	289	289	385	846	948
406	560	460	650	406	460	560	650
738	837	378	783	378	738	783	837
582	285	528	852	285	528	582	852
206	620	602	260	206	260	602	620
634	436	364	463	364	436	463	634
47	740	74	704	47	74	704	740
501	150	51	105	51	105	150	501
290	92	209	29	29	92	209	290
803	380	83	38	38	83	380	803
504	450	54	45	45	54	450	504

Make sure that children do not simply order the numbers according to the first digits.

Rounding

What is 327 rounded to the nearest 100?
300 310 320 330 340 350 360 370 380 390 400
300   327

What is each number rounded to the nearest 100?

478	500	231	200	147	100	687	700
342	300	812	800	973	1000	439	400
639	600	108	100	374	400	752	800
418	400	639	600	523	500	446	400
857	900	560	600	299	300	809	800

What is 250 rounded to the nearest 100?
200 210 220 230 240 250 260 270 280 290 300
300   250

What is each number rounded to the nearest 100?

450	500	850	900	650	700	87	100
21	0	405	400	150	200	950	1000
655	700	540	500	980	1000	50	100
750	800	250	300	90	100	59	100
550	600	105	100	955	1000	350	400

Children should recognize that amounts of 50 and above are rounded up, and amounts below 50 are rounded down. Make sure that children increase the hundreds digit by 1 when they round up.

Dividing by 2s, 5s, and 10s

$\frac{1}{2}$ of 12 is 6 $\frac{1}{5}$ of 10 is 2 $\frac{1}{10}$ of 20 is 2

What is $\frac{1}{2}$ of each number?

4	2	8	4	10	5	2	1
6	3	18	6	20	10	16	8
14	7	50	25	100	50	60	30

What is $\frac{1}{5}$ of each number?

5	1	25	5	40	8	70	14
50	10	65	13	20	4	30	6
45	9	60	12	35	7	75	15

What is $\frac{1}{10}$ of each number?

10	1	50	5	30	3	60	6
20	2	40	4	80	8	70	7

What is $\frac{1}{2}$ of each number?

22	11	30	15	24	12	28	14
32	16	26	13	36	18	34	17

What is $\frac{1}{10}$ of each number?

120	12	140	14	180	18	100	10
110	11	130	13	150	15	90	9

Each of the fractions on this page is a unit fraction—it has a numerator of 1. Children should realize that multiplying by these fractions is the same as dividing by the denominator.

Multiplying

Write the answer in the box.

7 x 3 = 21   9 x 5 = 45   6 x 10 = 60

Write the answer in the box.

2 x 3 = 6   7 x 4 = 28   4 x 3 = 12   6 x 4 = 24
9 x 5 = 45   8 x 3 = 24   6 x 3 = 18   10 x 9 = 90
3 x 2 = 6   9 x 4 = 36   7 x 5 = 35   5 x 4 = 20
0 x 3 = 0   8 x 4 = 32   4 x 10 = 40   0 x 4 = 0
5 x 3 = 15   4 x 4 = 16   9 x 3 = 27   8 x 5 = 40

Write the answer in the box.

Three times a number is 18. What is the number?   6

A number multiplied by 4 is 36. What is the number?   9

A child draws 8 squares. How many sides have to be drawn?   32

Light bulbs come in packs of 3. Erin buys 6 packs. How many bulbs will she have?   18

Mari is given eight 5¢ coins. How much money is she given?   40¢

A box contains 4 cans of beans. A man buys 9 boxes. How many cans does he have?   36

A girl is given 3 stickers for every point she gains in a spelling test. How many will she receive if she gets 10 points?   30

Four times a number is 24. What is the number?   6

A bottle holds 4 litres of soda. How much will 7 bottles hold?   28 litres

Six times a number is 30. What is the number?   5

Children should be able to answer all the questions on this page using mental math.

Dividing

Work out each division problem. Some will have remainders, some will not.

15 ÷ 3 = 5

17 ÷ 4 = 4 r 1

```
    5 r 1        2 r 2
2)11          3)8
 -10           -6
   1            2
```

Work out each division problem.

24 ÷ 3 = 8   32 ÷ 4 = 8   18 ÷ 9 = 2   24 ÷ 6 = 4
16 ÷ 4 = 4   24 ÷ 4 = 6   40 ÷ 10 = 4   28 ÷ 4 = 7
40 ÷ 10 = 4   20 ÷ 4 = 5   40 ÷ 4 = 10   12 ÷ 6 = 2
9 ÷ 3 = 3   24 ÷ 3 = 8   35 ÷ 7 = 5   60 ÷ 10 = 6
3 ÷ 1 = 3   25 ÷ 5 = 5   36 ÷ 4 = 9   44 ÷ 4 = 11

Work out each division problem. Some will have remainders, some will not.

```
     4          6 r 2         3 r 1         2 r 3
4)16          5)32          3)10          5)13
  16            30             9            10
   0             2             1             3

   3 r 2          7             7           6 r 1
4)14          3)21          10)70          3)19
  12            21             70            18
   2             0              0             1
```

Work out the answer to each problem.

23 carrots are shared equally by 4 rabbits. How many carrots does each rabbit receive and how many are left over?   5 carrots, 3 are left over

```
   5 r 3
4)23
  20
   3
```

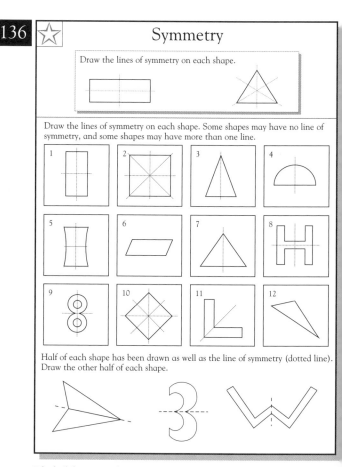

36 apples are shared equally between 5 horses. How many apples does each horse receive and how many are left over?   7 apples, 1 is left over

```
   7 r 1
5)36
  35
   1
```

Children should be able to answer all the questions on this page using mental math.

Bar graphs

Look at the bar graph. Then answer the question.

How many cherries does Robbie have?   6

Look at the bar graph. Then answer the questions.

Favourite seasons

This graph shows the favourite seasons of a group of children.

How many children were asked which season they liked best?   20

How many children liked autumn best?   6

Which season did four children like?   spring

Which was the favourite season?   summer

How many more children liked autumn than liked winter?   4

Look at the bar graph. Then answer the questions.

Favourite pets

This graph shows the favourite pets of a group of children.

How many children were asked about which pets they liked?   14

Which pet did eight children like?   guinea pigs

How many children liked rabbits?   3

How many children liked hamsters?   1

How many more children liked rabbits than liked hamsters?   2

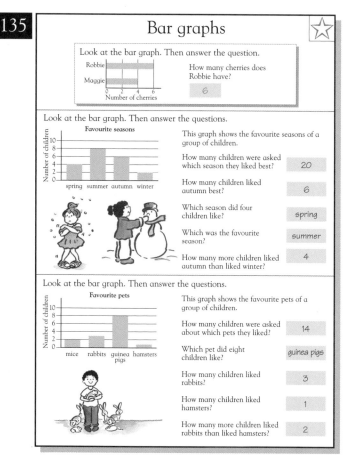

If children need help reading bar graphs, show them how to read across and up from the axis labels. To answer some of the questions, children will need to add and compare data.

Symmetry

Draw the lines of symmetry on each shape.

Draw the lines of symmetry on each shape. Some shapes may have no line of symmetry, and some shapes may have more than one line.

1   2   3   4

5   6   7   8

9   10   11   12

Half of each shape has been drawn as well as the line of symmetry (dotted line). Draw the other half of each shape.

If children pick an incorrect line of symmetry, you can use a small mirror to show them their mistake.

Ordering

Write these numbers in order starting with the smallest.

670	760	607	706	760
607	670	706	760	

Write these numbers in order starting with the smallest.

270	720	207	702		870	780	807	708
207	270	702	720		708	780	807	870

906	690	960	609		106	610	601	160
609	690	906	960		106	160	601	610

560	506	650	605		849	489	948	984
506	560	605	650		489	849	948	984

890	980	809	908		486	684	864	648
809	890	908	980		486	648	684	864

405	450	540	504		746	647	764	674
405	450	504	540		647	674	746	764

570	586	490	92		76	104	200	92
92	490	570	586		76	92	104	200

440	66	781	177		632	236	77	407
66	177	440	781		77	236	407	632

842	587	99	88		74	101	12	800
88	99	587	842		12	74	101	800

500	468	395	288		600	304	403	89
288	395	468	500		89	304	403	600

78	9	302	470		345	543	53	34
9	78	302	470		34	53	345	543

Make sure that children do not simply order the numbers according to the first digits.

Fractions of shapes

Shade half of each shape.

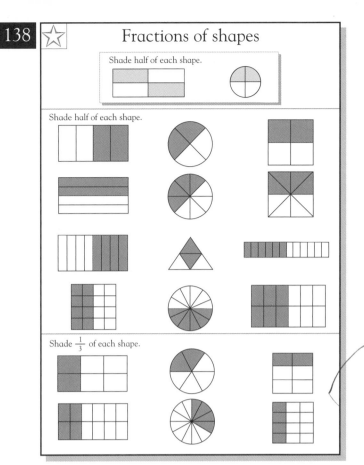

Shade half of each shape.

Shade $\frac{1}{3}$ of each shape.

Children may shade in any combination of the sections as long as the shaded area represents the fraction.

Choosing the operation

Write the answer in the box.

I add 25 to a number and the sum is 40. What number did I start with? — 15

I subtract 13 and have 24 left. What number did I start with? — 37

Write the answer in the box.

22 is added to a number and the sum is 30. What number did I begin with? — 8

I subtract 14 from a number and end up with 17. What number did I start with? — 31

I add 16 to a number and the total of the two numbers is 30. What number did I begin with? — 14

When 26 is subtracted from a number, the difference is 14. What is the number? — 40

After adding 22 to a number the total is 45. What is the number? — 23

What number must you subtract from 19 to find a difference of 7? — 12

I start with 29 and take away a number. The difference is 14. What number did I subtract? — 15

35 is added to a number and the total is 60. What is the number? — 25

I increase a number by 14 and the total is 30. What number did I start with? — 16

After taking 17 away from a number I am left with 3. What number did I start with? — 20

Paul starts with 50¢ but spends some money in a shop. He goes home with 18¢. How much did Paul spend? — 32¢

Sue starts out with 23¢ but is given some money by her aunt. Sue then has 50¢. How much was she given? — 27¢

Alice gives 20¢ to charity. If she started with 95¢, how much has she have left? — 75¢

Jane has a 500 millilitres bottle of orange soda. She drinks 350 millilitres. How many millilitres does she have left? — 150 ml

A box contains 60 pins and then some are added so that the new total is 85. How many pins have been added? — 25

A tower is made up of 30 blocks. 45 more are put on the top. How many blocks are in the tower now? — 75

Children must choose between addition and subtraction to solve each problem. If they make an error, have them substitute their answer in the problem to help them understand why it is incorrect.

Choosing the operation

Write the answer in the box.

A number is multiplied by 8 and the result is 24. What is the number? — 3

I divide a number by 4 and the answer is 9. What number did I begin with? — 36

Write the answer in the box.

A number is multiplied by 6 and the result is 30. What is the number? — 5

When a number is divided by 7 the result is 4. What is the number? — 28

I multiply a number by 10, and the final number is 70. What number did I multiply? — 7

After dividing a number by 8, I am left with 4. What number did I divide? — 32

When 20 is multiplied by a number the result is 100. What number is used to multiply? — 5

I divide a number by 3 and the result is 9. What is the number? — 27

After multiplying a number by 5, I have 40. What was the number I started with? — 8

When a number is divided by 10 the result is 3. What number was divided? — 30

I multiply a number by 4 and the result is 40. What number was multiplied? — 10

After dividing a number by 2, I am left with 30. What number was divided? — 60

45¢ is shared equally by some children. Each child receives 9¢. How many children are there? — 5

Each box contains 7 markers. I have 28 markers altogether. How many boxes do I have? — 4

I share 80¢ equally among some children. Each child is given 20¢. How many children have shared the money? — 4

A bag contains 10 chocolate bars. In all I have 100 chocolate bars. How many bags do I have? — 10

50 peanuts are shared equally between 2 squirrels. How many peanuts does each squirrel receive? — 25

I give $25 to each charity. I give away $200. How many charities did I give money to? — 8

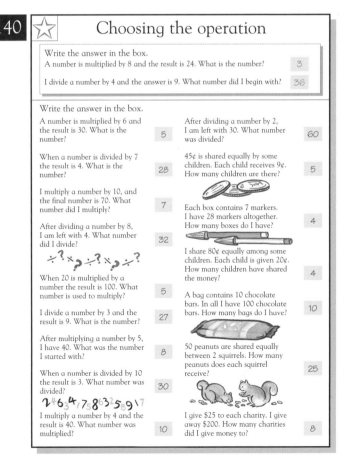

Children must choose between multiplication and division to solve each problem. If they make an error, have them substitute their answer in the problem to help them understand why it is incorrect.

Bar graphs and pictographs ☆

Look at the bar graph and answer the question.

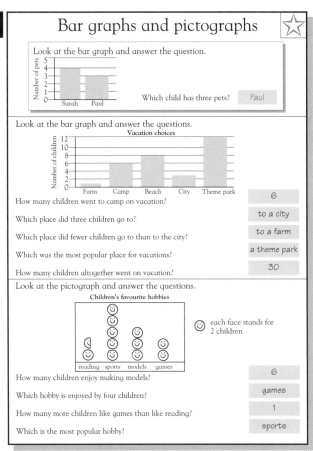

Which child has three pets? **Paul**

Look at the bar graph and answer the questions.

Vacation choices

How many children went to camp on vacation? **6**

Which place did three children go to? **to a city**

Which place did fewer children go to than to the city? **to a farm**

Which was the most popular place for vacations? **a theme park**

How many children altogether went on vacation? **30**

Look at the pictograph and answer the questions.

Children's favourite hobbies

😊 each face stands for 2 children

reading   sports   models   games

How many children enjoy making models? **6**

Which hobby is enjoyed by four children? **games**

How many more children like games than like reading? **1**

Which is the most popular hobby? **sports**

If children need help reading bar graphs, show them how to read across and up from the axis labels. To answer some of the questions, children will have to compare and add data.

Adding two numbers

Find each sum.

```
  2 7 1        3 8 3
+ 5 2 4      + 5 7 1
  7 9 5        9 5 4
```

Remember to regroup if you need to.

Find each sum.

```
  3 3 4      3 5 2      6 2 3      5 4 3
+ 2 6 5    + 1 2 7    + 3 4 5    + 2 9 1
  5 9 9      4 7 9      9 6 8      8 3 4

  3 8 5      3 6 3      5 3 5      3 9 2
+ 6 0 6    + 1 4 7    + 1 8 7    + 4 8 8
  9 9 1      5 1 0      7 2 2      8 8 0
```

Write the answer in the box.

213 + 137 = **350**   535 + 167 = **702**

Write the missing number in the box.

```
  3 6 2      2 5 6      7 2 1      7 3 9
+ 4 1 9    + 5 8 1    + 2 6 4    + 2 4 0
  7 8 1      8 3 7      9 8 5      9 7 9
```

Find each sum.

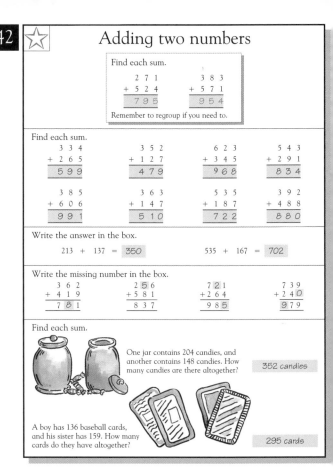

One jar contains 204 candies, and another contains 148 candies. How many candies are there altogether? **352 candies**

A boy has 136 baseball cards, and his sister has 159. How many cards do they have altogether? **295 cards**

The questions on this page involve straightforward addition work. If children have difficulty with the horizontal sums, suggest that they rewrite them in vertical form. Some errors may result from neglecting to regroup.

Adding two numbers ☆

Find each sum.

```
  3 2 1        5 9 4
+ 4 6 5      + 3 2 5
  7 8 6        9 1 9
```

Remember to carry if you need to.

Find each sum.

```
  6 4 2      3 2 5      4 7 1
+ 2 4 1    + 6 5 3    + 2 3 8
  8 8 3      9 7 8      7 0 9

  2 4 9      7 6 4      4 8 2
+ 4 7 1    + 2 1 5    + 3 4 9
  7 2 0      9 7 9      8 3 1
```

Write the answer in the box.

342 + 264 = **606**   531 + 236 = **767**

13 + 642 = **655**   338 + 261 = **599**

Write the missing number in the box.

```
  2 4 1      6 5 2      3 4 2
+ 4 4 3    + 2 7 4    + 1 3 1
  6 8 4      9 2 6      4 7 3
```

Find each sum.

621 people saw the local soccer team play on Saturday, and 246 people watched the midweek match. How many people saw the soccer team play that week? **867 people**

214 people went to the rock concert on Saturday night, and 471 people went on Sunday night. How many people saw rock concerts that weekend? **685 people**

This page is similar to the previous page. If children have difficulty with the section on finding missing numbers, have them try various digits until they find the correct one.

Subtracting three-digit numbers

Write the difference between the lines.

```
  3 6 4        4 7 1 cm
- 2 2 3      - 2 5 2 cm
  1 4 1        2 1 9 cm
```

Write the difference between the lines.

```
  2 6 3      4 7 8      8 4 5      7 9 3
- 1 5 1    - 2 3 4    - 6 2 4    - 5 8 1
  1 1 2      2 4 4      2 2 1      2 1 2

  5 8 0 cm    6 5 9 m     8 5 0 cm    3 7 2 m
- 2 3 0 cm  - 3 1 8 m   - 7 4 0 cm  - 2 6 2 m
  3 5 0 cm    3 4 1 m     1 1 0 cm    1 1 0 m
```

Write the difference in the box.

365 – 123 = **242**   799 – 354 = **445**

$876 – $515 = **$361** $940 – $730 = **$210**

$684 – $574 = **$110** $220 – $120 = **$100**

Write the difference between the lines.

```
  3 6 3      4 8 4      5 6 1      3 9 4
- 1 4 5    - 2 3 7    - 3 4 2    - 1 8 5
  2 1 8      2 4 7      2 1 9      2 0 9

  9 3 7      5 6 8      2 2 5      7 5 2
- 7 1 9    - 2 0 9    - 1 1 6    - 3 2 9
  2 1 8      3 5 9      1 0 9      4 2 3
```

Find the answer to each problem.

A grocer has 234 apples. He sells 127. How many apples does he have left? **107 apples**

A store has 860 movie videos to rent. 420 are rented. How many are left in the store? **440 videos**

There are 572 children in a school. 335 are girls. How many are boys? **237 boys**

In some of these sums, children may incorrectly subtract the smaller digit from the larger one, when they should be subtracting the larger digit from the smaller one. In such cases, point out that they should regroup.

Subtracting three-digit numbers ☆

Write the difference between the lines.

$$\begin{array}{r} \scriptstyle 3\ 11 \\ 4\cancel{1}5 \\ -\ 152 \\ \hline 263 \end{array} \qquad \begin{array}{r} \scriptstyle 6\,10\,11 \\ 7\cancel{1}\cancel{1}\ m \\ -\ 392\ m \\ \hline 319\ m \end{array}$$

Write the difference between the lines.

524 m − 263 m = **261 m**	319 m − 137 m = **182 m**	647 cm − 456 cm = **191 cm**	915 cm − 193 cm = **722 cm**
714 − 407 = **307**	926 − 827 = **99**	421 − 355 = **66**	815 − 786 = **29**

Write the difference in the box.

512 − 304 = **208**   648 − 239 = **409**

831 − 642 = **189**   377 − 198 = **179**

Write the difference between the lines.

423 − 136 = **287**	615 − 418 = **197**	312 − 113 = **199**	924 − 528 = **396**

Write the missing number in the box.

$$\begin{array}{r} 7\ 2\ 3 \\ -\ 1\ 2\ \boxed{8} \\ \hline 5\ 9\ 5 \end{array} \qquad \begin{array}{r} 5\ \boxed{6}\ 2 \\ -\ 3\ 1\ 7 \\ \hline 2\ 4\ 5 \end{array} \qquad \begin{array}{r} 8\ 3\ \boxed{4} \\ -\ 2\ 5\ 7 \\ \hline 5\ 7\ 7 \end{array} \qquad \begin{array}{r} 5\ 3\ 2 \\ -\ 1\ \boxed{8}\ 5 \\ \hline 3\ 4\ 7 \end{array}$$

Find the answer to each problem.

A theatre holds 645 people. 257 people buy tickets. How many seats are empty?   **388 seats**

There are 564 people in a park. 276 are boating on the lake. How many are taking part in other activities?   **288 people**

If children have difficulty with the section on missing numbers, have them use trial and error until they find the correct number. Encourage them to use addition and subtraction fact families to find the number.

☆ Multiplying by one-digit numbers

Find each product.

$$\begin{array}{r} 32 \\ \times\ 2 \\ \hline 64 \end{array} \qquad \begin{array}{r} \scriptstyle 1 \\ 26 \\ \times\ 3 \\ \hline 78 \end{array} \qquad \begin{array}{r} \scriptstyle 1 \\ 34 \\ \times\ 4 \\ \hline 136 \end{array}$$

Find each product.

27 × 2 = **54**	32 × 3 = **96**	16 × 4 = **64**	19 × 2 = **38**
22 × 3 = **66**	25 × 4 = **100**	18 × 6 = **108**	33 × 5 = **165**
39 × 2 = **78**	26 × 2 = **52**	41 × 2 = **82**	38 × 3 = **114**
29 × 3 = **87**	45 × 2 = **90**	28 × 3 = **84**	16 × 6 = **96**
10 × 5 = **50**	40 × 2 = **80**	20 × 4 = **80**	50 × 3 = **150**

Find the answer to each problem.

Laura has 36 marbles, and Sarah has twice as many. How many marbles does Sarah have?   **72 marbles**

A ruler is 30 cm long. How long will 4 rulers be altogether?   **120 cm**

Errors made on this page generally highlight gaps in children's knowledge of the 2, 3, 4, and 5 times tables. Other errors can also result from neglecting to regroup.

Multiplying by one-digit numbers ☆

Find each product.

$$\begin{array}{r} 53 \\ \times\ 3 \\ \hline 159 \end{array} \qquad \begin{array}{r} \scriptstyle 3 \\ 76 \\ \times\ 6 \\ \hline 456 \end{array} \qquad \begin{array}{r} \scriptstyle 3 \\ 25 \\ \times\ 7 \\ \hline 175 \end{array}$$

Find each product.

56 × 8 = **448**	46 × 7 = **322**	32 × 6 = **192**	36 × 9 = **324**	45 × 4 = **180**
73 × 5 = **365**	96 × 3 = **288**	58 × 7 = **406**	33 × 6 = **198**	48 × 5 = **240**
24 × 9 = **216**	19 × 8 = **152**	64 × 4 = **256**	52 × 6 = **312**	81 × 3 = **243**
37 × 7 = **259**	40 × 8 = **320**	50 × 3 = **150**	30 × 7 = **210**	20 × 9 = **180**

Find the answer to each problem.

A school bus holds 36 children. How many children can travel in 6 busloads?   **216 children**

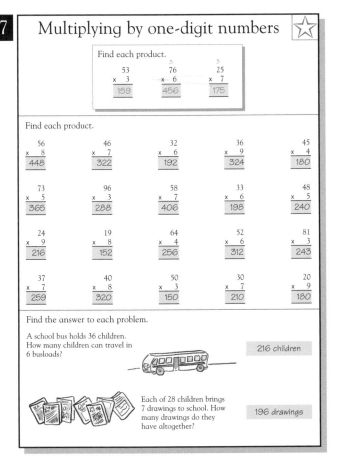

Each of 28 children brings 7 drawings to school. How many drawings do they have altogether?   **196 drawings**

Errors made on this page generally highlight gaps in children's knowledge of the 6, 7, 8, and 9 times tables. As on the previous page, the other most likely error will result from neglecting to regroup.

☆ Division with remainders

Find each quotient.

$$\begin{array}{r} 5\ r\ 1 \\ 3\overline{)16} \\ \underline{15} \\ 1 \end{array} \qquad \begin{array}{r} 6\ r\ 2 \\ 4\overline{)26} \\ \underline{24} \\ 2 \end{array}$$

Find each quotient.

17 r 1 2)35	**11 r 2** 4)46	**7 r 1** 3)22	**9 r 4** 5)49
14 r 2 4)58	**12 r 3** 5)63	**7 r 2** 5)37	**12 r 2** 4)50
25 r 1 3)76	**14 r 3** 4)59	**18 r 4** 5)94	**16 r 3** 5)83
49 r 1 2)99	**18 r 3** 4)75	**15 r 2** 5)77	**18 r 1** 2)37

Write the answer in the box.

What is 27 divided by 4?   **6 r 3**   Divide 78 by 5.   **15 r 3**

What is 46 divided by 3?   **15 r 1**   Divide 63 by 2.   **31 r 1**

Children may have difficulty finding quotients with remainders. Have them perform long division until the remaining value to be divided is less than the divisor. That value is the remainder.

Division with remainders

Find each quotient.

$$5 \text{ r } 4$$
$$6\overline{)34}$$
$$\underline{30}$$
$$4$$

$$7 \text{ r } 1$$
$$7\overline{)50}$$
$$\underline{49}$$
$$1$$

Find each quotient.

$$16 \text{ r } 3 \quad 6\overline{)99}$$
$$7 \text{ r } 1 \quad 6\overline{)43}$$
$$3 \text{ r } 3 \quad 9\overline{)30}$$
$$9 \text{ r } 4 \quad 8\overline{)76}$$

$$7 \text{ r } 3 \quad 7\overline{)52}$$
$$11 \text{ r } 6 \quad 7\overline{)83}$$
$$5 \text{ r } 7 \quad 9\overline{)52}$$
$$15 \text{ r } 1 \quad 6\overline{)91}$$

$$9 \text{ r } 3 \quad 7\overline{)66}$$
$$7 \text{ r } 7 \quad 8\overline{)63}$$
$$4 \text{ r } 3 \quad 6\overline{)27}$$
$$5 \text{ r } 6 \quad 8\overline{)46}$$

$$10 \text{ r } 3 \quad 9\overline{)93}$$
$$12 \text{ r } 1 \quad 7\overline{)85}$$
$$8 \text{ r } 3 \quad 8\overline{)67}$$
$$3 \text{ r } 5 \quad 7\overline{)26}$$

Write the answer in the box.

What is 87 divided by 7?   12 r 3

Divide 84 by 8.   10 r 4

What is 75 divided by 6?   12 r 3

Divide 73 by 9.   8 r 1

This page is similar to the previous page, but the divisors are numbers greater than 5. Children will need to know their 6, 7, 8, and 9 times tables to solve the problems.

Appropriate units of measure

Choose the best units to measure the length of each item.

millimetres	centimetres	metres
desk	tooth	swimming pool
centimetres	millimetres	metres

Choose the best units to measure the length of each item.

centimetres	metres	kilometres
bed	bicycle	toothbrush	football field
centimetres	centimetres	centimetres	metres
shoe	driveway	sailboat	highway
centimetres	metres	metres	kilometres

The height of a door is about 2   metres .

The length of a pencil is about 17 centimetres.

The height of a flagpole is about 7   metres .

Choose the best units to measure the mass of each item.

grams	kilograms	tonnes
train	kitten	watermelon	tennis ball
tonnes	grams	kilograms	grams
shoe	bag of potatoes	elephant	washing machine
grams	kilograms	tonnes	kilograms

The mass of a hamburger is about 26   grams .

The mass of a bag of apples is about 1   kilogram .

The mass of a truck is about 4   tonnes .

Children might come up with their own examples of items that measure about 1 millimetre, 1 centimetre, and 1 metre, as well as items that have a mass weigh about 1 gram, 1 kilogram, and 1 tonne. They can use these as benchmarks to find the appropriate unit

Real-life problems

Find the answer to each problem.

Jacob spent $4.68 at the store and had $4.77 left. How much did he have to start with?

$9.45

$$\begin{array}{r} 1 \\ 4.77 \\ + 4.68 \\ \hline 9.45 \end{array}$$

Tracy receives a weekly allowance of $3.00 a week. How much will she have if she saves all of it for 8 weeks?

$24.00

$$\begin{array}{r} 3.00 \\ \times \quad 8 \\ \hline 24.00 \end{array}$$

Find the answer to each problem.

A theatre charges $4 for each matinee ticket. If it sells 360 tickets for a matinee performance, how much does it take in?

$1440

$$\begin{array}{r} 2 \\ 360 \\ \times \quad 4 \\ \hline 1440 \end{array}$$

David has saved $9.59. His sister has $3.24 less. How much does she have?

$6.35

$$\begin{array}{r} 9.59 \\ - 3.24 \\ \hline 6.35 \end{array}$$

The cost for 9 children to go to a theme park is $72. How much does each child pay? If only 6 children go, what will the cost be?

$8 per child
$48 for 6 children

$$9\overline{)72} \quad \begin{array}{r} 8 \\ \underline{72} \\ 0 \end{array}$$
$$6 \times 8 = 48$$

Paul has $3.69. His sister gives him another $5.25, and he goes out and buys a CD single for $3.99. How much does he have left?

$4.95

$$\begin{array}{r} 1 \\ 3.69 \\ + 5.25 \\ \hline 8.94 \end{array} \quad \begin{array}{r} 7 \; 18 \; 14 \\ 8.94 \\ - 3.99 \\ \hline 4.95 \end{array}$$

Ian has $20 in savings. He decides to spend $\frac{1}{4}$ of it. How much will he have left?

$15

$$20 \div 4 = 5$$
$$20 - 5 = 15$$

This page provides children an opportunity to apply the skills they have practised. To select the appropriate operation, discuss if they expect the answer to be larger or smaller. This can help them decide whether to add, multiply, subtract or divide.

Perimeters of squares and rectangles

Find the perimeter of this rectangle.

To find the perimeter of a rectangle or a square, add the lengths of the four sides.
6 cm + 6 cm + 4 cm + 4 cm = 20 cm
You can also do this with multiplication.
(2 × 6) cm + (2 × 4) cm
= 12 cm + 8 cm = 20 cm

6 cm
4 cm

20 cm

Find the perimeters of these rectangles and squares.

4 cm, 1 cm   →   10 cm

3 m, 3 m   →   12 m

2 km, 3 km   →   10 km

3 cm, 2 cm   →   10 cm

1 m, 1 m   →   4 m

4 km, 2 km   →   12 km

4 m, 4 m   →   16 m

4 cm, 3 cm   →   14 cm

2 km, 2 km   →   8 km

Make sure that children do not simply add the lengths of two sides of a figure rather than all four sides. Help children realize that the perimeter of a square can be found by multiplying the length of one side by 4.

Comparing areas

Write how many units are in each figure.

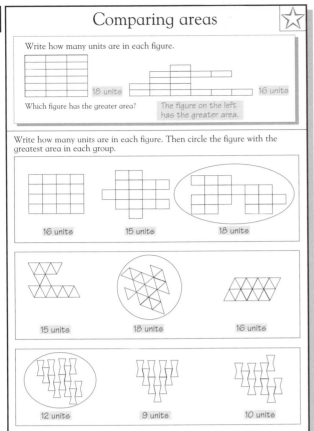

18 units   16 units

Which figure has the greater area?   The figure on the left has the greater area.

Write how many units are in each figure. Then circle the figure with the greatest area in each group.

16 units   15 units   18 units

15 units   18 units   16 units

12 units   9 units   10 units

Children may not realize that they can compare the areas of irregular figures. Make sure that they take care to count the units in each figure, rather than incorrectly assuming that the longest or tallest figure has the greater area.

Adding fractions

Write the sum in the simplest form.

$\frac{1}{8} + \frac{3}{8} = \frac{4}{8} = \frac{1}{2}$ $\frac{3}{5} + \frac{3}{5} = \frac{6}{5} = 1\frac{1}{5}$

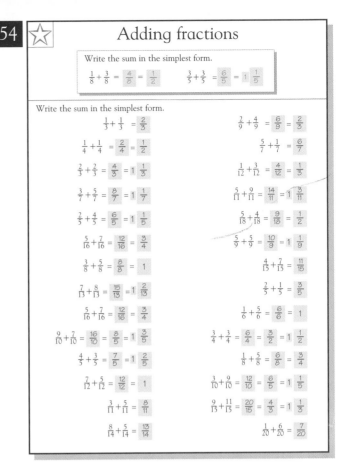

Write the sum in the simplest form.

$\frac{1}{3} + \frac{1}{3} = \frac{2}{3}$ $\frac{2}{9} + \frac{4}{9} = \frac{6}{9} = \frac{2}{3}$

$\frac{1}{4} + \frac{1}{4} = \frac{2}{4} = \frac{1}{2}$ $\frac{5}{7} + \frac{1}{7} = \frac{6}{7}$

$\frac{2}{3} + \frac{2}{3} = \frac{4}{3} = 1\frac{1}{3}$ $\frac{1}{12} + \frac{3}{12} = \frac{4}{12} = \frac{1}{3}$

$\frac{3}{7} + \frac{5}{7} = \frac{8}{7} = 1\frac{1}{7}$ $\frac{5}{11} + \frac{9}{11} = \frac{14}{11} = 1\frac{3}{11}$

$\frac{2}{5} + \frac{4}{5} = \frac{6}{5} = 1\frac{1}{5}$ $\frac{5}{18} + \frac{4}{18} = \frac{9}{18} = \frac{1}{2}$

$\frac{5}{16} + \frac{7}{16} = \frac{12}{16} = \frac{3}{4}$ $\frac{5}{9} + \frac{5}{9} = \frac{10}{9} = 1\frac{1}{9}$

$\frac{3}{8} + \frac{5}{8} = \frac{8}{8} = 1$ $\frac{4}{15} + \frac{7}{15} = \frac{11}{15}$

$\frac{7}{13} + \frac{8}{13} = \frac{15}{13} = 1\frac{2}{13}$ $\frac{2}{5} + \frac{1}{5} = \frac{3}{5}$

$\frac{5}{16} + \frac{7}{16} = \frac{12}{16} = \frac{3}{4}$ $\frac{1}{6} + \frac{5}{6} = \frac{6}{6} = 1$

$\frac{9}{10} + \frac{7}{10} = \frac{16}{10} = \frac{8}{5} = 1\frac{3}{5}$ $\frac{3}{4} + \frac{3}{4} = \frac{6}{4} = \frac{3}{2} = 1\frac{1}{2}$

$\frac{4}{5} + \frac{3}{5} = \frac{7}{5} = 1\frac{2}{5}$ $\frac{1}{8} + \frac{5}{8} = \frac{6}{8} = \frac{3}{4}$

$\frac{7}{12} + \frac{5}{12} = \frac{12}{12} = 1$ $\frac{3}{10} + \frac{9}{10} = \frac{12}{10} = \frac{6}{5} = 1\frac{1}{5}$

$\frac{3}{11} + \frac{5}{11} = \frac{8}{11}$ $\frac{9}{13} + \frac{11}{13} = \frac{20}{15} = \frac{4}{3} = 1\frac{1}{3}$

$\frac{8}{14} + \frac{5}{14} = \frac{13}{14}$ $\frac{1}{20} + \frac{6}{20} = \frac{7}{20}$

Some children may incorrectly add both the numerators and the denominators. Demonstrate that only the numerators should be added when the fractions have the same denominators: $\frac{1}{2} + \frac{1}{2}$ equals $\frac{2}{2}$ or 1, not $\frac{2}{4}$.

Subtracting fractions

Write the sum in the simplest form.

$\frac{5}{6} - \frac{4}{6} = \frac{1}{6}$ $\frac{5}{8} - \frac{3}{8} = \frac{2}{8} = \frac{1}{4}$

Write the answer in the simplest form.

$\frac{2}{3} - \frac{1}{3} = \frac{1}{3}$ $\frac{7}{9} - \frac{4}{9} = \frac{3}{9} = \frac{1}{3}$

$\frac{1}{4} - \frac{1}{4} = 0$ $\frac{5}{7} - \frac{1}{7} = \frac{4}{7}$

$\frac{7}{12} - \frac{5}{12} = \frac{2}{12} = \frac{1}{6}$ $\frac{5}{11} - \frac{3}{11} = \frac{2}{11}$

$\frac{6}{7} - \frac{5}{7} = \frac{1}{7}$ $\frac{9}{12} - \frac{5}{12} = \frac{4}{12} = \frac{1}{3}$

$\frac{18}{30} - \frac{15}{30} = \frac{3}{30} = \frac{1}{10}$ $\frac{4}{5} - \frac{2}{5} = \frac{2}{5}$

$\frac{3}{6} - \frac{1}{6} = \frac{2}{6} = \frac{1}{3}$ $\frac{7}{8} - \frac{1}{8} = \frac{6}{8} = \frac{3}{4}$

$\frac{11}{16} - \frac{7}{16} = \frac{4}{16} = \frac{1}{4}$ $\frac{5}{9} - \frac{2}{9} = \frac{3}{9} = \frac{1}{3}$

$\frac{7}{13} - \frac{5}{13} = \frac{2}{13}$ $\frac{14}{15} - \frac{4}{15} = \frac{10}{15} = \frac{2}{3}$

$\frac{12}{13} - \frac{8}{13} = \frac{4}{13}$ $\frac{4}{5} - \frac{1}{5} = \frac{3}{5}$

$\frac{9}{10} - \frac{7}{10} = \frac{2}{10} = \frac{1}{5}$ $\frac{5}{6} - \frac{1}{6} = \frac{4}{6} = \frac{2}{3}$

$\frac{8}{17} - \frac{4}{17} = \frac{4}{17}$ $\frac{11}{18} - \frac{8}{18} = \frac{3}{18} = \frac{1}{6}$

$\frac{4}{5} - \frac{3}{5} = \frac{1}{5}$ $\frac{9}{11} - \frac{5}{11} = \frac{4}{11}$

$\frac{7}{8} - \frac{5}{8} = \frac{2}{8} = \frac{1}{4}$ $\frac{3}{16} - \frac{2}{16} = \frac{1}{16}$

$\frac{7}{12} - \frac{5}{12} = \frac{2}{12} = \frac{1}{6}$ $\frac{8}{14} - \frac{5}{14} = \frac{3}{14}$

$\frac{9}{10} - \frac{3}{10} = \frac{6}{10} = \frac{3}{5}$ $\frac{17}{20} - \frac{6}{20} = \frac{11}{20}$

On this page, children subtract fractions that have the same denominators. Some children may neglect to simplify their answers. Help them do so by finding common factors in the numerator and the denominator.

Volumes of cubes

This cube is 1 cm long, 1 cm high, and 1 cm wide. We say it has a volume of 1 cubic centimetre (1 cm³).

1 cm   1 cm   1 cm

If we put 4 of these cubes together the new shape has a volume of 4 cm³.

These shapes are made of 1 cm³ cubes. What are their volumes?

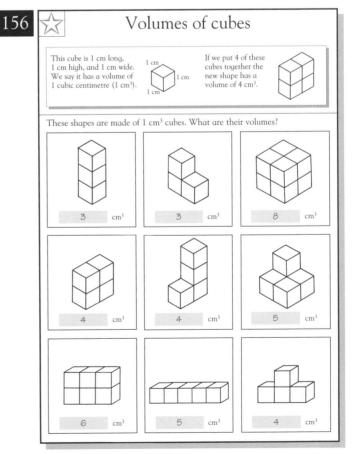

3 cm³   3 cm³   8 cm³

4 cm³   4 cm³   5 cm³

6 cm³   5 cm³   4 cm³

To find the volume of some of the shapes on this page, children will need to visualize how many blocks cannot be seen in the illustrations. For example, in the third and sixth shapes, there is one block that is not shown.

Extra Practice

Answer Section
with Parents' Notes

This section provides answers for the Extra Practice section on pages 158–201. There are also notes for each page, indicating the skills being developed, pointing out potential issues, or providing ideas for extra activities and ways to help children.

Children should be able to read the more specialized math words ("multiples," for example), but be prepared to assist. Working alongside children can also help you to understand how they are thinking and where the stumbling blocks may be.

There is an increasing emphasis on solving problems and applying the four operations (+, –, x, and ÷). Children are expected to be able to represent the problems symbolically and communicate the mathematical process clearly using objects and drawings. If children really understand the math, they will be able to reason critically and explain their reasoning.

Occasionally, you may find that a particular problem is slightly beyond your child's capabilities. Offer as much help and support as needed, and encourage them to reason out the solutions to the best of their abilities.

Around the home, provide opportunities for practical use of measuring equipment and appropriate tools, such as calculators and rulers. This will help children to visualize situations when answering math problems.

Build your child's confidence with words of praise. If they are getting answers wrong, encourage them to return to try again another time. Good luck, and remember to have fun!

★ Place value

Circle the "ones" digit in each number.

4(5)   45(8)   21(9)   5(6)7   70(0)

Circle the "tens" digit in each number.

1(8)4   1(6)5   4(5)6   7(8)6   2(0)0

Circle the "hundreds" digit in each number.

(6)00   (1)63   (5)46   (2)34   (3)34

654 can be written as 600 + 50 + 4. This is called the **expanded form**.
Write each number in its expanded form.

423 400 + 20 + 3   406 400 + 6

710 700 + 10   805 800 + 5

612 600 + 10 + 2   428 400 + 20 + 8

649 600 + 40 + 9   417 400 + 10 + 7

700 + 60 + 9 can be written as 769. This is called the **standard form**.
Write each number in its standard form.

400 + 7 407   200 + 30 + 5 235

50 + 8 58   900 + 4 904

Recognizing the value of a digit is important in many ways and will help children when it comes to solving more complicated problems. Being able to "split" numbers as shown in the last two questions can be very helpful.

Negative numbers ★

Look at this number line.

-10 -9 -8 -7 -6 -5 -4 -3 -2 -1 0 1 2 3 4 5 6 7 8 9 10

Add 1 to each number.
Note: When you add, you move to the right on the number line.

3 4   7 8   9 10   1 2   0 1   -2 -1

-10 -9   8 9   4 5   6 7   -3 -2   -9 -8

Subtract 1 from each number.
Note: When you subtract, you move left on the number line.

8 7   5 4   10 9   1 0   -3 -4   -9 -10

2 1   9 8   -5 -6   4 3   -8 -9   -7 -8

Add 3 to each number. **Hint:** Move to the right.

4 7   7 10   0 3   -7 -4   -5 -2

5 8   -3 0   -9 -6   6 9   -10 -7

Subtract 4 from each number. **Hint:** Move to the left.

4 0   -5 -9   9 5   10 6   -4 -8

5 1   2 -2   3 -1   -1 -5   -6 -10

At this stage questions about negative numbers are usually shown with a number line so that children can actually see "where to go" when adding and subtracting.

★ Counting forward and backward

What is 2 more than these numbers?

7 9   28 30   99 101   80 82   107 109

What is 2 less than these numbers?

11 9   70 68   92 90   48 46   101 99

What is 5 more than these numbers?

6 11   17 22   59 64   31 36   98 103

What is 5 less than these numbers?

11 6   34 29   43 38   98 93   102 97

Fill in the missing numbers.

90 95 100 105 110 115 120 125

110 120 130 140 150 160 170 180

25 50 75 100 125 150 175 200

100 200 300 400 500 600 700 800

This work should be straightforward. Encourage the children to work the simple problems quickly and without using fingers. Children may have a slight problem when crossing into the 100s if they are unsure about place values.

Ordering numbers ★

Order each row of numbers, starting with the smallest.

213	312	123	230	32
32	123	213	230	312

841	148	184	481	814
148	184	481	814	841

Order each row of numbers, starting with the largest.

627	276	672	267	726
726	672	627	276	267

150	100	105	500	510
510	500	150	105	100

Order this row, starting with the smallest amount.

$2.60	$6.20	$2.06	$6.02	$0.26
$0.26	$2.06	$2.60	$6.02	$6.20

Order this row, starting with the largest amount.

$12.34	$21.43	$43.21	$43.12	$34.21
$43.21	$43.12	$34.21	$21.43	$12.34

For each sum, put these numbers in order, starting with the largest. Then add.

50 + 200 + 8 = 200 + 50 + 8 = 258

7 + 60 + 400 = 400 + 60 + 7 = 467

12 + 750 = 750 + 12 = 762

24 + 370 = 370 + 24 = 394

Children will generally be able to order smaller numbers but can become confused with higher numbers. Help them by looking at the first digit first, e.g., the 2 of 276 and ordering the hundreds and then the tens and then the ones.

★ Rounding

Round each number to the nearest 10.

14	10	9	10	55	60	26	30
11	10	38	40	99	100	72	70
883	880	451	450	724	720	906	910
107	110	345	350	189	190	503	500
263	260	485	490	214	210	895	900
481	480	673	670	957	960	426	430
762	760	381	380	266	270	751	750
107	110	143	140	376	380	288	290
452	450	673	670	924	920	649	650
805	810	637	640	751	750	948	950

162

As with all rounding, it is the "5" or "55" situation that can cause confusion. The simple convention is to round upward so that 15 will become 20 for example.

Comparing numbers ★

Circle the smaller number each time.

(3 x 4) or 7 + 6   (7 + 8) or 20 – 4   2 x 8 or (3 x 5)

(10 x 3) or 18 + 13   5 x 4 or (10 + 9)   (15 – 3) or 8 + 6

Circle the larger number each time.

(10 x 4) or 19 + 13   8 + 9 or (3 x 6)   (12 + 12) or 7 x 3

(5 x 3) or 8 + 6   10 + 12 or (5 x 5)   7 + 13 or (30 – 9)

Circle the smaller amount each time.

$2.00 or (80 ¢ + 70 ¢)   65 ¢ – 25 ¢ or (56 ¢ – 30 ¢)

($1.00) or 70 ¢ + 35 ¢   90 ¢ – 25 ¢ or (65 ¢ – 10 ¢)

Circle the larger amount each time.

($5 + $2) or 250 ¢ + 250 ¢   (47 ¢ – 8 ¢) or 35 ¢ + 3 ¢

$2.50 or ($3.00 – 40 ¢)   60 ¢ – 15 ¢ or (70 ¢ – 20 ¢)

Circle the amount that is between $3.00 and $4.00.

$2.30 + 65 ¢   ($5.00 – $1.50) $5.00 – 35 ¢

Circle the amount that is between 2 cm and 3 cm.

1.5 cm + 2.5 cm   6.5 cm – 2.5 cm   (4 cm – 1.5 cm)

163

Children should be encouraged to read the question carefully as with this selection they are sometimes asked to "circle the larger number" and sometimes "circle the smaller number."

★ Fractions of numbers

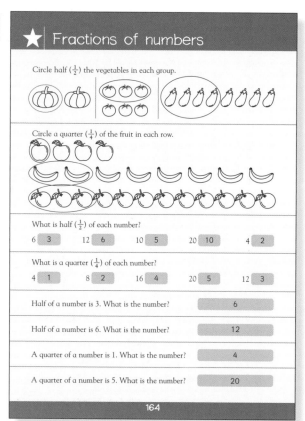

Circle half (½) the vegetables in each group.

Circle a quarter (¼) of the fruit in each row.

What is half (½) of each number?

6 | 3   12 | 6   10 | 5   20 | 10   4 | 2

What is a quarter (¼) of each number?

4 | 1   8 | 2   16 | 4   20 | 5   12 | 3

Half of a number is 3. What is the number?   6

Half of a number is 6. What is the number?   12

A quarter of a number is 1. What is the number?   4

A quarter of a number is 5. What is the number?   20

164

Once children have counted the number of each item they should be able to work out a half or quarter fairly quickly. Where images are not given and children are struggling, encourage them to draw circles to then split up equally.

Fractions of shapes ★

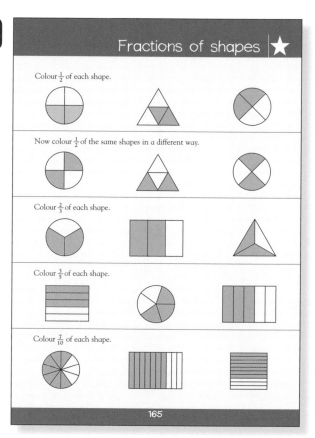

Colour ½ of each shape.

Now colour ½ of the same shapes in a different way.

Colour ⅔ of each shape.

Colour ⅗ of each shape.

Colour 7/10 of each shape.

165

Children should realize that the actual sections that are coloured do not matter as long as the correct number are coloured.

★ Quarters

What is a quarter ($\frac{1}{4}$) of each number?

12 [3]　　16 [4]　　40 [10]　　28 [7]

What is a quarter ($\frac{1}{4}$) of each amount?

4 ¢ [1 ¢]　　20 ¢ [5 ¢]　　12 ¢ [3 ¢]　　16 ¢ [4 ¢]

How much is a quarter ($\frac{1}{4}$) of 40 ¢?

[10 ¢]

Fido eats 8 biscuits each day. Fido has a quarter ($\frac{1}{4}$) of the biscuits for breakfast. How many biscuits does Fido have for breakfast? [2]

Daisy is given 20 CDs by her sister. Daisy gives a quarter ($\frac{1}{4}$) of the CDs to her brother. How many CDs does Daisy give to her brother? [5]

Shen has to work for one hour but stops after a quarter of an hour. How long is a quarter of an hour in minutes? [15 minutes]

Darius has to wait 24 minutes for a bus. He has waited a quarter ($\frac{1}{4}$) of that time. How long does Darius still have to wait? [18 minutes]

Children generally find quarters a little trickier than halves so the more practice the better. They need to be careful answering the last question, which is deliberately a bit more complicated.

Calculator ★

Use a calculator to work out these problems.

7 x 12 = [84]	9 x 9 = [81]	10 x 12 = [120]
7 x 6 = [42]	14 x 10 = [140]	12 x 50 = [600]
16 x 3 = [48]	200 x 6 = [1200]	120 x 7 = [840]
12 x 8 = [96]	20 x 20 = [400]	150 x 6 = [900]
26 + 49 + 58 = [133]	74 + 59 + 82 = [215]	29 + 69 + 84 = [182]
546 + 512 = [1058]	785 + 897 = [1682]	209 + 109 + 56 = [374]
432 + 777 = [1209]	812 + 564 = [1376]	231 + 321 + 412 = [964]
576 − 299 = [277]	600 − 345 = [255]	708 − 544 = [164]
1000 − 564 = [436]	1645 − 789 = [856]	1705 − 805 = [900]
634 − 486 = [148]	554 − 366 = [188]	904 − 904 = [0]
86 ÷ 2 = [43]	100 ÷ 25 = [4]	40 ÷ 8 = [5]
160 ÷ 8 = [20]	240 ÷ 12 = [20]	300 ÷ 15 = [20]
480 ÷ 20 = [24]	500 ÷ 25 = [20]	196 ÷ 14 = [14]

Jake has to share $280 equally between himself and his four sisters.

How much will they each receive? [$56]

Children usually pick up calculator skills very quickly. Encourage them to make estimates of answers before pressing the keys. Estimates can be done by rounding the numbers, a skill that should already have been learned.

★ Keeping skills sharp

Which child has the most money?

Nada	Barbara	Ann	Harris
$230	$432	$402	$340

.......Barbara.......

This thermometer shows the temperature during the day. Overnight, the temperature drops by 14°. What is the temperature at night?

[−2°C]

Write the children's names in order of height, starting with the shortest.

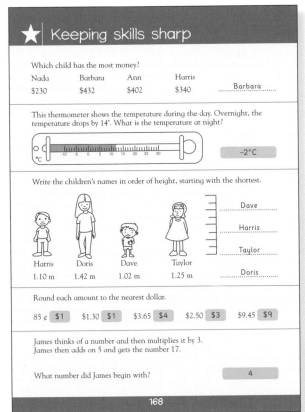

Harris 1.10 m　Doris 1.42 m　Dave 1.02 m　Taylor 1.25 m

Dave
Harris
Taylor
Doris

Round each amount to the nearest dollar.

85 ¢ [$1]　　$1.30 [$1]　　$3.65 [$4]　　$2.50 [$3]　　$9.45 [$9]

James thinks of a number and then multiplies it by 3. James then adds on 5 and gets the number 17.

What number did James begin with? [4]

The questions here and on the following page cover the work practised so far and should act as a little reminder and also a test of how well topics have been understood.

Keeping skills sharp ★

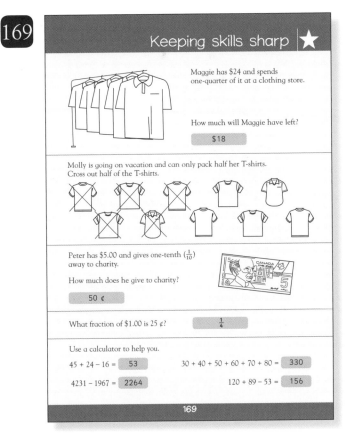

Maggie has $24 and spends one-quarter of it at a clothing store.

How much will Maggie have left? [$18]

Molly is going on vacation and can only pack half her T-shirts. Cross out half of the T-shirts.

Peter has $5.00 and gives one-tenth ($\frac{1}{10}$) away to charity.

How much does he give to charity? [50 ¢]

What fraction of $1.00 is 25 ¢? [$\frac{1}{4}$]

Use a calculator to help you.

45 + 24 − 16 = [53]　　30 + 40 + 50 + 60 + 70 + 80 = [330]

4231 − 1967 = [2264]　　120 + 89 − 53 = [156]

★ Adding three numbers

Write the answers.

9 + 8 + 7 = 24   10 + 8 + 7 = 25   20 + 17 + 14 = 51

11 + 5 + 3 = 19   15 + 10 + 5 = 30   30 + 20 + 10 = 60

50 + 30 + 10 = 90   12 + 11 + 10 = 33   21 + 11 + 1 = 33

7 + 14 + 21 = 42   9 + 18 + 30 = 57   50 + 30 + 20 = 100

40 + 18 + 20 = 78   30 + 19 + 10 = 59   10 + 23 + 40 = 73

70 + 9 + 10 = 89   50 + 17 + 20 = 87   40 + 20 + 40 = 100

17 + 18 + 19 = 54   23 + 24 + 25 = 72   36 + 37 + 38 = 111

51 + 52 + 53 = 156   35 + 45 + 55 = 135   20 + 80 + 60 = 160

Write the answers.

23	45	19	56	38	73
34	16	15	42	13	12
+ 42	+ 18	+ 32	+ 17	+ 25	+ 15
99	79	66	115	76	100

Generally it is good to have the children re-arrange the numbers in descending order before adding. Column addition is often taught at this age—the key is to "carry" a number from the ones to the tens if it totals more than 9.

Subtracting ★

Write the answers.

20 − 7 = 13   34 − 18 = 16   42 − 19 = 23   23 − 22 = 1

50 − 27 = 23   44 − 35 = 9   21 − 19 = 2   50 − 36 = 14

53 − 26 = 27   71 − 68 = 3   49 − 17 = 32   60 − 12 = 48

50 − 19 = 31   40 − 18 = 22   30 − 17 = 13   20 − 16 = 4

100 − 40 = 60   100 − 65 = 35   100 − 32 = 68   100 − 17 = 83

100 − 45 = 55   100 − 70 = 30   100 − 23 = 77   100 − 71 = 29

Write the answers.

43	67	80	120	105	102
− 21	− 14	− 54	− 30	− 45	− 56
22	53	26	90	60	46

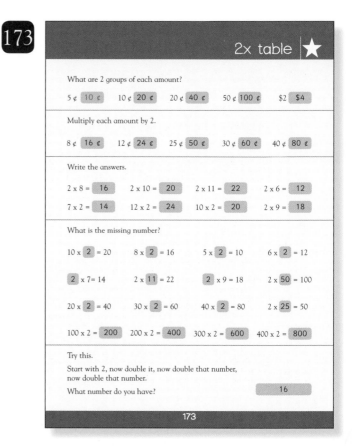

Matilda owns 145 pairs of shoes but gives 62 pairs away to a charity store.

How many pairs of shoes does Matilda have left?

83

Schools will teach different ways of working subtraction questions and children may easily become confused so take everything very slowly. A common method is to "add upward," which may not have be the way you have been taught.

★ Groups of 2

Write the answers.

3 sets of 2 = 6
3 x 2 = 6

4 sets of 2 = 8
4 x 2 = 8

2 sets of 2 = 4
2 x 2 = 4

2 sets of 5 = 10
2 x 5 = 10

Write the answers.

1 x 2 = 2   2 x 2 = 4   3 x 2 = 6   4 x 2 = 8

5 x 2 = 10   6 x 2 = 12   9 x 2 = 18   10 x 2 = 20

2 x 3 = 6   2 x 4 = 8   2 x 6 = 12   2 x 8 = 16

2 x 1 = 2   2 x 3 = 6   2 x 5 = 10   2 x 7 = 14

Which number is missing?

2 x 3 = 6   2 x 5 = 10   2 x 8 = 16   2 x 7 = 14

2 x 4 = 8   2 x 10 = 20   2 x 6 = 12   2 x 9 = 18

This page provides the starting point for the type of multiplication problems the children will be encountering. At this stage, the more formal questions will usually be laid out horizontally rather than vertically.

2x table ★

What are 2 groups of each amount?

5 ¢ 10 ¢   10 ¢ 20 ¢   20 ¢ 40 ¢   50 ¢ 100 ¢ $2 $4

Multiply each amount by 2.

8 ¢ 16 ¢   12 ¢ 24 ¢   25 ¢ 50 ¢   30 ¢ 60 ¢   40 ¢ 80 ¢

Write the answers.

2 x 8 = 16   2 x 10 = 20   2 x 11 = 22   2 x 6 = 12

7 x 2 = 14   12 x 2 = 24   10 x 2 = 20   2 x 9 = 18

What is the missing number?

10 x 2 = 20   8 x 2 = 16   5 x 2 = 10   6 x 2 = 12

2 x 7 = 14   2 x 11 = 22   2 x 9 = 18   2 x 50 = 100

20 x 2 = 40   30 x 2 = 60   40 x 2 = 80   2 x 25 = 50

100 x 2 = 200   200 x 2 = 400   300 x 2 = 600   400 x 2 = 800

Try this.

Start with 2, now double it, now double that number, now double that number.

What number do you have?   16

By now children should have a good knowledge of the 2-times tables and this page gives further practice. Look out for two things: the children's accurate recall of the tables and a fast recall.

★ 7x table

Match each dog to the right bone with a line.

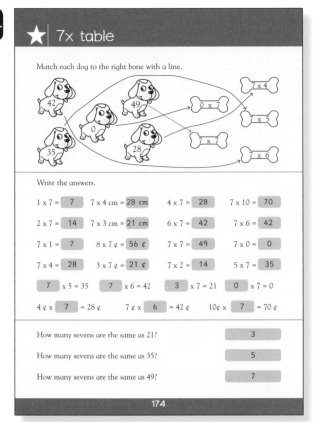

Write the answers.

1 x 7 = 7	7 x 4 cm = 28 cm	4 x 7 = 28	7 x 10 = 70
2 x 7 = 14	7 x 3 cm = 21 cm	6 x 7 = 42	7 x 6 = 42
7 x 1 = 7	8 x 7 ¢ = 56 ¢	7 x 7 = 49	7 x 0 = 0
7 x 4 = 28	3 x 7 ¢ = 21 ¢	7 x 2 = 14	5 x 7 = 35

7 x 5 = 35   7 x 6 = 42   3 x 7 = 21   0 x 7 = 0

4 ¢ x 7 = 28 ¢   7 ¢ x 6 = 42 ¢   10¢ x 7 = 70 ¢

How many sevens are the same as 21?   3

How many sevens are the same as 35?   5

How many sevens are the same as 49?   7

Similarly, the children will be gaining confidence with the 7-times table as well. Keep a record of how quickly and accurately they complete this page. Encourage them to try it again on another occasion if further practice is needed.

5x table ★

Match each mouse to the right cheese with a line.

0 x 5   8 x 5   2 x 5   5 x 5

25   0   10   40

Write the answers.

4 x 5 = 20	8 x 5 = 40	5 x 3 ¢ = 15 ¢	5 x 0 = 0
1 x 5 = 5	11 x 5 = 55	5 x 9 ¢ = 45 ¢	5 x 12 ¢ = 60 ¢
6 x 5 = 30	7 x 5 = 35	5 x 10 = 50	5 x 6 = 30
12 x 5 = 60	0 x 5 = 0	5 x 6 = 30	5 x 9 = 45

Circle the numbers that are **not** multiples of 5.

5   10   (13)   40   90   55   120   (18)   (22)   (47)   100

Write the answers.

5 + 5 = 10   2 groups of 5 = 10   5 groups of 2 are 10

5 x 2 = 10   3 groups of 5 = 15   3 groups of 5 are 15

This 5-times table practice also reinforces the different ways of presenting multiplication problems and the terminology used.

★ Some times tables!

Complete the grids.

X	2	6	8	11	9
2	4	12	16	22	18
5	10	30	40	55	45

X	0	1	8	6	4
2	0	2	16	12	8
5	0	5	40	30	20
10	0	10	80	60	40

X	2	5	6	7	4	3	1
2	4	10	12	14	8	6	2
5	10	25	30	35	20	15	5
10	20	50	60	70	40	30	10

X	3	6	5	4	0
2	6	12	10	8	0
5	15	30	25	20	0
0	0	0	0	0	0

These grids give practice in recall of the 2-times, 5-times, and 10-times tables. As before, it is not just accurate recall but very quick recall that needs to be achieved.

Multiplying ★

Write the answers.

9 x 3 = 27	10 x 6 = 60	8 x 4 = 32	6 x 7 = 42
7 x 5 = 35	9 x 4 = 36	6 x 5 = 30	10 x 10 = 100
6 x 2 = 12	6 x 4 = 24	6 x 10 = 60	12 x 0 = 0
4 x 7 = 28	5 x 9 = 45	3 x 8 = 24	7 x 10 = 70
1 x 1 = 1	3 x 3 = 9	5 x 5 = 25	6 x 6 = 36
7 x 7 = 49	2 x 2 = 4	4 x 4 = 16	0 x 0 = 0

Write the answers.

8	7	9	10
x 4	x 6	x 5	x 8
32	42	45	80

12	13	14	15
x 7	x 4	x 6	x 8
84	52	84	120

Don collects 6 new sports cards every day for a week.

How many cards will Don have at the end of the week?

42

These are straightforward practice problems in multiplication. It is important the children realize that for example, 5 x 9 gives the same result as 9 x 5, which they should already know.

★ Multiples

Circle the numbers that are multiples of 3.
(12) 14 16 (18) 20 22 (24) 26 28 (30)

Circle the numbers that are multiples of 4.
2 (4) 6 (8) 10 (12) 14 (16) 18 (20)

Circle the numbers that are multiples of 5.
2 7 (10) 14 19 (20) (25) 28 33 42

Circle the numbers that are multiples of 6.
4 (6) 8 10 (12) 14 16 (18) 20 (24)

Circle the numbers that are multiples of 10.
5 (10) (20) (30) 55 75 (90) 95 (100) (200)

What is the smallest number that is a multiple of 3 and 4?	12
What is the smallest number that is a multiple of 2 and 5?	10
What is the smallest number that is a multiple of 3 and 5?	15
What is the smallest number that is a multiple of 2 and 4?	4
What is the smallest number that is a multiple of 3 and 10?	30

Children will associate multiples with "numbers in the times tables." The last five questions are a little more challenging but will test understanding.

Dividing ★

Write the answers.

20 ÷ 4 = 5	20 ÷ 2 = 10	20 ÷ 5 = 4
20 ÷ 10 = 2	12 ÷ 2 = 6	12 ÷ 6 = 2
12 ÷ 3 = 4	12 ÷ 4 = 3	18 ÷ 3 = 6
18 ÷ 6 = 3	18 ÷ 9 = 2	18 ÷ 2 = 9
30 ÷ 6 = 5	24 ÷ 2 = 12	40 ÷ 10 = 4
28 ÷ 7 = 4	44 ÷ 4 = 11	25 ÷ 5 = 5
32 ÷ 8 = 4	24 ÷ 6 = 4	12 ÷ 12 = 1
14 ÷ 2 = 7	32 ÷ 4 = 8	56 ÷ 7 = 8
10 ÷ 5 = 2	14 ÷ 2 = 7	20 ÷ 4 = 5
24 ÷ 3 = 8	12 ÷ 2 = 6	15 ÷ 5 = 3
21 ÷ 3 = 7	27 ÷ 3 = 9	16 ÷ 4 = 4
36 ÷ 4 = 9	28 ÷ 4 = 7	30 ÷ 5 = 6
50 ÷ 10 = 5	70 ÷ 10 = 7	60 ÷ 10 = 6
40 ÷ 10 = 4	16 ÷ 2 = 8	22 ÷ 2 = 11
4 ÷ 2 = 2	14 ÷ 2 = 7	24 ÷ 3 = 8
45 ÷ 5 = 9	44 ÷ 4 = 11	12 ÷ 6 = 2

It is most important children realize the connection between simple division and times tables.

★ Choosing the operation

I add 16 to a number and then have 40. What number did I begin with?	24
I subtract 25 from a number and have 14 left. What number did I start with?	39
I multiplied a number by 6 and now have 54. What number did I begin with?	9
Danny has a collection of 28 comics and buys another 14. How many comics does Danny have now?	42
I divided a number by 8 and now have 2. What number did I begin with?	16
After adding 20 ¢ to some money, Gill has 75 ¢. How much did Gill have to start with?	55 ¢
Margaret has to share 100 grapes with her three sisters. How many grapes do they each receive? **Hint:** Margaret wants some grapes too.	25
Peter adds three numbers together. Two of the numbers are 8 and 7 and the total is 20. What number is missing?	5
Justin knows that six times a number is 48 but has forgotten the number! Remind Justin what the number is.	8
Jonas has lost some money. He started with $1.00 but now has only 58 ¢. How much has Jonas lost?	42 ¢

Remind children about the practical application of addition, subtraction, multiplication, and division. Subtraction is the reverse of addition and division is the reverse of multiplication.

Working with money ★

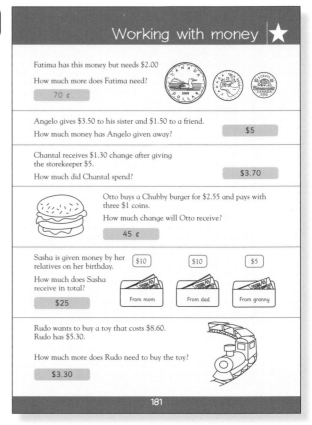

Fatima has this money but needs $2.00

How much more does Fatima need?
70 ¢

Angelo gives $3.50 to his sister and $1.50 to a friend. How much money has Angelo given away? — $5

Chantal receives $1.30 change after giving the storekeeper $5. How much did Chantal spend? — $3.70

Otto buys a Chubby burger for $2.55 and pays with three $1 coins. How much change will Otto receive?
45 ¢

Sasha is given money by her relatives on her birthday. $10 $10 $5 How much does Sasha receive in total?
$25
From mom From dad From granny

Rudo wants to buy a toy that costs $8.60. Rudo has $5.30.

How much more does Rudo need to buy the toy?
$3.30

Be prepared to have some coins and even a few bills available to help the children with these problems although they might be able to do them without any practical help.

★ Money problems

When Henry's dad empties his pockets he finds he has one loonie, two toonies, four 25 ¢ coins, and five 10 ¢ coins.

How much money has Henry's dad found? **$6.50**

Henry's mom finds this money behind some cushions – four loonies, five 25 ¢ coins, two 10 ¢ coins, and seven 1 ¢ coins.

How much money has Henry's mom found? **$5.52**

Henry's mom and dad put their money together.
How much do they have in total?
$12.02

Jack and Jane together have $25.
They spend their money on a takeout meal that costs $30.

How much more do they need? **$5**

What amount is missing?

$5   + $5   + $10   + $20   +   **$10**   = $50

Write the answer.

How many 5 ¢ coins are the same as $1.00? **20**

How many 10 ¢ coins are the same as $1.80? **18**

How many 25 ¢ coins are the same as $2.00? **8**

The last question helps to check that the children know how many 5¢, 10 ¢, and 25¢ coins are needed to make up $1.00, and then can use this information to calculate the number for other amounts too.

Decimals with money ★

Write each amount in two ways.

Example: Thirty-five cents is either 35 ¢ or $0.35

Seven cents **7 ¢** **$0.07**   Ninety cents **90 ¢** **$0.90**

Twenty-nine cents **29 ¢** **$0.29**   Forty-two cents **42 ¢** **$0.42**

Thirty-one cents **31 ¢** **$0.31**   Fifteen cents **15 ¢** **$0.15**

Sixty-seven cents **67 ¢** **$0.67**   Fifty-five cents **55 ¢** **$0.55**

Ninety-three cents **93 ¢** **$0.93**   Seventy-eight cents **78 ¢** **$0.78**

Write the answers.

$1.20 + $0.80 = **$2** $1.30 + $1.60 = **$2.90** $2.10 + $1.70 = **$3.80**

$1.30 + $0.50 = **$1.80** $5.00 − $2.50 = **$2.50** $1.45 + $0.65 = **$2.10**

$2.50 + $1.50 = **$4.00** $1.40 + $2.30 = **$3.70** $5.25 + $1.15 = **$6.40**

$1.35 + $1.45 = **$2.80** $0.60 + $0.85 = **$1.45** $1.60 + $1.60 = **$3.20**

$4.45 + $0.70 = **$5.15** $2.05 + $1.75 = **$3.80** $1.00 − $0.73 = **$0.27**

$1.00 − $0.30 = **$0.70** $5.90 + $0.20 = **$6.10** $2.00 − $1.50 = **$0.50**

$2.00 − $0.50 = **$1.50** $5.00 − $3.00 = **$2.00** $10.00 − $7.50 = **$2.50**

Write the answers.

What is $1.60 plus 45 ¢? **$2.05**   How much is $5.00 minus 8 ¢? **$4.92**

What is $3.80 plus 70 ¢? **$4.50**   How much is $2.00 minus 30 ¢? **$1.70**

Children should understand the conventions we use in writing money, e.g., $3.45 or $0.24 or 24¢.

★ Keeping skills sharp

Complete this grid.

X	4	9	10	6
5	20	45	50	30
2	8	18	20	12

Write the answers.

24	38	40	51
− 17	− 12	− 23	− 36
7	**26**	**17**	**15**

Bart has to mark these products for Homer.
Help Bart to mark the products right (✓) or wrong (✗).

8 x 3 = 42 **✗**   5 x 6 = 30 **✓**   2 x 10 = 22 **✗**

10 x 5 = 50 **✓**   3 x 9 = 24 **✗**   8 x 4 = 31 **✗**

What is the smallest number that is a multiple of 4 and 5? **20**

What is the largest number that is a multiple of 3 and 2 but less than 20? **18**

Lucy has to share 3 pizzas equally between herself and three friends. Each pizza has 8 pieces.

How many pieces of pizza will each girl receive? **6**

The test on this page and the following one covers work in the previous pages. It may be worth timing the children to see how quickly they can work through the questions but do not put pressure on them unnecessarily.

Keeping skills sharp ★

Share the 20 apples equally among the 4 children.

How many apples will each child get?
5

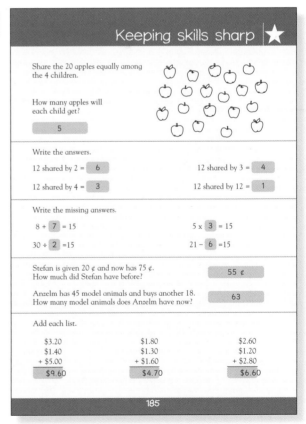

Write the answers.

12 shared by 2 = **6**   12 shared by 3 = **4**

12 shared by 4 = **3**   12 shared by 12 = **1**

Write the missing answers.

8 + **7** = 15   5 x **3** = 15

30 ÷ **2** = 15   21 − **6** = 15

Stefan is given 20 ¢ and now has 75 ¢.
How much did Stefan have before? **55 ¢**

Anzelm has 45 model animals and buys another 18.
How many model animals does Anzelm have now? **63**

Add each list.

$3.20	$1.80	$2.60
$1.40	$1.30	$1.20
+ $5.00	+ $1.60	+ $2.80
$9.60	**$4.70**	**$6.60**

★ Measuring length

This is a centimetres ruler.

| cm 0 1 2 3 4 5 6 7 8 9 10 11 12 13 14 15 |

What length is shown on each ruler?

0cm 1 2 3 4 5 6 7 8 9 10 11 12 13 14 15 → **5 cm**

0cm 1 2 3 4 5 6 7 8 9 10 11 12 13 14 15 → **8.5 cm**

0cm 1 2 3 4 5 6 7 8 9 10 11 12 13 14 15 → **11 cm**

0cm 1 2 3 4 5 6 7 8 9 10 11 12 13 14 15 → **2.5 cm**

Mark the lengths on the ruler.

3.7 cm ↓

10.3 cm ↓

3.5 cm ↓

5.5 cm ↓

Practical experience with using measuring equipment and units is invaluable so the more the better.

Measuring problems ★

This is a part of a measuring tape.

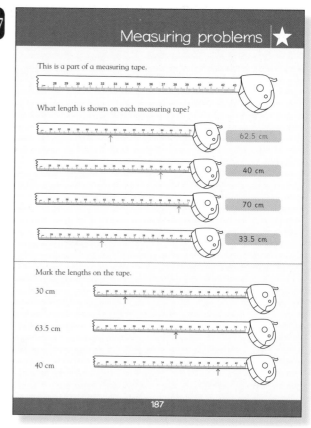

What length is shown on each measuring tape?

→ **62.5 cm**

→ **40 cm**

→ **70 cm**

→ **33.5 cm**

Mark the lengths on the tape.

30 cm

63.5 cm

40 cm

This page gives more measuring experience. If possible, let your child use a measuring tape at home.

★ Writing the time

Show the time on each clock.

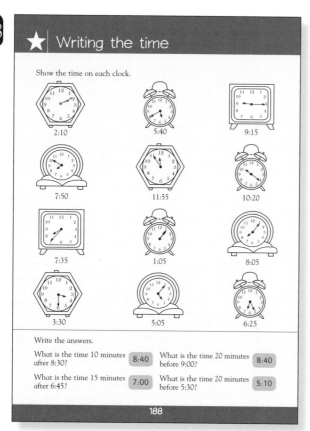

2:10   5:40   9:15

7:50   11:55   10:20

7:35   1:05   8:05

3:30   5:05   6:25

Write the answers.

What is the time 10 minutes after 8:30? **8:40**

What is the time 20 minutes before 9:00? **8:40**

What is the time 15 minutes after 6:45? **7:00**

What is the time 20 minutes before 5:30? **5:10**

Children might benefit from having an analog clock to practise with so they can actually turn the hands to show the times before drawing. Make sure they notice that at most times, e.g., 3:30, the hour hand does not actually point at the 3.

Telling time ★

What is the time on each clock face?

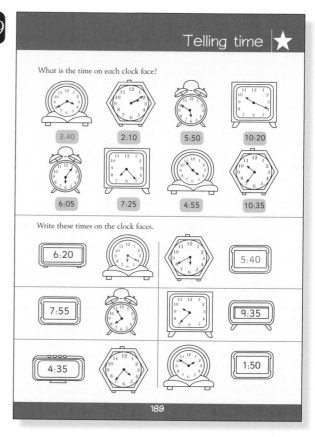

3.40   2:10   5:50   10:20

6:05   7:25   4:55   10:35

Write these times on the clock faces.

6:20

5:40

7:55

9:35

4:35

1:50

This page provides more experience of telling and writing time correctly.

★ Time problems

Yasir leaves for school at 8:35 and it is a 15-minute walk. At what time does Yasir arrive at school? — `8:50`

Matty starts her homework at 4:15 p.m. and it takes 30 minutes. What time will Matty finish? — `4:45 p.m.`

Simone spends 90 minutes at a friend's house. She arrived at noon. What time does Simone leave her friend's house? — `1:30 p.m.`

Ebba is waiting for a bus. The bus will arrive at 10:10 but the time is 9:50. How long does Ebba have to wait? — `20 minutes`

It is 9:15 when Emma starts to watch a movie. The movie lasts 90 minutes. What time will the movie end? — `10:45`

Konrad starts swimming at 8:45 and swims for half an hour. What time does Konrad finish swimming? — `9:15`

Mark cooks for two hours. He starts cooking at 11:00 in the morning. What time will Mark finish cooking? — `1:00 p.m.`

Salama runs for 25 minutes before she gets tired. She starts running at 3:40 p.m. What time will Salama finish running? — `4:05 p.m.`

Umi's watch is 20 minutes slow. The watch shows the time as 9:45. What time should the watch show? — `10:05`

Clara's bedside clock is 10 minutes fast. The clock shows 7:05. What is the correct time? — `6:55`

Children will need to work through these questions carefully and an actual watch or clock to help them may be very useful.

Days, weeks, months, years ★

How many days are in each number of weeks?

2 weeks `14` 3 weeks `21` 4 weeks `28`

5 weeks `35` 10 weeks `70` 8 weeks `56`

How many whole weeks are in each number of months? **Hint:** Multiply by 4.

1 month `4` 2 months `8` 3 months `12`

5 months `20` 6 months `24` 12 months `48`

A leap year is every four years. When are the next five leap years after 2012?

`2016` `2020` `2024` `2028` `2032`

How many days are in two weeks? — `14`

Which months begin with the letter J? — January, June, and July

Which day comes before Saturday? — Friday

Which days begin with the letter T? — Tuesday and Thursday

Which month comes before October? — September

Which month comes between February and April? — March

How many days are in February in a leap year? — `29`

What will the year after 2019 be? — `2020`

Children often pick up ideas about the days and weeks, etc., through general conversations at home or with friends so it is important to help them with some of the terminology.

★ Location

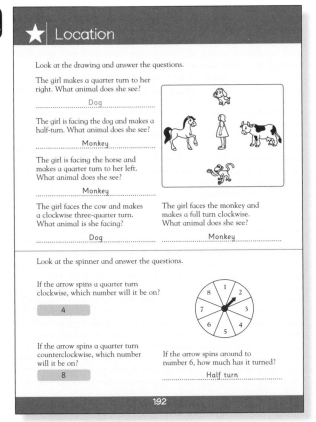

Look at the drawing and answer the questions.

The girl makes a quarter turn to her right. What animal does she see? — Dog

The girl is facing the dog and makes a half-turn. What animal does she see? — Monkey

The girl is facing the horse and makes a quarter turn to her left. What animal does she see? — Monkey

The girl faces the cow and makes a clockwise three-quarter turn. What animal is she facing? — Dog

The girl faces the monkey and makes a full turn clockwise. What animal does she see? — Monkey

Look at the spinner and answer the questions.

If the arrow spins a quarter turn clockwise, which number will it be on? — `4`

If the arrow spins a quarter turn counterclockwise, which number will it be on? — `8`

If the arrow spins around to number 6, how much has it turned? — Half turn

The idea of clockwise and counter-clockwise is normally picked up easily and reference can be made to the way the hands of a clock move.

Tally charts ★

Amy asked children in her school about favourite places to go on vacation. She recorded the information on a tally chart.

Favourite countries

Countries	Number of votes
France	LHT LHT LHT LHT LHT III
U.S.	LHT LHT LHT LHT LHT LHT LHT LHT LHT LHT
England	LHT LHT LHT II
Spain	LHT LHT IIII
Canada	LHT LHT LHT LHT II

Amy forgot to record 4 votes for the U.S. Add these to the chart.

Which was the most popular choice? — U.S.

How many children liked this country? — `45`

Which was the least popular country? — Spain

How many children liked this country? — `14`

How many more children preferred France to England? — `11`

How many children did Amy ask in total? — `126`

Which country had 17 votes? — England

How many votes did Canada and Spain have in total? — `36`

Put the countries in order of votes with the least popular first.

Spain   England   Canada   France   U.S.

Tally marks are a very useful way of recording information and are often used by adults as a simple shorthand method. Quickly seeing that the diagonal line through the four marks represents 5 can really help.

★ Graphs

Mike asks his class about their favourite countries visited during the summer vacations. He records his findings on a bar graph.

A survey of favourite countries

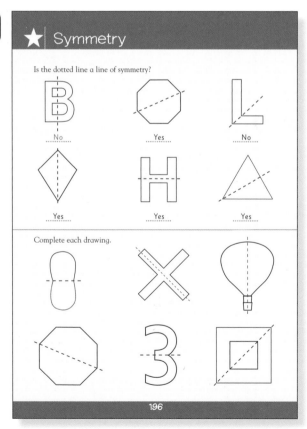

Rank the countries in order of popularity, starting with the least favourite.

Germany   France   U.S   Italy   Portugal   Spain

How many children preferred Spain? **9**

Which two countries had a total of 13? **Italy and Portugal**

The pictograph shows how many children took part in various sports.

A survey of favourite sports

= 2 children

= 1 child

Hockey   Soccer   Basketball   Tennis   Swimming

Which is the most popular sport? **Soccer**

Which sport had 7 votes? **Tennis**

How many children liked basketball? **3**

How many children took part in the survey? **28**

Different types of graphs come into the curriculum later on but they are essentially the same idea. Be careful with pictographs where a unit such as the running shoe in this question may represent more than one person or unit.

Give the correct name for each shape.

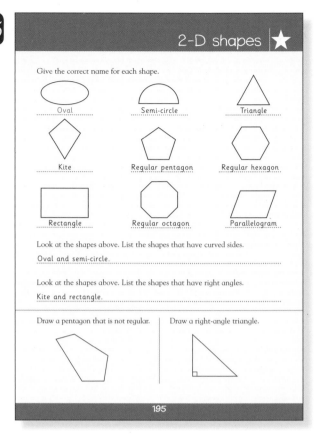

Oval   Semi-circle   Triangle

Kite   Regular pentagon   Regular hexagon

Rectangle   Regular octagon   Parallelogram

Look at the shapes above. List the shapes that have curved sides.

Oval and semi-circle.

Look at the shapes above. List the shapes that have right angles.

Kite and rectangle.

Draw a pentagon that is not regular. | Draw a right-angle triangle.

Children should be able to name each of these shapes although spelling may not always be accurate. Be sure to explain that the use of the word "regular" means all sides are the same length and the interior angles are the same.

★ Symmetry

Is the dotted line a line of symmetry?

B — No   octagon — Yes   L — No

kite — Yes   H — Yes   triangle — Yes

Complete each drawing.

This activity just needs a careful eye for accuracy. To help, encourage the children to use a small mirror to see if a shape is symmetrical.

Look carefully for the right angles and mark them on the shapes.

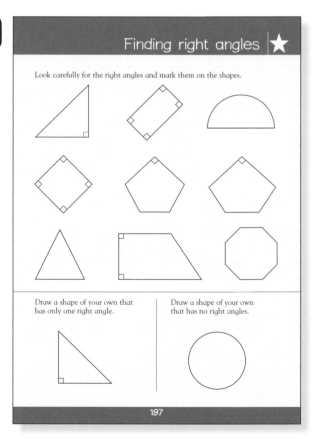

Draw a shape of your own that has only one right angle. | Draw a shape of your own that has no right angles.

Children generally spot right angles when the shape is level but can miss them when the right angle is tilted or in a place they are not expecting.

★ More angles

This angle is **less than** a right angle.

This angle is **more than** a right angle.

Look at each angle and write "more than," "less than," or "right angle."

Less than | Right angle | More than

Less than | More than | Less than

More than | Less than | More than

Less than | Right angle | Less than

Children should be able to spot angles that are more or less than a right angle. The terms "acute" (less than a right angle) and "obtuse" (more than a right angle) may not have been introduced yet and so are not used here.

Diagrams ★

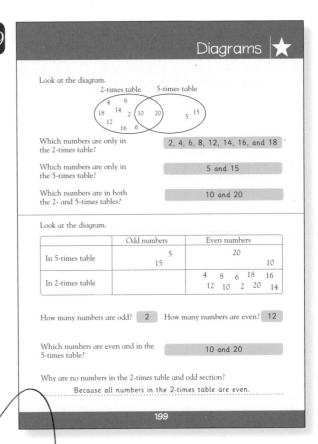

Look at the diagram.

2-times table 5-times table

Which numbers are only in the 2-times table? — 2, 4, 6, 8, 12, 14, 16, and 18

Which numbers are only in the 5-times table? — 5 and 15

Which numbers are in both the 2- and 5-times tables? — 10 and 20

Look at the diagram.

	Odd numbers	Even numbers
In 5-times table	5 15	20 10
In 2-times table		4 8 6 18 16 12 10 2 20 14

How many numbers are odd? 2 How many numbers are even? 12

Which numbers are even and in the 5-times table? — 10 and 20

Why are no numbers in the 2-times table and odd section?
Because all numbers in the 2-times table are even.

Venn diagrams and Carroll diagrams are used in displays of information and play a part in mathematics at the elementary school level and beyond. These questions will help children to understand and interpret them.

★ Keeping skills sharp

Barry's watch shows this time in the evening.

Val's watch shows this time in the evening.

What is the difference between the two times? — 10 minutes

Sean goes for a long walk and starts at 9:30. The walk takes two and a quarter hours. When does Sean arrive? — 11:45

The dogs have walked these distances.

14 kilometres

17 kilometres

28 kilometres

How far have the dogs walked in total? — 59 kilometres

A teacher found out that 24 children had packed lunches, 7 bought school lunch, and 1 went home to lunch.

Show this information as a tally chart. Remember to write labels.

Type of lunch	Number of children
Packed lunch	ЖЖ ЖЖ ЖЖ ЖЖ IIII
School lunch	ЖЖ II
Went home	I

These questions are designed to test the understanding of the work just covered. If children stumble over a question, just return to the relevant page to try again and give some extra help and explanation.

Keeping skills sharp ★

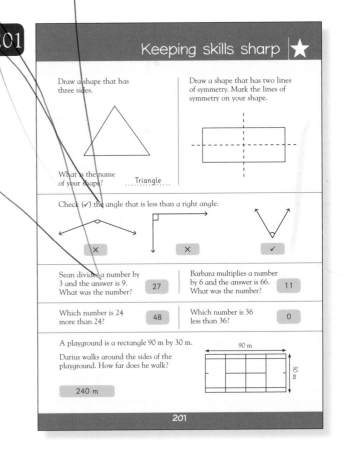

Draw a shape that has three sides.

Draw a shape that has two lines of symmetry. Mark the lines of symmetry on your shape.

What is the name of your shape? — Triangle

Check (✓) the angle that is less than a right angle.

✗ | ✗ | ✓

Sean divides a number by 3 and the answer is 9. What was the number? — 27

Barbara multiplies a number by 6 and the answer is 66. What was the number? — 11

Which number is 24 more than 24? — 48

Which number is 36 less than 36? — 0

A playground is a rectangle 90 m by 30 m.

Darius walks around the sides of the playground. How far does he walk? — 240 m

90 m

30 m

$3 \times 4 = 4 \times 3$

$3 \times 3 \times 3 \times 3 = 4 \times 4 \times 4$

$12 = 12$

DK
Senior Editor Deborah Lock
Art Director Martin Wilson
Publishing Director Sophie Mitchell
Pre-production Francesca Wardell
Jacket Designer Martin Wilson
Canadian Editor Barbara Campbell
Canadian Math Consultant Marilyn Wilson

DK Delhi
Editorial Monica Saigal, Tanya Desai
Design Pallavi Narain, Dheeraj Arora,
Tanvi Nathyal, Jyotsna Khosla
DTP Designer Anita Yadav

Expanded Canadian Edition, 2013
DK Publishing is represented in Canada by
Tourmaline Editions Inc.
662 King Street West, Suite 304
Toronto, Ontario M5V 1M7

Published in Great Britain in 2013
by Dorling Kindersley Limited
Copyright © 2005, 2013 Dorling Kindersley Limited
A Penguin Company
13 14 15 10 9 8 7 6 5 4 3 2 1
001-187483-August 2013

Library and Archives Canada Cataloguing in Publication
Math made easy : grade 3, ages 8-9 /
Canadian math consultant,
Marilyn Wilson. -- Expanded Canadian ed.
ISBN 978-1-55363-204-7
1. Mathematics--Problems, exercises, etc.
2. Mathematics--Study and teaching (Primary).
3. Mathematical recreations.
I. Wilson, Marilyn
QA107.2.M3884 2013   510.76   C2012-908196-5

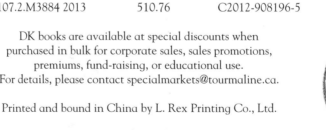

DK books are available at special discounts when
purchased in bulk for corporate sales, sales promotions,
premiums, fund-raising, or educational use.
For details, please contact specialmarkets@tourmaline.ca.

Printed and bound in China by L. Rex Printing Co., Ltd.

All images © Dorling Kindersley.
For further information see: www.dkimages.com
Discover more at
www.dk.com